C000263729

THE abc OF
BRITISH RAILWAYS
LOCOMOTIVES

COMBINED VOLUME
PARTS 1—4
Nos. 1-99999
ALSO DIESEL AND ELECTRIC
MULTIPLE UNITS

WINTER
1958/9
EDITION

LONDON :

Ian Allan Ltd

NOTES ON THE USE OF THIS BOOK

T HE following notes are a guide to the system of reference marks and other details given in the lists of dimensions shown for each class in the alphabetical list of classes.

1. Many of the classes listed are sub-divided by reason of mechanical or constructional differences (on the Eastern and North Eastern Regions the sub-divisions are denoted in some cases by "Parts," shown thus : D16/3). At the head of each class will be found a list of such sub-divisions, if any, usually arranged in order of introduction. Each part is given there a reference mark by which its relevant dimensions, if differing from those of other parts, and the locomotives included in this sub-division, or part, may be identified. Any other differences between locomotives are also indicated, with reference marks, below the details of the class's introduction.

2. The lists of dimensions at the head of each class show locomotives fitted with two inside cylinders, Stephenson valve gear and slide valves, unless otherwise stated, e.g. (O) = two outside cylinders, P.V. = piston valves.

3. The following method is used to denote superheated locomotives, the letters being inserted, where applicable, after the boiler pressure details : Su = All engines superheated.
SS = Some engines superheated.

4. The date on which the first locomotive of a class was built or modified is denoted by "Introduced."

5. S. denotes Service (Departmental) locomotive still carrying B.R. number. This reference letter is introduced only for the reader's guidance and is not borne by the locomotive concerned.

Note :

(a) On the Southern Region the letters "DS" preceding a number indicate a Service Locomotive. On the S.R. (only) this marking appears on the locomotive.

(b) The Eastern and North Eastern Regions number their departmental locomotives in a separate series, as shown in Part IV.

BRITISH RAILWAYS LOCOMOTIVE
SHEDS AND SHED CODES

**ALL B.R. LOCOMOTIVES CARRY THE CODE OF THEIR HOME DEPOT
ON A SMALL PLATE AFFIXED TO THE SMOKEBOX DOOR.**

LONDON MIDLAND REGION

1A	**Willesden**	9A	**Longsight (Manchester)**
1B	Camden	9B	Stockport (Edgeley)
1C	Watford	9C	Macclesfield
1D	Devons Road (Bow)	9D	Buxton
1E	Bletchley	9E	Trafford Park
	Leighton Buzzard		Glazebrook
		9F	Heaton Mersey
		9G	Gorton
2A	**Rugby**		Ardwick
2B	Nuneaton		Dinting
2C	Warwick (W.R.)		Guide Bridge
2D	Coventry		Mottram
2E	Northampton		Reddish
2F	Woodford Halse		
		11A	**Barrow**
3A	**Bescot**	11B	Workington
3B	Bushbury	11C	Oxenholme
3C	Walsall	11D	Tebay
3D	Aston		
3E	Monument Lane	12A	**Carlisle (Kingmoor)**
		12B	Carlisle (Upperby)
5A	**Crewe North**		Penrith
	Whitchurch	12C	Carlisle (Canal)
5B	Crewe South	12D	Kirkby Stephen
5C	Stafford		
5D	Stoke	14A	**Cricklewood**
5E	Alsager	14B	Kentish Town
5F	Uttoxeter	14C	St. Albans
		14D	Neasden
6A	**Chester (Midland)**		Aylesbury
6B	Mold Junction		Chesham
6C	Birkenhead		Marylebone
6D	Chester (Northgate)		Rickmansworth
6E	Chester (West)	14E	Bedford
6F	Bidston		
6G	Llandudno Junction	15A	**Wellingborough**
6H	Bangor	15B	Kettering
6J	Holyhead	15C	Leicester (Midland)
6K	Rhyl	15D	Coalville
		15E	Leicester (Central)
		15F	Market Harborough
8A	**Edge Hill**		Seaton
8B	Warrington (Dallam)		
	Warrington (Arpley)	16A	**Nottingham**
8C	Speke Junction	16B	Kirkby
8D	Widnes	16C	Mansfield
8E	Northwich	16D	Annesley
8F	Springs Branch (Wigan)		Nottingham (Victoria)
8G	Sutton Oak		Kirkby Bentinck

17A	**Derby**		24E	Blackpool
	Derby (Friargate)		24F	Fleetwood
17B	Burton		24G	Skipton
	Horninglow		24H	Hellifield
	Overseal		24J	Lancaster (Green Ayre)
17D	Rowsley		24K	Preston
	Cromford		24L	Carnforth
	Middleton			
	Sheep Pasture		26A	**Newton Heath**
			26B	Agecroft
18A	**Toton (Stapleford &**		26C	Bolton
	Sandiacre)		26D	Bury
18B	Westhouses		26E	Lees (Oldham)
18C	Hasland		26F	Patricroft
21A	**Saltley**		27A	**Bank Hall**
21B	Bournville		27B	Aintree
			27C	Southport
24A	**Accrington**		27D	Wigan
24B	Rose Grove		27E	Walton-on-the-Hill
24C	Lostock Hall		27F	Brunswick (Liverpool)
24D	Lower Darwen			Warrington (Central)

EASTERN REGION

30A	**Stratford**		32C	Lowestoft Central
	Chelmsford		32D	Yarmouth (South Town)
	Enfield Town		32E	Yarmouth (Vauxhall)
	Southend (Victoria)		32F	Yarmouth Beach
	Wood St. (Walthamstow)		32G	Melton Constable
30B	Hertford East			Norwich City
	Buntingford			
30C	Bishops Stortford			
30E	Colchester		33A	**Plaistow**
	Braintree		33B	Tilbury
	Clacton		33C	Shoeburyness
	Maldon			
	Walton-on-Naze		34A	**Kings Cross**
30F	Parkeston		34B	Hornsey
			34C	Hatfield
			34D	Hitchin
31A	**Cambridge**		34E	New England
	Ely		34F	Grantham
	Huntingdon East			
	Saffron Walden			
31B	March		36A	**Doncaster**
	Wisbech East		36C	Frodingham
31C	Kings Lynn		36E	Retford
	Hunstanton			Newark
31D	South Lynn			
31E	Bury St. Edmunds			
	Sudbury (Suffolk)		40A	**Lincoln**
31F	Spital Bridge (Peterboro')			Lincoln (St. Marks)
			40B	Immingham
				Grimsby
32A	**Norwich**			New Holland
	Cromer Beach		40E	Colwick
	Dereham		40F	Boston
	Wymondham			Sleaford
32B	Ipswich			Spalding
	Felixstowe Town			
	Stowmarket			

41A	Sheffield (Darnall)	41F	Mexborough
41B	Sheffield (Grimesthorpe)		Wath
41C	Millhouses	41G	Barnsley
41D	Canklow	41H	Staveley (ex-G.C.)
41E	Staveley (Barrow Hill)	41J	Langwith Junction
		41K	Tuxford

NORTH EASTERN REGION

50A	York	52F	North Blyth
50B	Leeds (Neville Hill)		South Blyth
50C	Selby	53A	Hull (Dairycoates)
50D	Starbeck	53B	Hull (Botanic Gardens)
50E	Scarborough	53C	Hull (Springhead)
50F	Malton		Alexandra Dock
	Pickering	53D	Bridlington
50G	Whitby	53E	Goole
		54A	Sunderland
			Durham
51A	Darlington	54B	Tyne Dock
	Middleton-in-Teesdale		Pelton Level
51C	West Hartlepool	54C	Borough Gardens
51E	Stockton	54D	Consett
51F	West Auckland	55A	Leeds (Holbeck)
51G	Haverton Hill	55B	Stourton
51J	Northallerton	55C	Farnley Junction
51K	Saltburn	55D	Royston
51L	Thornaby	55E	Normanton
		55F	Manningham
		55G	Huddersfield
52A	Gateshead	56A	Wakefield
	Bowes Bridge	56B	Ardsley
52B	Heaton	56C	Copley Hill
52C	Blaydon	56D	Mirfield
	Alston	56E	Sowerby Bridge
	Hexham	56F	Low Moor
52D	Tweedmouth	56G	Bradford
	Alnmouth		
52E	Percy Main		

SCOTTISH REGION

60A	Inverness	62A	Thornton
	Dingwall		Anstruther
	Kyle of Lochalsh		Burntisland
60B	Aviemore		Ladybank
	Boat of Garten		Methil
60C	Helmsdale	62B	Dundee (Tay Bridge)
	Dornoch		Arbroath
	Tain		Dundee West
60D	Wick		Montrose
	Thurso		St. Andrews
60E	Forres	62C	Dunfermline
			Alloa
61A	Kittybrewster	63A	Perth South
	Ballater		Aberfeldy
	Fraserburgh		Blair Atholl
	Inverurie		Crieff
	Peterhead	63B	Stirling South
61B	Aberdeen (Ferryhill)		Killin
61C	Keith	63C	Forfar
	Banff	63D	Oban
	Elgin		Ballachulish

64A	St. Margarets		65F	Grangemouth
		(Edinburgh)	65G	Yoker
	Dunbar		65H	Helensburgh
	Galashiels		65I	Balloch
	Longniddry		65J	Fort William
	North Berwick			Mallaig
	Seafield			
	South Leith		66A	Polmadie (Glasgow)
64B	Haymarket		66B	Motherwell
64C	Dalry Road		66C	Hamilton
64D	Carstairs		66D	Greenock (Ladyburn)
64E	Polmont			Greenock (Princes Pier)
64F	Bathgate			
64G	Hawick		67A	Corkerhill (Glasgow)
	Riccarton		67B	Hurlford
	St. Boswells			Beith
				Muirkirk
65A	Eastfield (Glasgow)		67C	Ayr
	Arrochar		67D	Ardrossan
65B	St. Rollox			
65C	Parkhead		68B	Dumfries
65D	Dawsholm		68C	Stranraer
	Dumbarton			Newton Stewart
65E	Kipps		68D	Beattock

SOUTHERN REGION

70A	Nine Elms		72B	Salisbury
70B	Feltham		72C	Yeovil
70C	Guildford		72E	Barnstaple Junction
70D	Basingstoke			Ilfracombe
70E	Reading			Torrington
70F	Fratton		72F	Wadebridge
70H	Ryde (I.O.W.)			
			73A	Stewarts Lane
71A	Eastleigh		73B	Bricklayers Arms
	Andover Junction		73C	Hither Green
	Lymington		73D	Gillingham (Kent)
	Winchester		73E	Faversham
71B	Bournemouth			
	Branksome		74A	Ashford (Kent)
71G	Weymouth		74B	Ramsgate
	Bridport		74C	Dover
71H	Yeovil (G.W.)			Folkestone
71I	Southampton Docks		74D	Tonbridge
			74E	St. Leonards
72A	Exmouth Junction			
	Bude		75A	Brighton
	Callington		75B	Redhill
	Exmouth		75C	Norwood Junction
	Lyme Regis		75D	Horsham
	Okehampton		75E	Three Bridges
	Seaton		75F	Tunbridge Wells West

WESTERN REGION

81A	Old Oak Common		82A	Bristol (Bath Road)
81B	Slough			Bath
	Marlow			Wells
81C	Southall			Weston-super-Mare
81D	Reading			Yatton
	Henley-on-Thames		82B	St. Philip's Marsh
81E	Didcot		82C	Swindon
81F	Oxford			Chippenham
	Fairford			

82D	Westbury
	Frome
82E	Bristol (Barrow Rd.)
82F	Bath (Green Park)
	Radstock
	Highbridge
82G	Templecombe

83A	**Newton Abbot**
	Ashburton
	Kingsbridge
83B	Taunton
	Bridgwater
83C	Exeter
	Tiverton Junction
83D	Laira (Plymouth)
	Launceston
83E	St. Blazey
	Bodmin
	Moorswater
83F	Truro
83G	Penzance
	Helston
	St. Ives
83H	Plymouth (Friary)

84A	**Wolverhampton**
	(Stafford Road)
84B	Oxley
84C	Banbury
84D	Leamington Spa
84E	Tyseley
	Stratford-on-Avon
84F	Stourbridge Junction
84G	Shrewsbury
	Builth Road
	Clee Hill
	Craven Arms
	Knighton
84H	Wellington (Salop)
84J	Croes Newydd
	Bala
	Penmaenpool
	Trawsfynydd
84K	Wrexham (Rhosddu)

85A	**Worcester**
	Evesham
	Kingham
85B	Gloucester
	Brimscombe
	Cheltenham
	Cirencester
	Lydney
	Tetbury
85C	Hereford
	Ledbury
	Leominster
	Ross
85D	Kidderminster

85E	Gloucester
	Dursley
	Tewkesbury
85F	Bromsgrove
	Redditch

86A	**Newport**
	(Ebbw Junction)
86B	Newport (Pill)
86C	Cardiff (Canton)
86D	Llantrisant
86E	Severn Tunnel Junction
86F	Tondu
86G	Pontypool Road
86H	Aberbeeg
86J	Aberdare
86K	Tredegar

87A	**Neath**
	Glyn Neath
	Neath (N. & B.
87B	Duffryn Yard
87C	Danygraig
87D	Swansea East Dock
87E	Landore
87F	Llanelly
	Burry Port
	Pantyfynnon
87G	Carmarthen
87H	Neyland
	Cardigan
	Milford Haven
	Pembroke Dock
	Whitland
87J	Goodwick
87K	Swansea (Victoria)
	Gurnos
	Llandovery
	Upper Bank

88A	**Cardiff (Cathays)**
	Radyr
88B	Cardiff East Dock
88C	Barry
88D	Merthyr
	Cae Harris
	Dowlais Centra
	Rhymney
88E	Abercynon
88F	Treherbert
	Ferndale

89A	**Oswestry**
	Llanidloes
	Moat Lane
89B	Brecon
89C	Machynlleth
	Aberayron
	Aberystwyth
	Aberystwyth (V. of R.)
	Portmadoc
	Pwllheli

SUMMARY OF WESTERN REGION
STEAM LOCOMOTIVE CLASSES
WITH HISTORICAL NOTES AND DIMENSIONS

The code given in smaller bold type at the head of each Class, e.g. "6MT" denotes its British Railways power classification.

The numbers of locomotives in service have been checked to July 12th, 1958.

4-6-0　6MT　1000 Class
"County"

Introduced 1945. Hawksworth design.
*Fitted with double chimney.
Weight: Loco.　76 tons 17 cwt.
　　　　Tender 49 tons 0 cwt.
Pressure: 280 lb. Su.
Cyls.: (O) 18½" × 30".
Driving Wheels: 6' 3".
T.E.: 32,580 lb.　P.V.

1005/6/8/11/5/7/9–21/5/6/9
*1000–4/7/9/10/2–4/6/8/22–4/7/8

　　　　　　　　　　　　Total 30

4-6-0　7P　4073 Class
"Castle"

*Introduced 1923.　Collett design, developed from "Star" (4037, 5083–92 converted from "Star").
†Introduced 1946. Fitted with 3-row superheater.
‡Introduced 1947. Fitted with 4-row superheater.
¶Introduced 1956. Fitted with double chimney.
Weight: Loco.　79 tons 17 cwt.
　　　　Tender 46 tons 14 cwt.
Pressure: 225 lb. Su.
Cyls.: (4) 16" × 26".
Driving Wheels: 6' 8½".
T.E.: 31,625 lb.
Inside Walschaerts valve gear and rocking shafts.　P.V.

*4037/73/5–9/81–6/9/90/1/4–6/8/9,5001–25/7–32/4/5/7–42/4–8/51–6/8–60/2/6–70/6/8/80/3–7/9–92
†5000/50/63/5/72/4/5/7/9/81/2/93/6–9,7000–3/5–12/4–7/20/1/5–8/31–3/5/7
‡4074/8, 5026/33/6/49/61/4/71/3/94/5,7019/24/9/30/4/6

†¶7023
‡¶4080/7/8/90/3/7, 5043/57/88, 7004/13/8/22　　**Total 166**

4-6-0　5MT　4900 Class
"Hall"

*Introduced 1924. Collett rebuild with 6' 0" driving wheels of "Saint" (built 1907).
†Introduced 1928. Modified design for new construction, with higher-pitched boiler, modified footplating and detail differences.
Weight: Loco. { 72 tons 10 cwt.*
　　　　　　　 { 75 tons 0 cwt.†
　　　　Tender 46 tons 14 cwt.
Pressure: 225 lb. Su.
Cyls.: (O) 18½" × 30".
Driving Wheels: 6' 0".
T.E.: 27,275 lb.
P.V.

*4900
†4901–10/2–99, 5900–99, 6900–58

　　　　　　　　　　　　Total 258

4-6-0　8P　6000 Class
"King"

Introduced 1927. Collett design.
All engines modified since 1947 with 4-row superheater and since 1955 with double chimney.
Weight: Loco.　89 tons 0 cwt.
　　　　Tender 46 tons 14 cwt.
Pressure: 250 lb. Su.
Cyls.: (4) 16¼" × 28".
Driving Wheels: 6' 6".
T.E.: 40,285 lb.
Inside Walschaerts valve gear and rocking shafts.　P.V.

6000–29

　　　　　　　　　　　　Total 30

4-6-0 5MT 6800 Class
"Grange"

Introduced 1936. Collett design, variation of "Hall" with smaller wheels, incorporating certain parts of withdrawn 4300 2-6-0 locos.

Weight: Loco.   74 tons 0 cwt.
        Tender 40 tons 0 cwt.
Pressure: 225 lb. Su.
Cyls.: (O) $18\frac{1}{2}'' \times 30''$.
Driving Wheels: 5' 8".
T.E.: 28,875 lb.
P.V.

6800–79   **Total 80**

4-6-0 5MT 6959 Class
"Modified Hall"

Introduced 1944. Hawksworth development of "Hall," with larger superheater, "one-piece" main frames and plate-framed bogie.

Weight: Loco.   75 tons 16 cwt.
        Tender 46 tons 14 cwt.
Pressure: 225 lb. Su.
Cyls.: (O) $18\frac{1}{2}'' \times 30''$.
Driving Wheels: 6' 0".
T.E.: 27,275 lb.
P.V.

6959–99, 7900–29   **Total 71**

4-6-0 5MT 7800 Class
"Manor"

Introduced 1938. Collett design for secondary lines, incorporating certain parts of withdrawn 4300 2-6-0 locos.

Weight: Loco.   68 tons 18 cwt.
        Tender 40 tons 0 cwt.
Pressure: 225 lb. Su.
Cyls.: (O) $18'' \times 30''$.
Driving Wheels: 5' 8".
T.E.: 27,340 lb.
P.V.

7800–29   **Total 30**

4-4-0 "City" Class

Introduced 1903. Churchward design.

Weight: Loco.   55 tons 6 cwt.
        Tender 36 tons 15 cwt.
Pressure: 200 lb. Su.
Cyls.: $18'' \times 26''$.
Driving Wheels: 6' $8\frac{1}{2}''$.
T.E.: 17,790 lb.

3440

Withdrawn 1931 and preserved in York Museum. Returned to service 1957.

                  Total 1

4-4-0 2P 9000 Class

Introduced 1936. Collett rebuild, incorporating "Duke" type boiler and "Bulldog" frames for light lines.

Weight: Loco.   49 tons 0 cwt.
        Tender $\begin{cases} 40 \text{ tons } 0 \text{ cwt.} \\ 36 \text{ tons } 15 \text{ cwt.} \end{cases}$
Pressure: 180 lb. SS.
Cyls.: $18'' \times 26''$.
Driving Wheels: 5' 8".
T.E.: 18,955 lb.

9004/5/13–5/7/8/21   **Total 8**

2-8-0 8F 2800 Class

*Introduced 1903. Churchward design, earlier locos. subsequently fitted with new boiler and superheater.

†Introduced 1938. Collett locos., with side-window cab and detail alterations.

Weight: Loco. $\begin{cases} 75 \text{ tons } 10 \text{ cwt.*} \\ 76 \text{ tons } 5 \text{ cwt.†} \end{cases}$
        Tender 40 tons 0 cwt.
Pressure: 225 lb. Su.
Cyls.: (O) $18\frac{1}{2}'' \times 30''$.
Driving Wheels: 4' $7\frac{1}{2}''$.
T.E.: 35,380 lb.
P.V.

*2801–83
†2884–99, 3800–66   **Total 166**

2-8-0　7F　R.O.D. Class

Introduced 1911. Robinson G.C. design (L.N.E.R. O4), built from 1917 for Railway Operating Division, R.E., taken into G.W. stock from 1919 and subsequently fitted with G.W. boiler mountings and details.
Weight: Loco.　73 tons 11 cwt.
　　　　　Tender 47 tons 6 cwt.
Pressure: 185 lb. Su.
Cyls.: (O) 21″ × 26″.
Driving Wheels: 4′ 8″.
T.E.: 32,200 lb.
P.V.

3011/5/24　　　　　　　　　**Total 3**

2-8-0　7F　4700 Class

Introduced 1919. Churchward mixed traffic design (4700 built with smaller boiler and later rebuilt).
Weight: Loco.　82 tons 0 cwt.
　　　　　Tender 46 tons 14 cwt.
Pressure: 225 lb. Su.
Cyls.: (O) 19″ × 30″.
Driving Wheels: 5′ 8″.
T.E.: 30,460 lb.
P.V.

4700–8　　　　　　　　　　**Total 9**

2-6-0　4MT　4300 Class

*Introduced 1911. Churchward design.
†Introduced 1925. Locos. with detail alterations affecting weight.
‡Introduced 1932. Locos. with side window cab and detail alterations.
Weight: Loco. { 62 tons 0 cwt.*
　　　　　　　{ 64 tons 0 cwt.†
　　　　　　　{ 65 tons 6 cwt.‡
　　　　　Tender 40 tons 0 cwt.
Pressure: 200 lb. Su.
Cyls.: (O) 18½″ × 30″.
Driving Wheels: 5′ 8″
T.E.: 25,670 lb.
P.V.

*4358/77, 5306/11/2/5/8/9/ 21/2/
4/6/30–3/5–9/41/4/5/50/1/3/5
–8/60/1/7–70/5–8/80–2/4–6/8
/90/2–4/6/8/9, 6300–14/6–20/2
–82/4–95/7–9, 7305–21
†7300–4
‡7322–6/8/9/33/6/9/40/1, 9305/8
–10/2/3/5　　　　　　　　**Total 192**

0-6-0　3MT　2251 Class

Introduced 1930. Collett design.
Weight:
　Loco.　　43 tons 8 cwt.
　Tender { 36 tons 15 cwt.
　　　　　{ 47 tons 6 cwt. (ex-R.O.D.
　　　　　　tender from 3000 Class
　　　　　　2-8-0).
Pressure: 200 lb. Su.
Cyls.: 17½″ × 24″.
Driving Wheels: 5′ 2″.
T.E.: 20,155 lb.

2200–99, 3200–19　　　　**Total 120**

2-8-2T　8F　7200 Class

Introduced 1934. Collett rebuild, with extended bunker and trailing wheels, of Churchward 4200 class 2-8-0T.
Weight: 92 tons 2 cwt.
Pressure: 200 lb. Su.
Cyls.: (O) 19″ × 30″.
Driving Wheels: 4′ 7½″.
T.E.: 33,170 lb.
P.V.

7200–53　　　　　　　　　**Total 54**

2-8-0T　{ 7F*　4200 Class
　　　　　{ 8F† }

*Introduced 1910. Churchward design.
†**5205 class.** Introduced 1923. With enlarged cyls. and detail alterations.
Weight: { 81 tons 12 cwt.*
　　　　 { 82 tons 2 cwt.†
Pressure: 200 lb. Su.
Cyls.: { (O) 18½″ × 30″*.
　　　 { (O) 19″ × 30″†.
Driving Wheels: 4′ 7½″.
T.E.: { 31,450 lb.*
　　　{ 33,170 lb.†
P.V.

*4200/1/3/6–8/11–5/7/8/21–33/5–
8/41–3/6–8/50–99, 5200–4
†5205–64　　　　　　　　**Total 151**

2-6-2T 4MT 3100 Class

Introduced 1938. Collett rebuild, with higher pressure and smaller wheels, of Churchward 3150 class (introduced 1906).

Weight: 81 tons 9 cwt.
Pressure: 225 lb. Su.
Cyls.: (O) $18\frac{1}{2}'' \times 30''$.
Driving Wheels: 5' 3".
T.E.: 31,170 lb.
P.V.

3102/3   **Total 2**

2-6-2T 4MT 3150 Class

Introduced 1906. Churchward design, developed from his original 3100 class of 1903, but with larger boiler, subsequently fitted with superheater.

Weight: 81 tons 12 cwt.
Pressure: 200 lb. Su.
Cyls.: (O) $18\frac{1}{2}'' \times 30''$.
Driving Wheels: 5' 8".
T.E.: 25,670 lb.
P.V.

3170   **Total 1**

2-6-2T 4MT 4500 Class

*Introduced 1906. Churchward design for light branches, developed from 4400 class with larger wheels, earlier locos. subsequently fitted with superheater.
†4575 class. Introduced 1927. With detail alterations and increased weight.
‡Introduced 1953. Push-and-pull fitted.

Weight: $\begin{cases} 57 \text{ tons } 0 \text{ cwt.}^* \\ 61 \text{ tons } 0 \text{ cwt.}†‡ \end{cases}$
Pressure: 200 lb. Su.
Cyls.: (O) $17'' \times 24''$.
Driving Wheels: 4' $7\frac{1}{2}''$.
T.E.: 21,250 lb.
P.V.

*4507/8/19/36/40/5/7/9/50/2–74
†4575–9/79/84/5/7/8/90–5/9, 5500/
3/4/7–10/4–23/5–8/30–3/6–44/6
–54/6–8/61–7/9–71/3
‡4578/89, 5511/24/9/34/45/55/9
/60/8/72/4   **Total 118**

2-6-2T 4MT 5100 & 6100 Classes

*5100 class. Introduced 1928. Collett rebuild, with detail alterations and increased weight, of Churchward 3100 class (introduced 1903 and subsequently fitted with superheater).
†5101 class. Introduced 1929. Modified design for new construction.
‡6100 class. Introduced 1931. Locos. for London suburban area with increased boiler pressure.

Weight: $\begin{cases} 75 \text{ tons } 10 \text{ cwt}^*. \\ 78 \text{ tons } 9 \text{ cwt.}†‡ \end{cases}$
Pressure: $\begin{cases} 200 \text{ lb. Su.}^*† \\ 225 \text{ lb. Su.}‡ \end{cases}$
Cyls.: (O) $18'' \times 30''$.
Driving Wheels: 5' 8".
T.E.: $\begin{cases} 24,300 \text{ lb.}^*† \\ 27,340 \text{ lb.}‡ \end{cases}$
P.V.

*5148
†4100–37/40–79, 5101–6/10/50–
6/8/60/3/4/6–70/2–99
‡6100–69   **Total 200**

2-6-2T 4MT 8100 Class

Introduced 1938. Collett rebuild, with higher pressure and smaller wheels, of Churchward locos. in 5100 class.

Weight: 76 tons 11 cwt.
Pressure: 225 lb. Su.
Cyls.: (O) $18'' \times 30''$.
Driving Wheels: 5' 6".
T.E.: 28,165 lb.
P.V.

8100–4/6–9   **Total 9**

2-6-2T unclass. V. of R.

*Introduced 1902. Davies and Metcalfe design for V. of R. 1' $11\frac{1}{2}''$ gauge.
†Introduced 1923. G.W. development of V. of R. design.

Weight: 25 tons 0 cwt.
Gauge: 1' $11\frac{1}{2}''$.
Pressure: 165 lb.
Cyls.: (O) $\begin{cases} 11'' \times 17''.^* \\ 11\frac{1}{2}'' \times 17''.† \end{cases}$
Driving Wheels: 2' 6".
T.E.: $\begin{cases} 9,615 \text{ lb.}^* \\ 10,510 \text{ lb.}† \end{cases}$
Walschaerts valve gear.

*9   †7/8   **Total 3**

0-6-2T   5MT   5600 Class

*Introduced 1924. Collett design for service in Welsh valleys.
†Introduced 1927. Locos. with detail alterations.
Weight: { 68 tons 12 cwt.*
          { 69 tons 7 cwt.†
Pressure: 200 lb. Su.
Cyls.: 18″ × 26″.
Driving Wheels: 4′ 7½″.
T.E.: 25,800 lb.
P.V.

*5600–99

†6600–99   Total 200

0-6-0PT   2F   850 Class

Introduced 1910. Dean saddletanks, subsequently rebuilt with pannier tanks.
Weight: 36 tons 3 cwt.
Pressure: 165 lb.
Cyls.: 16″ × 24″.
Driving Wheels: 4′ 1½″.
T.E.: 17,410 lb.

2012   Total 1

0-6-0ST   0F   1361 Class

Introduced 1910. Churchward design for dock shunting.
Weight: 35 tons 4 cwt.
Pressure: 150 lb.
Cyls.: (O) 16″ × 20″.
Driving Wheels: 3′ 8″.
T.E.: 14,835 lb.
1361–5   Total 5

0-6-0PT   1F   1366 Class

Introduced 1934. Collett development of 1361 class, with pannier tanks.
Weight: 35 tons 15 cwt.
Pressure: 165 lb.
Cyls.: (O) 16″ × 20″.
Driving Wheels: 3′ 8″.
T.E.: 16,320 lb.
1366–71   Total 6

0-6-0PT   4F   1500 Class

Introduced 1949. Hawksworth short-wheelbase heavy shunting design.
Weight: 58 tons 4 cwt.
Pressure: 200 lb.
Cyls.: (O) 17½″ × 24″.
Driving Wheels: 4′ 7½″.
T.E.: 22,515 lb.
Walschaerts valve gear. P.V.
1500–9   Total 10

0-6-0PT   2F   1600 Class

Introduced 1949. Hawksworth light branch line and shunting design.
Weight: 41 tons 12 cwt.
Pressure: 165 lb.
Cyls.: 16½″ × 24″.
Driving Wheels: 4′ 1½″.
T.E.: 18,515 lb.
1600–69   Total 70

0-6-0PT   2F   2021 Class

Introduced 1897. Dean saddletank, subsequently rebuilt with pannier tanks.
Weight: 39 tons 15 cwt.
Pressure: 165 lb.
Cyls.: 16½″ × 24″.
Driving Wheels: 4′ 1½″.
T.E.: 18,515 lb.
2069   Total 1

0-6-0PT   1P   5400 Class

Introduced 1931. Collett design for light passenger work, push-and-pull fitted.

Weight: 46 tons 12 cwt.
Pressure: 165 lb.
Cyls.: $16\frac{1}{2}'' \times 24''$.
Driving Wheels: 5' 2".
T.E.: 14,780 lb.

5400/2/7/9/10/2/4/6–8/20–4

Total 15

0-6-0PT 3F 5700 Class

*Introduced 1929. Collett design for shunting and light goods work developed from 2021 class.

†Introduced 1930. Locos. with steam brake and no A.T.C. fittings, for shunting only.

§Introduced 1933. Locos. with detail alterations, modified cab (except 8700) and increased weight.

‡Introduced 1933. Locos. with condensing apparatus for working over L.T. Metropolitan line.

¶Introduced 1948. Steam brake locos. with increased weight.

Weight: $\begin{cases} 47 \text{ tons } 10 \text{ cwt.}^{*\dagger} \\ 50 \text{ tons } 15 \text{ cwt.}^{\ddagger} \\ 49 \text{ tons } 0 \text{ cwt.}^{\S\P} \end{cases}$

Pressure: 200 lb.
Cyls.: $17\frac{1}{2}'' \times 24''$.
Driving Wheels: 4' 7½".
T.E.: 22,515 lb.

*5702–9/13/5/7/9–22/5–8/31/3/4/
7–40/2–5 /7–50/3–9/61/3–71/3
–6/8–85/7–91/3–9,7700–10/2
–91/3/4/6–9,8701/2/4–49

†6700–2/7/11/2/4/6/7/9–21/3–5/
8/9/34–6/8/9/41–3/5/6/9

§3600–3799, 4600–99, 8700/50–4/
6–99, 9600–82, 9711–99

‡9700–10

¶6750–70/2–9   **Total 810**

0-6-0PT 2P* 2F†
6400 & 7400 Classes

*6400 class. Introduced 1932. Collett design for light passenger work, variation of 5400 class with smaller wheels, push-and-pull fitted.

†7400 class. Introduced 1936. Non-push-and-pull fitted locos.

Weight: $\begin{cases} 45 \text{ tons } 12 \text{ cwt.}^* \\ 45 \text{ tons } 9 \text{ cwt.}^\dagger \end{cases}$

Pressure: 180 lb.
Cyls.: $16\frac{1}{2}'' \times 24''$.
Driving Wheels: 4' 7½".
T.E.: 18,010 lb.

*6400–39

†7400–49

**Total : 6400 Class 40
7400 Class 50**

0-6-0PT 4F 9400 Class

*Introduced 1947. Hawksworth taper boiler design for heavy shunting.

†Introduced 1949. Locos. with non-superheated boiler.

Weight: 55 tons 7 cwt.
Pressure: 200 lb. SS.
Cyls.: $17\frac{1}{2}'' \times 24''$.
Driving Wheels: 4' 7½".
T.E.: 22,515 lb.

*9400–9

†3400–9, 8400–99, 9410–99

Total 210

0-6-0T 1F B.P.G.V.

Introduced 1910. Hudswell Clarke design for B.P.G.V., rebuilt by G.W.R.
Weight: 37 tons 15 cwt.
Pressure: 165 lb.
Cyls.: (O) 15" × 22".
Driving Wheels: 3' 9".
T.E.: 15,430 lb.

2198   **Total 1**

0-6-0T Unclass. W. & L.

(Line closed: locos stored.)

Introduced 1902. Beyer Peacock design for 2' 6" gauge W. & L. Section, Cambrian Railways.
Weight: 19 tons 18 cwt.

Gauge: 2' 6".
Pressure: 150 lb.
Cyls.: (O) 11½" × 16".
Driving Wheels: 2' 9".
T.E.: 8,175 lb.
Walschaerts valve gear.

822/3 **Total 2**

0-4-2T IP
1400 & 5800 Classes

*1400 class introduced 1932. Collett design for light branch work (originally designated 4800 class). Push-and-pull fitted.

†5800 class introduced 1933. Non-push-and-pull fitted locos.
Weight: 41 tons 6 cwt.
Pressure: 165 lb.
Cyls.: 16" × 24".
Driving Wheels: 5' 2".
T.E.: 13,900 lb.

*1401/5/7/9/10/2/7–21/3/4/6–
38/40–2/4–59/62–74
†5801/2/4/9/10/5/8

Total 65

0-4-0T 3F 1101 Class

Introduced 1926. Avonside Engine Co. design to G.W. requirements for dock shunting.
Weight: 38 tons 4 cwt.
Pressure: 170 lb.
Cyls.: (O) 16" × 24".
Driving Wheels: 3' 9½".
T.E.: 19,510 lb.
Walschaerts valve gear.

1101–6 **Total 6**

0-4-0ST OF Cardiff Rly.

Introduced 1893. Kitson design for Cardiff Railway.
Weight: 25 tons 10 cwt.
Pressure: 160 lb.
Cyls.: (O) 14" × 21".

Driving Wheels: 3' 2¼".
T.E.: 14,540 lb.
Hawthorn Kitson valve gear.

1338 **Total 1**

0-4-0ST OF P. & M.

Introduced 1907. Peckett design for P. & M.
Weight: 33 tons 10 cwt.
Pressure: 150 lb.
Cyls.: (O) 15" × 21".
Driving Wheels: 3' 7".
T.E.: 14,010 lb.

1151/2 **Total 2**

0-4-0ST S.H.T.

Introduced 1906. Peckett design for S.H.T. (similar to 1151/2).
Weight: 33 tons 10 cwt.
Pressure: 150 lb.
Cyls.: (O) 15" × 21".
Driving Wheels: 3' 7"
T.E.: 14,010 lb.

1143/5 **Total 2**

Introduced 1909. Hawthorn Leslie design for S.H.T.
Weight: 26 tons 17 cwt.
Pressure: 150 lb.
Cyls.: (O) 14" × 22".
Driving Wheels: 3' 6".
T.E.: 13,090 lb.

1144 **Total 1**

Introduced 1911. Hudswell Clarke design for S.H.T.
Weight: 28 tons 15 cwt.
Pressure: 160 lb.
Cyls.: (O) 15" × 22".
Driving Wheels: 3' 4"
T.E.: 16,830 lb.

1142 **Total 1**

NUMERICAL LIST OF WESTERN REGION STEAM LOCOMOTIVES

Locomotives are of G.W. origin except where indicated by other initials

2-6-2T   V. of R.

7   Owain Glyndŵr
8   Llywelyn
9   Prince of Wales

0-6-0T   W. & L.

822   823
(Line closed : locos. stored.)

4-6-0   1000 Class
" County "

1000	County of Middlesex
1001	County of Bucks
1002	County of Berks
1003	County of Wilts
1004	County of Somerset
1005	County of Devon
1006	County of Cornwall
1007	County of Brecknock
1008	County of Cardigan
1009	County of Carmarthen
1010	County of Caernarvon
1011	County of Chester
1012	County of Denbigh
1013	County of Dorset
1014	County of Glamorgan
1015	County of Gloucester
1016	County of Hants
1017	County of Hereford
1018	County of Leicester
1019	County of Merioneth
1020	County of Monmouth
1021	County of Montgomery
1022	County of Northampton
1023	County of Oxford
1024	County of Pembroke
1025	County of Radnor
1026	County of Salop
1027	County of Stafford
1028	County of Warwick
1029	County of Worcester

0-4-0T   1101 Class

1101	1103	1105
1102	1104	1106

0-4-0ST   S.H.T.

1142	1143	1144	1145

0-4-0ST   P.M.

1151	1152

0-4-0ST   Car. R.

1338

0-6-0ST   1361 Class

1361	1363	1365
1362	1364	

0-6-0PT   1366 Class

1366	1368	1370
1367	1369	1371

0-4-2T   1400 Class

1401	1418	1427	1434
1405	1419	1428	1435
1407	1420	1429	1436
1409	1421	1430	1437
1410	1423	1431	1438
1412	1424	1432	1440
1417	1426	1433	1441

1442-2864

1442	1451	1459	1468
1444	1452	1462	1469
1445	1453	1463	1470
1446	1454	1464	1471
1447	1455	1465	1472
1448	1456	1466	1473
1449	1457	1467	1474
1450	1458		

0-6-0PT   1500 Class

1500	1503	1506	1509
1501	1504	1507	
1502	1505	1508	

0-6-0PT   1600 Class

1600	1618	1636	1654
1601	1619	1637	1655
1602	1620	1638	1656
1603	1621	1639	1657
1604	1622	1640	1658
1605	1623	1641	1659
1606	1624	1642	1660
1607	1625	1643	1661
1608	1626	1644	1662
1609	1627	1645	1663
1610	1628	1646	1664
1611	1629	1647	1665
1612	1630	1648	1666
1613	1631	1649	1667
1614	1632	1650	1668
1615	1633	1651	1669
1616	1634	1652	
1617	1635	1653	

0-6-0PT   850 Class

2012

0-6-0PT   2021 Class

2069

0-6-0T   B.P.G.V.

2198

0-6-0   2251 Class

2200	2225	2250	2275
2201	2226	2251	2276
2202	2227	2252	2277
2203	2228	2253	2278
2204	2229	2254	2279
2205	2230	2255	2280
2206	2231	2256	2281
2207	2232	2257	2282
2208	2233	2258	2283
2209	2234	2259	2284
2210	2235	2260	2285
2211	2236	2261	2286
2212	2237	2262	2287
2213	2238	2263	2288
2214	2239	2264	2289
2215	2240	2265	2290
2216	2241	2266	2291
2217	2242	2267	2292
2218	2243	2268	2293
2219	2244	2269	2294
2220	2245	2270	2295
2221	2246	2271	2296
2222	2247	2272	2297
2223	2248	2273	2298
2224	2249	2274	2299

2-8-0   2800 Class

2801	2817	2833	2849
2802	2818	2834	2850
2803	2819	2835	2851
2804	2820	2836	2852
2805	2821	2837	2853
2806	2822	2838	2854
2807	2823	2839	2855
2808	2824	2840	2856
2809	2825	2841	2857
2810	2826	2842	2858
2811	2827	2843	2859
2812	2828	2844	2860
2813	2829	2845	2861
2814	2830	2846	2862
2815	2831	2847	2863
2816	2832	2848	2864

2865	2874	2883	2892
2866	2875	2884	2893
2867	2876	2885	2894
2868	2877	2886	2895
2869	2878	2887	2896
2870	2879	2888	2897
2871	2880	2889	2898
2872	2881	2890	2899
2873	2882	2891	

2-8-0　　　　R.O.D. Class

3011	3015	3024

2-6-2T　　　　3100 Class

3102	3103

2-6-2T　　　　3150 Class

3170

0-6-0　　　　2251 Class

3200	3205	3210	3215
3201	3206	3211	3216
3202	3207	3212	3217
3203	3208	3213	3218
3204	3209	3214	3219

0-6-0PT　　　　9400 Class

3400	3403	3406	3408
3401	3404	3407	3409
3402	3405		

4-4-0　　　"City" Class

3440	City of Truro

0-6-0PT　　　　5700 Class

3600	3605	3610	3615
3601	3606	3611	3616
3602	3607	3612	3617
3603	3608	3613	3618
3604	3609	3614	3619

3620	3667	3714	3761
3621	3668	3715	3762
3622	3669	3716	3763
3623	3670	3717	3764
3624	3671	3718	3765
3625	3672	3719	3766
3626	3673	3720	3767
3627	3674	3721	3768
3628	3675	3722	3769
3629	3676	3723	3770
3630	3677	3724	3771
3631	3678	3725	3772
3632	3679	3726	3773
3633	3680	3727	3774
3634	3681	3728	3775
3635	3682	3729	3776
3636	3683	3730	3777
3637	3684	3731	3778
3638	3685	3732	3779
3639	3686	3733	3780
3640	3687	3734	3781
3641	3688	3735	3782
3642	3689	3736	3783
3643	3690	3737	3784
3644	3691	3738	3785
3645	3692	3739	3786
3646	3693	3740	3787
3647	3694	3741	3788
3648	3695	3742	3789
3649	3696	3743	3790
3650	3697	3744	3791
3651	3698	3745	3792
3652	3699	3746	3793
3653	3700	3747	3794
3654	3701	3748	3795
3655	3702	3749	3796
3656	3703	3750	3797
3657	3704	3751	3798
3658	3705	3752	3799
3659	3706	3753	
3660	3707	3754	
3661	3708	3755	
3662	3709	3756	
3663	3710	3757	
3664	3711	3758	
3665	3712	3759	
3666	3713	3760	

2-8-0 2800 Class

3800	3817	3834	3851
3801	3818	3835	3852
3802	3819	3836	3853
3803	3820	3837	3854
3804	3821	3838	3855
3805	3822	3839	3856
3806	3823	3840	3857
3807	3824	3841	3858
3808	3825	3842	3859
3809	3826	3843	3860
3810	3827	3844	3861
3811	3828	3845	3862
3812	3829	3846	3863
3813	3830	3847	3864
3814	3831	3848	3865
3815	3832	3849	3866
3816	3833	3850	

4-6-0 4073 Class
" Castle "

4037	The South Wales Borderers
4073	Caerphilly Castle
4074	Caldicot Castle
4075	Cardiff Castle
4076	Carmarthen Castle
4077	Chepstow Castle
4078	Pembroke Castle
4079	Pendennis Castle
4080	Powderham Castle
4081	Warwick Castle
4082	Windsor Castle
4083	Abbotsbury Castle
4084	Aberystwyth Castle
4085	Berkeley Castle
4086	Builth Castle
4087	Cardigan Castle
4088	Dartmouth Castle
4089	Donnington Castle
4090	Dorchester Castle
4091	Dudley Castle
4092	Dunraven Castle
4093	Dunster Castle
4094	Dynevor Castle
4095	Harlech Castle
4096	Highclere Castle
4097	Kenilworth Castle
4098	Kidwelly Castle
4099	Kilgerran Castle

2-6-2T 5100 Class

4100	4120	4142	4161
4101	4121	4143	4162
4102	4122	4144	4163
4103	4123	4145	4164
4104	4124	4146	4165
4105	4125	4147	4166
4106	4126	4148	4167
4107	4127	4149	4168
4108	4128	4150	4169
4109	4129	4151	4170
4110	4130	4152	4171
4111	4131	4153	4172
4112	4132	4154	4173
4113	4133	4155	4174
4114	4134	4156	4175
4115	4135	4157	4176
4116	4136	4158	4177
4117	4137	4159	4178
4118	4140	4160	4179
4119	4141		

2-8-0T 4200 Class

4200	4222	4237	4256
4201	4223	4238	4257
4203	4224	4241	4258
4206	4225	4242	4259
4207	4226	4243	4260
4208	4227	4246	4261
4211	4228	4247	4262
4212	4229	4248	4263
4213	4230	4250	4264
4214	4231	4251	4265
4215	4232	4252	4266
4217	4233	4253	4267
4218	4235	4254	4268
4221	4236	4255	4269

4270	4278	4286	4294
4271	4279	4287	4295
4272	4280	4288	4296
4273	4281	4289	4297
4274	4282	4290	4298
4275	4283	4291	4299
4276	4284	4292	
4277	4285	4293	

2-6-0   4300 Class

4358	4377

2-6-2T   4500 Class

4507	4556	4568	4584
4508	4557	4569	4585
4519	4558	4570	4587
4536	4559	4571	4588
4540	4560	4572	4589
4545	4561	4573	4590
4547	4562	4574	4591
4549	4563	4575	4592
4550	4564	4576	4593
4552	4565	4577	4594
4553	4566	4578	4595
4554	4567	4579	4599
4555			

0-6-0PT   5700 Class

4600	4609	4618	4627
4601	4610	4619	4628
4602	4611	4620	4629
4603	4612	4621	4630
4604	4613	4622	4631
4605	4614	4623	4632
4606	4615	4624	4633
4607	4616	4625	4634
4608	4617	4626	4635

4636	4652	4668	4684
4637	4653	4669	4685
4638	4654	4670	4686
4639	4655	4671	4687
4640	4656	4672	4688
4641	4657	4673	4689
4642	4658	4674	4690
4643	4659	4675	4691
4644	4660	4676	4692
4645	4661	4677	4693
4646	4662	4678	4694
4647	4663	4679	4695
4648	4664	4680	4696
4649	4665	4681	4697
4650	4666	4682	4698
4651	4667	4683	4699

2-8-0   4700 Class

4700	4703	4705	4707
4701	4704	4706	4708
4702			

4-6-0 " Hall " 4900 Class

4900	Saint Martin
4901	Adderley Hall
4902	Aldenham Hall
4903	Astley Hall
4904	Binnegar Hall
4905	Barton Hall
4906	Bradfield Hall
4907	Broughton Hall
4908	Broome Hall
4909	Blakesley Hall
4910	Blaisdon Hall
4912	Berrington Hall
4913	Baglan Hall
4914	Cranmore Hall
4915	Condover Hall
4916	Crumlin Hall
4917	Crosswood Hall
4918	Dartington Hall
4919	Donnington Hall
4920	Dumbleton Hall
4921	Eaton Hall
4922	Enville Hall

4923	Evenley Hall
4924	Eydon Hall
4925	Eynsham Hall
4926	Fairleigh Hall
4927	Farnborough Hall
4928	Gatacre Hall
4929	Goytrey Hall
4930	Hagley Hall
4931	Hanbury Hall
4932	Hatherton Hall
4933	Himley Hall
4934	Hindlip Hall
4935	Ketley Hall
4936	Kinlet Hall
4937	Lanelay Hall
4938	Liddington Hall
4939	Littleton Hall
4940	Ludford Hall
4941	Llangedwyn Hall
4942	Maindy Hall
4943	Marrington Hall
4944	Middleton Hall
4945	Milligan Hall
4946	Moseley Hall
4947	Nanhoran Hall
4948	Northwick Hall
4949	Packwood Hall
4950	Patshull Hall
4951	Pendeford Hall
4952	Peplow Hall
4953	Pitchford Hall
4954	Plaish Hall
4955	Plaspower Hall
4956	Plowden Hall
4957	Postlip Hall
4958	Priory Hall
4959	Purley Hall
4960	Pyle Hall
4961	Pyrland Hall
4962	Ragley Hall
4963	Rignall Hall
4964	Rodwell Hall
4965	Rood Ashton Hall
4966	Shakenhurst Hall
4967	Shirenewton Hall
4968	Shotton Hall
4969	Shrugborough Hall

4970	Sketty Hall
4971	Stanway Hall
4972	Saint Brides Hall
4973	Sweeney Hall
4974	Talgarth Hall
4975	Umberslade Hall
4976	Warfield Hall
4977	Watcombe Hall
4978	Westwood Hall
4979	Wootton Hall
4980	Wrottesley Hall
4981	Abberley Hall
4982	Acton Hall
4983	Albert Hall
4984	Albrighton Hall
4985	Allesley Hall
4986	Aston Hall
4987	Brockley Hall
4988	Bulwell Hall
4989	Cherwell Hall
4990	Clifton Hall
4991	Cobham Hall
4992	Crosby Hall
4993	Dalton Hall
4994	Downton Hall
4995	Easton Hall
4996	Eden Hall
4997	Elton Hall
4998	Eyton Hall
4999	Gopsal Hall

4-6-0 "Castle" 4073 Class

5000	Launceston Castle
5001	Llandovery Castle
5002	Ludlow Castle
5003	Lulworth Castle
5004	Llanstephan Castle
5005	Manorbier Castle
5006	Tregenna Castle
5007	Rougemont Castle
5008	Raglan Castle
5009	Shrewsbury Castle
5010	Restormel Castle
5011	Tintagel Castle
5012	Berry Pomeroy Castle

5013	Abergavenny Castle	5059	Earl St. Aldwyn
5014	Goodrich Castle	5060	Earl of Berkeley
5015	Kingswear Castle	5061	Earl of Birkenhead
5016	Montgomery Castle	5062	Earl of Shaftesbury
5017	The Gloucestershire	5063	Earl Baldwin
	Regiment 28th, 61st	5064	Bishop's Castle
5018	St. Mawes Castle	5065	Newport Castle
5019	Treago Castle	5066	Sir Felix Pole
5020	Trematon Castle	5067	St. Fagans Castle
5021	Whittington Castle	5068	Beverston Castle
5022	Wigmore Castle	5069	Isambard Kingdom Brunel
5023	Brecon Castle	5070	Sir Daniel Gooch
5024	Carew Castle	5071	Spitfire
5025	Chirk Castle	5072	Hurricane
5026	Criccieth Castle	5073	Blenheim
5027	Farleigh Castle	5074	Hampden
5028	Llantilio Castle	5075	Wellington
5029	Nunney Castle	5076	Gladiator
5030	Shirburn Castle	5077	Fairey Battle
5031	Totnes Castle	5078	Beaufort
5032	Usk Castle	5079	Lysander
5033	Broughton Castle	5080	Defiant
5034	Corfe Castle	5081	Lockheed Hudson
5035	Coity Castle	5082	Swordfish
5036	Lyonshall Castle	5083	Bath Abbey
5037	Monmouth Castle	5084	Reading Abbey
5038	Morlais Castle	5085	Evesham Abbey
5039	Rhuddlan Castle	5086	Viscount Horne
5040	Stokesay Castle	5087	Tintern Abbey
5041	Tiverton Castle	5088	Llanthony Abbey
5042	Winchester Castle	5089	Westminster Abbey
5043	Earl of Mount Edgcumbe	5090	Neath Abbey
5044	Earl of Dunraven	5091	Cleeve Abbey
5045	Earl of Dudley	5092	Tresco Abbey
5046	Earl Cawdor	5093	Upton Castle
5047	Earl of Dartmouth	5094	Tretower Castle
5048	Earl of Devon	5095	Barbury Castle
5049	Earl of Plymouth	5096	Bridgwater Castle
5050	Earl of St. Germans	5097	Sarum Castle
5051	Earl Bathurst	5098	Clifford Castle
5052	Earl of Radnor	5099	Compton Castle
5053	Earl Cairns		
5054	Earl of Ducie		
5055	Earl of Eldon		
5056	Earl of Powis		
5057	Earl Waldegrave		
5058	Earl of Clancarty		

2-6-2T   5100 Class

5101	5103	5105	5110
5102	5104	5106	5148

21

5150	5166	5178	5189
5151	5167	5179	5190
5152	5168	5180	5191
5153	5169	5181	5192
5154	5170	5182	5193
5155	5172	5183	5194
5156	5173	5184	5195
5158	5174	5185	5196
5160	5175	5186	5197
5163	5176	5187	5198
5164	5177	5188	5199

5376	5382	5388	5394
5377	5384	5390	5396
5378	5385	5392	5398
5380	5386	5393	5399
5381			

0-6-0PT 5400 Class

5400	5410	5417	5422
5402	5412	5418	5423
5407	5414	5420	5424
5409	5416	5421	

2-8-0T 4200 Class

5200	5217	5234	5251
5201	5218	5235	5252
5202	5219	5236	5253
5203	5220	5237	5254
5204	5221	5238	5255
5205	5222	5239	5256
5206	5223	5240	5257
5207	5224	5241	5258
5208	5225	5242	5259
5209	5226	5243	5260
5210	5227	5244	5261
5211	5228	5245	5262
5212	5229	5246	5263
5213	5230	5247	5264
5214	5231	5248	
5215	5232	5249	
5216	5233	5250	

2-6-2T 4500 Class

5500	5523	5541	5558
5503	5524	5542	5559
5504	5525	5543	5560
5507	5526	5544	5561
5508	5527	5545	5562
5509	5528	5546	5563
5510	5529	5547	5564
5511	5530	5548	5565
5514	5531	5549	5566
5515	5532	5550	5567
5516	5533	5551	5568
5517	5534	5552	5569
5518	5536	5553	5570
5519	5537	5554	5571
5520	5538	5555	5572
5521	5539	5556	5573
5522	5540	5557	5574

2-6-0 4300 Class

5306	5326	5339	5357
5311	5330	5341	5358
5312	5331	5344	5360
5315	5332	5345	5361
5318	5333	5350	5367
5319	5335	5351	5368
5321	5336	5353	5369
5322	5337	5355	5370
5324	5338	5356	5375

0-6-2T 5600 Class

5600	5603	5606	5609
5601	5604	5607	5610
5602	5605	5608	5611

5612	5634	5656	5678
5613	5635	5657	5679
5614	5636	5658	5680
5615	5637	5659	5681
5616	5638	5660	5682
5617	5639	5661	5683
5618	5640	5662	5684
5619	5641	5663	5685
5620	5642	5664	5686
5621	5643	5665	5687
5622	5644	5666	5688
5623	5645	5667	5689
5624	5646	5668	5690
5625	5647	5669	5691
5626	5648	5670	5692
5627	5649	5671	5693
5628	5650	5672	5694
5629	5651	5673	5695
5630	5652	5674	5696
5631	5653	5675	5697
5632	5654	5676	5698
5633	5655	5677	5699

5791	5794	5796	5798
5793	5795	5797	5799

0-4-2T   5800 Class

5801	5804	5810	5818
5802	5809	5815	

4-6-0   4900 Class
" Hall "

5900	Hinderton Hall
5901	Hazel Hall
5902	Howick Hall
5903	Keele Hall
5904	Kelham Hall
5905	Knowsley Hall
5906	Lawton Hall
5907	Marble Hall
5908	Moreton Hall
5909	Newton Hall
5910	Park Hall
5911	Preston Hall
5912	Queen's Hall
5913	Rushton Hall
5914	Ripon Hall
5915	Trentham Hall
5916	Trinity Hall
5917	Westminster Hall
5918	Walton Hall
5919	Worsley Hall
5920	Wycliffe Hall
5921	Bingley Hall
5922	Caxton Hall
5923	Colston Hall
5924	Dinton Hall
5925	Eastcote Hall
5926	Grotrian Hall
5927	Guild Hall
5928	Haddon Hall
5929	Hanham Hall
5930	Hannington Hall
5931	Hatherley Hall

0-6-0PT   5700 Class

5702	5727	5750	5771
5703	5728	5753	5773
5704	5731	5754	5774
5705	5733	5755	5775
5706	5734	5756	5776
5707	5737	5757	5778
5708	5738	5758	5779
5709	5739	5759	5780
5713	5740	5761	5781
5715	5742	5763	5782
5717	5743	5764	5783
5719	5744	5765	5784
5720	5745	5766	5785
5721	5746	5767	5787
5722	5747	5768	5788
5725	5748	5769	5789
5726	5749	5770	5790

23

5932	Haydon Hall
5933	Kingsway Hall
5934	Kneller Hall
5935	Norton Hall
5936	Oakley Hall
5937	Stanford Hall
5938	Stanley Hall
5939	Tangley Hall
5940	Whitbourne Hall
5941	Campion Hall
5942	Doldowlod Hall
5943	Elmdon Hall
5944	Ickenham Hall
5945	Leckhampton Hall
5946	Marwell Hall
5947	Saint Benet's Hall
5948	Siddington Hall
5949	Trematon Hall
5950	Wardley Hall
5951	Clyffe Hall
5952	Cogan Hall
5953	Dunley Hall
5954	Faendre Hall
5955	Garth Hall
5956	Horsley Hall
5957	Hutton Hall
5958	Knolton Hall
5959	Mawley Hall
5960	Saint Edmund Hall
5961	Toynbee Hall
5962	Wantage Hall
5963	Wimpole Hall
5964	Wolseley Hall
5965	Woollas Hall
5966	Ashford Hall
5967	Bickmarsh Hall
5968	Cory Hall
5969	Honington Hall
5970	Hengrave Hall
5971	Merevale Hall
5972	Olton Hall
5973	Rolleston Hall
5974	Wallsworth Hall
5975	Winslow Hall
5976	Ashwicke Hall
5977	Beckford Hall
5978	Bodinnick Hall

5979	Cruckton Hall
5980	Dingley Hall
5981	Frensham Hall
5982	Harrington Hall
5983	Henley Hall
5984	Linden Hall
5985	Mostyn Hall
5986	Arbury Hall
5987	Brocket Hall
5988	Bostock Hall
5989	Cransley Hall
5990	Dorford Hall
5991	Gresham Hall
5992	Horton Hall
5993	Kirby Hall
5994	Roydon Hall
5995	Wick Hall
5996	Mytton Hall
5997	Sparkford Hall
5998	Trevor Hall
5999	Wollaton Hall

4-6-0   6000 Class
" King "

6000	King George V
6001	King Edward VII
6002	King William IV
6003	King George IV
6004	King George III
6005	King George II
6006	King George I
6007	King William III
6008	King James II
6009	King Charles II
6010	King Charles I
6011	King James I
6012	King Edward VI
6013	King Henry VIII
6014	King Henry VII
6015	King Richard III
6016	King Edward V
6017	King Edward IV
6018	King Henry VI
6019	King Henry V
6020	King Henry IV

6021	King Richard II
6022	King Edward III
6023	King Edward II
6024	King Edward I
6025	King Henry III
6026	King John
6027	King Richard I
6028	King George VI
6029	King Edward VIII

6354	6366	6378	6391
6355	6367	6379	6392
6356	6368	6380	6393
6357	6369	6381	6394
6358	6370	6382	6395
6359	6371	6384	6397
6360	6372	6385	6398
6361	6373	6386	6399
6362	6374	6387	
6363	6375	6388	
6364	6376	6389	
6365	6377	6390	

2-6-2T   6100 Class

6100	6118	6136	6154
6101	6119	6137	6155
6102	6120	6138	6156
6103	6121	6139	6157
6104	6122	6140	6158
6105	6123	6141	6159
6106	6124	6142	6160
6107	6125	6143	6161
6108	6126	6144	6162
6109	6127	6145	6163
6110	6128	6146	6164
6111	6129	6147	6165
6112	6130	6148	6166
6113	6131	6149	6167
6114	6132	6150	6168
6115	6133	6151	6169
6116	6134	6152	
6117	6135	6153	

0-6-0PT   6400 Class

6400	6410	6420	6430
6401	6411	6421	6431
6402	6412	6422	6432
6403	6413	6423	6433
6404	6414	6424	6434
6405	6415	6425	6435
6406	6416	6426	6436
6407	6417	6427	6437
6408	6418	6428	6438
6409	6419	6429	6439

0-6-2T   5600 Class

6600	6620	6640	6660
6601	6621	6641	6661
6602	6622	6642	6662
6603	6623	6643	6663
6604	6624	6644	6664
6605	6625	6645	6665
6606	6626	6646	6666
6607	6627	6647	6667
6608	6628	6648	6668
6609	6629	6649	6669
6610	6630	6650	6670
6611	6631	6651	6671
6612	6632	6652	6672
6613	6633	6653	6673
6614	6634	6654	6674
6615	6635	6655	6675
6616	6636	6656	6676
6617	6637	6657	6677
6618	6638	6658	6678
6619	6639	6659	6679

2-6-0   4300 Class

6300	6313	6328	6341
6301	6314	6329	6342
6302	6316	6330	6343
6303	6317	6331	6344
6304	6318	6332	6345
6305	6319	6333	6346
6306	6320	6334	6347
6307	6322	6335	6348
6308	6323	6336	6349
6309	6324	6337	6350
6310	6325	6338	6351
6311	6326	6339	6352
6312	6327	6340	6353

6680	6685	6690	6695
6681	6686	6691	6696
6682	6687	6692	6697
6683	6688	6693	6698
6684	6689	6694	6699

0-6-0PT   5700 Class

6700	6728	6751	6765
6701	6729	6752	6766
6702	6734	6753	6767
6707	6735	6754	6768
6711	6736	6755	6769
6712	6738	6756	6770
6714	6739	6757	6772
6716	6741	6758	6773
6717	6742	6759	6774
6719	6743	6760	6775
6720	6745	6761	6776
6721	6746	6762	6777
6723	6749	6763	6778
6724	6750	6764	6779
6725			

4-6-0   6800 Class
" Grange "

6800	Arlington Grange
6801	Aylburton Grange
6802	Bampton Grange
6803	Bucklebury Grange
6804	Brockington Grange
6805	Broughton Grange
6806	Blackwell Grange
6807	Birchwood Grange
6808	Beenham Grange
6809	Burghclere Grange
6810	Blakemere Grange
6811	Cranbourne Grange
6812	Chesford Grange
6813	Eastbury Grange
6814	Enborne Grange
6815	Frilford Grange
6816	Frankton Grange
6817	Gwenddwr Grange
6818	Hardwick Grange
6819	Highnam Grange
6820	Kingstone Grange
6821	Leaton Grange
6822	Manton Grange
6823	Oakley Grange
6824	Ashley Grange
6825	Llanvair Grange
6826	Nannerth Grange
6827	Llanfrechfa Grange
6828	Trellech Grange
6829	Burmington Grange
6830	Buckenhill Grange
6831	Bearley Grange
6832	Brockton Grange
6833	Calcot Grange
6834	Dummer Grange
6835	Eastham Grange
6836	Estevarney Grange
6837	Forthampton Grange
6838	Goodmoor Grange
6839	Hewell Grange
6840	Hazeley Grange
6841	Marlas Grange
6842	Nunhold Grange
6843	Poulton Grange
6844	Penhydd Grange
6845	Paviland Grange
6846	Ruckley Grange
6847	Tidmarsh Grange
6848	Toddington Grange
6849	Walton Grange
6850	Cleeve Grange
6851	Hurst Grange
6852	Headbourne Grange
6853	Morehampton Grange
6854	Roundhill Grange
6855	Saighton Grange
6856	Stowe Grange
6857	Tudor Grange
6858	Woolston Grange
6859	Yiewsley Grange
6860	Aberporth Grange

6861	Crynant Grange
6862	Derwent Grange
6863	Dolhywel Grange
6864	Dymock Grange
6865	Hopton Grange
6866	Morfa Grange
6867	Peterston Grange
6868	Penrhos Grange
6869	Resolven Grange
6870	Bodicote Grange
6871	Bourton Grange
6872	Crawley Grange
6873	Caradoc Grange
6874	Haughton Grange
6875	Hindford Grange
6876	Kingsland Grange
6877	Llanfair Grange
6878	Longford Grange
6879	Overton Grange

4-6-0   4900 Class
" Hall "

6900	Abney Hall
6901	Arley Hall
6902	Butlers Hall
6903	Belmont Hall
6904	Charfield Hall
6905	Claughton Hall
6906	Chicheley Hall
6907	Davenham Hall
6908	Downham Hall
6909	Frewin Hall
6910	Gossington Hall
6911	Holker Hall
6912	Helmster Hall
6913	Levens Hall
6914	Langton Hall
6915	Mursley Hall
6916	Misterton Hall
6917	Oldlands Hall
6918	Sandon Hall
6919	Tylney Hall
6920	Barningham Hall
6921	Borwick Hall
6922	Burton Hall
6923	Croxteth Hall

6924	Grantley Hall
6925	Hackness Hall
6926	Holkham Hall
6927	Lilford Hall
6928	Underley Hall
6929	Whorlton Hall
6930	Aldersey Hall
6931	Aldborough Hall
6932	Burwarton Hall
6933	Birtles Hall
6934	Beachamwell Hall
6935	Browsholme Hall
6936	Breccles Hall
6937	Conyngham Hall
6938	Corndean Hall
6939	Calveley Hall
6940	Didlington Hall
6941	Fillongley Hall
6942	Eshton Hall
6943	Farnley Hall
6944	Fledborough Hall
6945	Glasfryn Hall
6946	Heatherden Hall
6947	Helmingham Hall
6948	Holbrooke Hall
6949	Haberfield Hall
6950	Kingsthorpe Hall
6951	Impney Hall
6952	Kimberley Hall
6953	Leighton Hall
6954	Lotherton Hall
6955	Lydcott Hall
6956	Mottram Hall
6957	Norcliffe Hall
6958	Oxburgh Hall

4-6-0   6959 Class
" Modified Hall "

6959	Peatling Hall
6960	Raveningham Hall
6961	Stedham Hall
6962	Soughton Hall
6963	Throwley Hall
6964	Thornbridge Hall
6965	Thirlestaine Hall
6966	Witchingham Hall

6967	Willesley Hall	7009	Athelney Castle
6968	Woodcock Hall	7010	Avondale Castle
6969	Wraysbury Hall	7011	Banbury Castle
6970	Whaddon Hall	7012	Barry Castle
6971	Athelhampton Hall	7013	Bristol Castle
6972	Beningbrough Hall	7014	Caerhays Castle
6973	Bricklehampton Hall	7015	Carn Brea Castle
6974	Bryngwyn Hall	7016	Chester Castle
6975	Capesthorne Hall	7017	G. J. Churchward
6976	Graythwaite Hall	7018	Drysllwyn Castle
6977	Grundisburgh Hall	7019	Fowey Castle
6978	Haroldstone Hall	7020	Gloucester Castle
6979	Helperly Hall	7021	Haverfordwest Castle
6980	Llanrumney Hall	7022	Hereford Castle
6981	Marbury Hall	7023	Penrice Castle
6982	Melmerby Hall	7024	Powis Castle
6983	Otterington Hall	7025	Sudeley Castle
6984	Owsden Hall	7026	Tenby Castle
6985	Parwick Hall	7027	Thornbury Castle
6986	Rydal Hall	7028	Cadbury Castle
6987	Shervington Hall	7029	Clun Castle
6988	Swithland Hall	7030	Cranbrook Castle
6989	Wightwick Hall	7031	Cromwell's Castle
6990	Witherslack Hall	7032	Denbigh Castle
6991	Acton Burnell Hall	7033	Hartlebury Castle
6992	Arborfield Hall	7034	Ince Castle
6993	Arthog Hall	7035	Ogmore Castle
6994	Baggrave Hall	7036	Taunton Castle
6995	Benthall Hall	7037	Swindon
6996	Blackwell Hall		
6997	Bryn-Ivor Hall		
6998	Burton Agnes Hall		
6999	Capel Dewi Hall		

4-6-0   4073 Class
" Castle "

7000	Viscount Portal
7001	Sir James Milne
7002	Devizes Castle
7003	Elmley Castle
7004	Eastnor Castle
7005	Sir Edward Elgar
7006	Lydford Castle
7007	Great Western
7008	Swansea Castle

2-8-2T   7200 Class

7200	7214	7228	7242
7201	7215	7229	7243
7202	7216	7230	7244
7203	7217	7231	7245
7204	7218	7232	7246
7205	7219	7233	7247
7206	7220	7234	7248
7207	7221	7235	7249
7208	7222	7236	7250
7209	7223	7237	7251
7210	7224	7238	7252
7211	7225	7239	7253
7212	7226	7240	
7213	7227	7241	

2-6-0   4300 Class

7300	7309	7318	7326
7301	7310	7319	7328
7302	7311	7320	7329
7303	7312	7321	7333
7304	7313	7322	7336
7305	7314	7323	7339
7306	7315	7324	7340
7307	7316	7325	7341
7308	7317		

0-6-0PT   7400 Class

7400	7413	7426	7438
7401	7414	7427	7439
7402	7415	7428	7440
7403	7416	7429	7441
7404	7417	7430	7442
7405	7418	7431	7443
7406	7419	7432	7444
7407	7420	7433	7445
7408	7421	7434	7446
7409	7422	7435	7447
7410	7423	7436	7448
7411	7424	7437	7449
7412	7425		

0-6-0PT   5700 Class

7700	7721	7741	7761
7701	7722	7742	7762
7702	7723	7743	7763
7703	7724	7744	7764
7704	7725	7745	7765
7705	7726	7746	7766
7706	7727	7747	7767
7707	7728	7748	7768
7708	7729	7749	7769
7709	7730	7750	7770
7710	7731	7751	7771
7712	7732	7752	7772
7713	7733	7753	7773
7714	7734	7754	7774
7715	7735	7755	7775
7716	7736	7756	7776
7717	7737	7757	7777
7718	7738	7758	7778
7719	7739	7759	7779
7720	7740	7760	7780

7781	7786	7790	7796
7782	7787	7791	7797
7783	7788	7793	7798
7784	7789	7794	7799
7785			

4-6-0   7800 Class
" Manor "

7800	Torquay Manor
7801	Anthony Manor
7802	Bradley Manor
7803	Barcote Manor
7804	Baydon Manor
7805	Broome Manor
7806	Cockington Manor
7807	Compton Manor
7808	Cookham Manor
7809	Childrey Manor
7810	Draycott Manor
7811	Dunley Manor
7812	Erlestoke Manor
7813	Freshford Manor
7814	Fringford Manor
7815	Fritwell Manor
7816	Frilsham Manor
7817	Garsington Manor
7818	Granville Manor
7819	Hinton Manor
7820	Dinmore Manor
7821	Ditcheat Manor
7822	Foxcote Manor
7823	Hook Norton Manor
7824	Iford Manor
7825	Lechlade Manor
7826	Longworth Manor
7827	Lydham Manor
7828	Odney Manor
7829	Ramsbury Manor

4-6-0   6959 Class
" Modified Hall "

7900	Saint Peter's Hall
7901	Dodington Hall
7902	Eaton Mascot Hall
7903	Foremarke Hall
7904	Fountains Hall

7905	Fowey Hall
7906	Fron Hall
7907	Hart Hall
7908	Henshall Hall
7909	Heveningham Hall
7910	Hown Hall
7911	Lady Margaret Hall
7912	Little Linford Hall
7913	Little Wyrley Hall
7914	Lleweni Hall
7915	Mere Hall
7916	Mobberley Hall
7917	North Aston Hall
7918	Rhose Wood Hall
7919	Runter Hall
7920	Coney Hall
7921	Edstone Hall
7922	Salford Hall
7923	Speke Hall
7924	Thornycroft Hall
7925	Westol Hall
7926	Willey Hall
7927	Willington Hall
7928	Wolf Hall
7929	Wyke Hall

8456	8467	8478	8489
8457	8468	8479	8490
8458	8469	8480	8491
8459	8470	8481	8492
8460	8471	8482	8493
8461	8472	8483	8494
8462	8473	8484	8495
8463	8474	8485	8496
8464	8475	8486	8497
8465	8476	8487	8498
8466	8477	8488	8499

2-6-2T   8100 Class

8100	8103	8106	8108
8101	8104	8107	8109
8102			

0-6-0PT   9400 Class

8400	8414	8428	8442
8401	8415	8429	8443
8402	8416	8430	8444
8403	8417	8431	8445
8404	8418	8432	8446
8405	8419	8433	8447
8406	8420	8434	8448
8407	8421	8435	8449
8408	8422	8436	8450
8409	8423	8437	8451
8410	8424	8438	8452
8411	8425	8439	8453
8412	8426	8440	8454
8413	8427	8441	8455

0-6-0PT   5700 Class

8700	8726	8751	8777
8701	8727	8752	8778
8702	8728	8753	8779
8704	8729	8754	8780
8705	8730	8756	8781
8706	8731	8757	8782
8707	8732	8758	8783
8708	8733	8759	8784
8709	8734	8760	8785
8710	8735	8761	8786
8711	8736	8762	8787
8712	8737	8763	8788
8713	8738	8764	8789
8714	8739	8765	8790
8715	8740	8766	8791
8716	8741	8767	8792
8717	8742	8768	8793
8718	8743	8769	8794
8719	8744	8770	8795
8720	8745	8771	8796
8721	8746	8772	8797
8722	8747	8773	8798
8723	8748	8774	8799
8724	8749	8775	
8725	8750	8776	

4-4-0   9000 Class

9004	9013	9015	9018
9005	9014	9017	9021

2-6-0   4300 Class

9305	9309	9312	9315
9308	9310	9313	

0-6-0PT   9400 Class

9400	9425	9450	9475
9401	9426	9451	9476
9402	9427	9452	9477
9403	9428	9453	9478
9404	9429	9454	9479
9405	9430	9455	9480
9406	9431	9456	9481
9407	9432	9457	9482
9408	9433	9458	9483
9409	9434	9459	9484
9410	9435	9460	9485
9411	9436	9461	9486
9412	9437	9462	9487
9413	9438	9463	9488
9414	9439	9464	9489
9415	9440	9465	9490
9416	9441	9466	9491
9417	9442	9467	9492
9418	9443	9468	9493
9419	9444	9469	9494
9420	9445	9470	9495
9421	9446	9471	9496
9422	9447	9472	9497
9423	9448	9473	9498
9424	9449	9474	9499

0-6-0PT   5700 Class

9600	9610	9620	9630
9601	9611	9621	9631
9602	9612	9622	9632
9603	9613	9623	9633
9604	9614	9624	9634
9605	9615	9625	9635
9606	9616	9626	9636
9607	9617	9627	9637
9608	9618	9628	9638
9609	9619	9629	9639

9640	9676	9729	9765
9641	9677	9730	9766
9642	9678	9731	9767
9643	9679	9732	9768
9644	9680	9733	9769
9645	9681	9734	9770
9646	9682	9735	9771
9647	9700	9736	9772
9648	9701	9737	9773
9649	9702	9738	9774
9650	9703	9739	9775
9651	9704	9740	9776
9652	9705	9741	9777
9653	9706	9742	9778
9654	9707	9743	9779
9655	9708	9744	9780
9656	9709	9745	9781
9657	9710	9746	9782
9658	9711	9747	9783
9659	9712	9748	9784
9660	9713	9749	9785
9661	9714	9750	9786
9662	9715	9751	9787
9663	9716	9752	9788
9664	9717	9753	9789
9665	9718	9754	9790
9666	9719	9755	9791
9667	9720	9756	9792
9668	9721	9757	9793
9669	9722	9758	9794
9670	9723	9759	9795
9671	9724	9760	9796
9672	9725	9761	9797
9673	9726	9762	9798
9674	9727	9763	9799
9675	9728	9764	

SERVICE LOCOMOTIVES

Diesel Mechanical

20
PWM 650   **Total 2**

Petrol

22   24   27
                    Total 3

POWER AND WEIGHT CLASSIFICATION

Since 1920 Western Region locomotives have been classified for power and weight by a letter on a coloured disc on the cab side. The letter represents the power of the locomotive and is approximately proportional to the tractive effort as under :

Power class	Tractive effort lb.	Power class	Tractive effort lb.
Special	Over 38,000	B	18,501–20,500
E	33,001–38,000	A	16,500–18,500
D	25,001–33,000	Un-grouped	
C	20,501–25,000		Below 16,500

The colour of the circle represents the routes over which the engine may work. Red engines are limited to the main lines and lines capable of carrying the heaviest locomotives ; blue engines are allowed over additional routes, yellow engines over nearly the whole system and uncoloured engines are more or less unrestricted. The double red circles on the " King " class represent special restrictions for these engines.

Class	Power Class	Route Restriction Colour	Class	Power Class	Route Restriction Colour
4-6-0			**0-6-2T**		
1000	D	Red	5600	D	Red
4073	D	Red			
4900	D	Red	**0-6-0T**		
6000	Special	Double Red	850	—	—
6800	D	Red	1361	—	—
6959	D	Red	1366	—	Red
7800	D	Blue	1500	C	Red
4-4-0			1600	A	—
9000	B	Yellow	2021	A	—
2-8-0			5400	—	Yellow
2800	E	Blue	5700	C	Yellow
R.O.D.	D	Blue	9700–10	C	Blue
4700	D	Red	6400	A	Yellow
2-6-0			7400	A	Yellow
4300	D	Blue	9400	C	Red
9305	D	Red	(2198)	—	—
0-6-0					
2251	B	Yellow	**0-4-2T**		
2-8-2T			1400	—	—
7200	E	Red	5800	—	—
2-8-0T					
4200	E	Red	**0-4-0T**		
2-6-2T			1101	B	Red
3100	D	Red	(1338)	—	—
4500	C	Yellow	(1151)	—	—
5100	D	Blue	(1143)	—	Blue
6100	D	Blue	(1144)	—	Yellow
8100	D	Blue	(1142)	A	Yellow
(7)	—	—			

Ex-S.H.T. 0-4-0ST No. 1144

[*P. J. Sharpe*

x-S.H.T. 0-4-0ST No. 1142

[*R. A. Panting*

Ex-P.M. 0-4-0ST No. 1152

[*A. R. Carpenter*

7400 Class 0-6-0PT No. 7402   *[A. R. Carpenter*

5700 Class 0-6-0PT No. 6707   *B. K. B. Green*

5700 Class 0-6-0PT No. 9602   *[P. Ransome-Wallis*

Above: 6000 Class 4-6-0 No. 6009 *King Charles II* [R. C. Riley

Left: Smokebox of 6000 Class 4-6-0 No. 6021 *King Richard II* as modified, showing new pattern basket-type spark arrester and steampipe layout [G. Wheeler

Below: 6000 Class 4-6-0 No. 6014 *King Henry VII* (fitted with double chimney and retaining 1935 stream-lined cab) [G. Wheeler

4073 Class 4-6-0 No. 7013 *Bristol Castle*

[B. K. B. Gree

4073 Class 4-6-0 No. 4093 *Dunster Castle* (fitted with four-row superheater and double chimney)

[J. Hodge

1000 Class 4-6-0 No. 1003 *County of Wilts* (fitted with double chimney)

[G. Wheeler

900 Class 4-6-0 No. 4900 *Saint Martin* (with lower-pitched boiler than class standard)

[*B. K. B. Green*

4900 Class 4-6-0 No. 6957 *Norcliffe Hall*

[*G. Wheeler*

6959 Class 4-6-0 No. 6970 *Whaddon Hall*

G. Wheeler

6800 Class 4-6-0 No. 6849 *Walton Grange*

[G. Wheeler

7800 Class 4-6-0 No. 7800 *Torquay Manor*

[G. Wheeler

4700 Class 2-8-0 No. 4704

[R. C. Riley

4300 Class 2-6-0 No 4358

[*J. A. Young*

4300 Class 2-6-0 No. 6339 (with detail differences to No. 4358)

[*R. K. Evans*

4300 Class 2-6-0 No. 7333 (with side-window cab)

[*G. Wheeler*

2800 Class 2-8-0 No. 2813 [Brian E. Morrison

2800 Class 2-8-0 Nc. 3819 (with side-window cab) [P. J. Sharpe

R.O.D. Class 2-8-0 No. 3011 [B. K. B. Green

7200 Class 2-8-2T No. 7242

[B. K. B. Green

4200 Class 2-8-0T No. 4217

[B K. B. Green

4200 Class 2-8-0T No. 5259 (with outside steampipes and raised framing over cylinders)

[B. K. B. Green

3150 Class 2-6-2T No. 3170

[K. R. Pirt

8100 Class 2-6-2T No. 8109

[R. C. Riley

6100 Class 2-6-2T No. 6125

[G. Wheeler

4500 Class 2-6-2T No. 4574 [G Wheeler

4575 Class 2-6-2T No. 5509 [G. Wheeler

2251 Class 0-6-0 No. 2276 G. Wheeler

" City " Class 4-4-0 No. 3440 *City of Truro*

[*J. Hodge*

9000 Class 4-4-0 No. 9013

[*Brian E. Morrison*

5600 Class 0-6-2T No 6664

[*G. Wheeler*

SUMMARY OF SOUTHERN REGION STEAM LOCOMOTIVE CLASSES

IN ALPHABETICAL ORDER
WITH HISTORICAL NOTES AND DIMENSIONS

The code given in smaller bold type at the head of each Class,
e.g. " 2F " denotes its British Railways power classification.
The numbers of locomotives in service have been checked to May 6th, 1958.

Classes

0-6-0T 0P A1 & A1X

*A1. Introduced 1872. Stroudley L.B.S.C. "Terrier", later fitted with Marsh boiler, retaining original type smokebox.

†A1X. Introduced 1911. Rebuild of A1 with Marsh boiler and extended smokebox.

‡A1X. Loco. with increased cylinder diameter.

Weight: { 27 tons 10 cwt.*
{ 28 tons 5 cwt.†‡

Pressure: 150 lb.

Cyls.: { 12″ × 20″.*†
{ 14 3/16″ × 20″.‡

Driving Wheels: 4′ 0″.

T.E.: { 7,650 lb.*†
{ 10,695 lb.‡

*DS680

†DS377 DS681, 32640/6/50/5/61/2/70/7/8

‡32636　　　Total A1　1
　　　　　　　　　　　A1X　12

0-4-0T 1F Class B4

*Introduced 1891. Adams L.S.W. design for dock shunting.

†Introduced 1908. Drummond K14 locos., with smaller boiler and detail alterations.

Weight: { 33 tons 9 cwt.*
{ 32 tons 18 cwt.†

Pressure: 140 lb. Cyls. (O): 16″ × 22″.

Driving Wheels: 3′ 9¾″.

T.E.: 14,650 lb.

*30086–9/93/6, 30102

†30083/4　　　　　　　Total 9

0-6-0 2F Class C

Introduced 1900. Wainwright S.E.C. design.

Weight: Loco. 43 tons 16 cwt.

Pressure: 160 lb.

Cyls.: 18½″ × 26″.

Driving Wheels: 5′ 2″.

T.E.: 19,520 lb.

31004/18/33/7/54/61/8/71/86, 31102/12/3/50/91, 31218/9/21/3/7/9/42–5/52/3/5/6/67/8/70–2/80/7/93/7/8, 31317, 31461/80/1/95/8, 31510/73/5/6/8/9/81/3–5/8–90/2, 31681–4/6/8–95, 31714–7/9–25　　　Total 82

0-6-0 2F Class C2X

Introduced 1908. Marsh rebuild of R. J. Billinton L.B.S.C. C2 with larger C3-type boiler, extended smokebox, etc.

Weight: Loco. 45 tons 5 cwt.

Pressure: 170 lb.

Cyls.: 17½″ × 26″.

Driving Wheels: 5′ 0″.

T.E.: 19,175 lb.

32437/8/40–51, 32521–3/5–9/32/4–6/8/9/41/3–54　　Total 41

0-4-0T 0P Class C14

Introduced 1923. Urie rebuild as shunting locos. of Drummond L.S.W. motor-train 2-2-0T (originally introduced 1906).

Weight: 25 tons 15 cwt.

Pressure: 150 lb.

Cyls.: (O) 14″ × 14″.

Driving Wheels: 3′ 0″.

T.E.: 9,720 lb.

Walschaerts valve gear.

DS77　　　　　　　Total 1

Class D1-E3

4-4-0   3P   Class D1

Introduced 1921. Maunsell rebuild of Wainwright D, with larger super-heated boiler, Belpaire firebox and long-travel piston valves.
Weight: Loco. 52 tons 4 cwt.
Pressure: 180 lb. Su.
Cyls.: 19" × 26".
Driving Wheels: 6' 8"
T.E.: 17,950 lb.

31145, 31246/7, 31470/87/9/92/4,
31505/9/45, 31727/35/9/41/3/9

Total 17

4-4-0   3P   Class E1

Introduced 1919. Maunsell rebuild o Wainwright E, with larger super-heated boiler, Belpaire firebox and long-travel piston valves.
Weight: Loco. 53 tons 9 cwt.
Pressure: 180 lb.
Cyls.: 19" × 26".
Driving Wheels: 6' 6".
T.E.: 18,410 lb.

31019/67,   31165,   31497,
31506/7

Total 6

0-6-0T   2F   Class E1

Introduced 1874. Stroudley L.B.S.C. design, reboilered by Marsh.
Weight: 44 tons 3 cwt.
Pressure: 170 lb.
Cyls.: 17" × 24".
Driving Wheels: 4' 6".
T.E.: 18,560 lb.

3/4,   32113/39/51,   32689/94

Total 7

0-6-2T   1P2F   Class E1/R

Introduced 1927. Maunsell rebuild of Stroudley E1, with radial trailing axle and larger bunker for passenger service in West of England.
Weight: 50 tons 5 cwt.
Pressure: 170 lb.
Cyls.: 17" × 24".
Driving Wheels: 4' 6".
T.E.: 18,560 lb.

32124/35, 32697

Total 3

0-6-0T   3F   Class E2

*Introduced 1913. L. B. Billinton L.B.S.C. design.
†Introduced 1915. Later locos. with tanks extended further forward.
Weight: $\begin{cases} 52 \text{ tons 15 cwt.}^* \\ 53 \text{ tons 10 cwt.}† \end{cases}$
Pressure: 170 lb.
Cyls.: 17½" × 26".
Driving Wheels: 4' 6".
T.E.: 21,305 lb.

*32100–4
†32105–9

Total 10

0-6-2T   2F   Class E3

Introduced 1894. R. J. Billinton L.B.S.C. design, development of Stroudley " West Brighton " (intro-duced 1891), reboilered and fitted with extended smokebox, 1918 onwards; cylinder diameter reduced from 18" by S.R.
Weight: 56 tons 10 cwt.
Pressure: 170 lb.
Cyls.: 17½" × 26".
Driving Wheels: 4' 6".
T.E.: 21,305 lb.

32165/6, 32456

Total 3

Classes
0-6-2T 2P2F E4 & E4X

*E4. Introduced 1897. R. J. Billinton L.B.S.C. design, development of E3 with larger wheels, reboilered with Marsh boiler and extended smokebox, cylinder diameter reduced from 18″ by S.R.
†E4X. Introduced 1909. E4 reboilered with larger I2 4-4-2T type boiler.

Weight: { 57 tons 10 cwt.*
{ 59 tons 5 cwt.†
Pressure: 170 lb.
Cyls.: $17\frac{1}{4}$″ × 26″
Driving Wheels: 5′ 0″.
T.E.: 19,175 lb.

*32463/8–75/9/80/4/6/7/91/4/
5/7/8, 32500 3–10/2/5/7/9/56/
7/9/60/2–6/77–81

†32466/77

Total E4 46
E4X 2

Classes
0-6-2T 3F E6 & E6X

*‡E6. Introduced 1904. R. J. Billinton L.B.S.C. design, development of E5 with smaller wheels, some with higher pressure.
†E6X. Introduced 1911. E6 reboilered with larger C3-type boiler.

Weight: { 61 tons.*‡
{ 63 tons.†
Pressure: { 160 lb.*
{ 175 lb.‡
{ 170 lb.†
Cyls.: 18″ × 26″.
Driving Wheels: 4′ 6″.
T.E.: { 21,215 lb.*
{ 23,205 lb.‡
{ 22,540 lb.†

*‡32408/10/3/5 -8   †32411

Total E6 7
E6X 1

Classes E4 & E4X·H

0-6-0T 2F Class G6

*Introduced 1894. Adams L.S.W design, later additions by Drummond, but with Adams type boiler.
†Introduced 1925. Fitted with Drummond type boiler.
Weight: 47 tons 13 cwt.
Pressure: 160 lb.
Cyls.: $17\frac{1}{2}$″ × 24″.
Driving Wheels: 4′ 10″.
T.E.: 17,235 lb.

*30238/58/60/6/70/7, 30349,
DS3152

†30160, 30274

Total 10

4-8-0T 8F Class G16

Introduced 1921. Urie L.S.W. " Hump " loco.
Weight: 95 tons 2 cwt.
Pressure: 180 lb. Su.
Cyls.: (O) 22″ × 28″.
Driving Wheels: 5′ 1″.
T.E.: 33,990 lb.
Walschaerts valve gear. P.V.

30492–5   Total 4

0-4-4T 1P Class H

Introduced 1904. Wainwright S.E.C. design.
*Introduced 1949. Fitted for push-and-pull working.
Weight: 54 tons 8 cwt.
Pressure: 160 lb.
Cyls.: 18″ × 26″.
Driving Wheels: 5′ 6″.
T.E.: 17,360 lb.

31005, 31259/61/3/5/6, 31305–7/
24/6/8, 31500/3/33/40/2/50–3

*31161/2/4/77/93, 31239/69/76/
8/9/95, 31308/10/9/22/7/9,
31512/7–23/30/43/4/8/54

Total 51

Classes H15-LN

4-6-0   4P5F   Class H15

*Introduced 1914. Urie L.S.W. design, fitted with " Maunsell " superheater from 1927, replacing earlier types.

†Introduced 1915. Urie rebuild with two outside cylinders of Drummond E14 4-cyl. 4-6-0 introduced 1907, retaining original boiler retubed and fitted with superheater.

‡Introduced 1924. Maunsell locos. with N15-type boiler and smaller tender.

§Introduced 1924. Maunsell rebuild of Drummond F13 4-cyl. 4-6-0 introduced 1905, with detail differences from rebuild of E14.

¶Introduced 1927. Urie loco. (built 1914 saturated), rebuilt with later N15-type boiler, with smaller fire-box.

Weight: Loco. $\begin{cases} 81 \text{ tons } 5 \text{ cwt.*} \\ 82 \text{ tons } 1 \text{ cwt.†} \\ 79 \text{ tons } 19 \text{ cwt.‡¶} \\ 80 \text{ tons } 11 \text{ cwt.§} \end{cases}$

Pressure: $\begin{cases} 180 \text{ lb. Su.*‡¶} \\ 175 \text{ lb. Su.†§} \end{cases}$

Cyls.: (O) 21″ × 28″.
Driving Wheels: 6′ 0″.

T.E.: $\begin{cases} 26,240 \text{ lb.*‡¶} \\ 25,510 \text{ lb.†§} \end{cases}$

Walschaerts valve gear.   P.V.

*30482/4/6/8/9   †30335
‡30473-8, 30521-4   §30331/3/4
¶30491   **Total 20**

4-6-2T   6F   Class H16

Introduced 1921. Urie L.S.W. design for heavy freight traffic.
Weight: 96 tons 8 cwt.
Pressure: 180 lb. Su.
Cyls.: (O) 21″ × 28″.
Driving Wheels: 5′ 7″.
T.E.: 28,200 lb.
Walschaerts valve gear.   P.V.
30516-20   **Total 5**

2-6-0   4P5F   Class K

Introduced 1913. L. B. Billinton L.B.S.C. design.
Weight: Loco. 63 tons 15 cwt.
Pressure: 180 lb. Su.
Cyls.: (O) 21″ × 26″.
Driving Wheels: 5′ 6″.
T.E.: 26,580 lb.
P.V.
32337-53   **Total 17**

4-4-0   3P   Class L

Introduced 1914. Wainwright S.E.C. design, with detail alterations by Maunsell.
Weight: Loco. 57 tons 9 cwt.
Pressure: 160 lb. Su.
Cyls.: 20½″ × 26″.
Driving Wheels: 6′ 8″.
T.E.: 18,575 lb.
P.V.

31760/2–8/70–81   **Total 20**

4-4-0   3P   Class L1

Introduced 1926. Maunsell post-grouping development of L, with long-travel valves, side window cab and detail alterations.
Weight: Loco. 57 tons 16 cwt.
Pressure: 180 lb. Su.
Cyls.: 19½″ × 26″.
Driving Wheels: 6′ 8″.
T.E.: 18,910 lb.
P.V.

31753–9/82–9   **Total 15**

4-6-0   7P   Class LN

*Introduced 1926. Maunsell design, cylinders and tender modified by Bulleid from 1938, and fitted with multiple-jet blastpipe and large-diameter chimney.

†Introduced 1929. Loco. fitted experimentally with smaller driving wheels.

‡Introduced 1929. Loco. fitted experimentally with longer boiler.

Weight: Loco. $\begin{cases} 83 \text{ tons } 10 \text{ cwt.*†} \\ 84 \text{ tons } 16 \text{ cwt.‡} \end{cases}$

Pressure: 220 lb. Su.
Cyls.: (4) 16½″ × 26″.

Driving Wheels: $\begin{cases} 6′ 7″.*‡ \\ 6′ 3″.† \end{cases}$

T.E.: $\begin{cases} 33,510 \text{ lb.*‡} \\ 35,300 \text{ lb.†} \end{cases}$

Walschaerts valve gear.   P.V.

*30850–8/61–5
†30859   ‡30860
                       Total 16

0-4-4T 2P Class M7

*Introduced 1897. Drummond L.S.W. M7 design.

†Introduced 1903. Drummond X14 design, with increased front over-hang, steam reverser and detail alterations, now classified M7 (30254 originally M7).

‡Introduced 1925. X14 design fitted for push-and-pull working.

Weight: { 60 tons 4 cwt.*
{ 60 tons 3 cwt.†
{ 62 tons 0 cwt.‡

Pressure: 175 lb.
Cyls.: 18½″ × 26″.
Driving Wheels: 5′ 7″.
T.E.: 19,755 lb.

*30023–6/31–6/9/40/3/4, 30112, 30241–3/5–9/51–3/5/6, 30318–24/56/7,30667–71/3/4/6

†30030, 30123/4/7/30/2/3, 30254, 30374–8, 30479

‡30021/7/8/9/45–60, 30104–11/ 25/8/9/31, 30328/79, 30480/1

Total 96

4-6-2 8P Class MN

*Introduced 1941. Bulleid design originally with 280 lb. pressure, multiple-jet blastpipe and Bulleid valve gear.

†Introduced 1956. Rebuilt with Walschaerts valve gear, modified details and air-smoothed casing removed.

Weight: Loco.{ 94 tons 15 cwt.*
{ 97 tons 18 cwt.†

Pressure: 250 lb.
Cyls.: (3) 18″ × 24″.
Driving Wheels: 6′ 2″.
T.E.: 33,495 lb.
P.V.

*35001/3/5/6/11/9/21/4/8/9
†35002/4/7–10/2–8/20/2/3/5–7/30

Total 30

Classes N & NI 2-6-0 4P5F

*N. Introduced 1917. Maunsell S.E.C mixed traffic design.

†NI. Introduced 1922. 3-cylinder development of N.

Weight: Loco.{ 61 tons 4 cwt.*
{ 64 tons 5 cwt.†

Pressure: 200 lb. Su.
Cyls.: { (O) 19″ × 28″.*
{ (3) 16″ × 28″.†

Driving Wheels: 5′ 6″.
T.E.: { 26,035 lb.*
{ 27,695 lb.†

Walschaerts valve gear. P.V.

*31400–14, 31810–21/3–75
†31822/76–80

Total Class N 80

Class NI 6

4-6-0 5P Class NI5

*Introduced 1925. Maunsell locos. with long-travel valves, increased boiler pressure, smaller fireboxes, and tenders from Drummond G14 4-6-0's.

†Introduced 1925. Later locos. with detail alterations and increased weight.

‡Introduced 1925. Locos. with modified cabs to suit Eastern Section, and new bogie tenders.

§Introduced 1926. Locos. with detail alterations and most with six-wheeled tenders for Central Section.

Weight: Loco.{ 79 tons 18 cwt.*
{ 80 tons 19 cwt.†‡
{ 81 tons 17 cwt.§

Pressure: 200 lb. Su.
Cyls.: (O) 20½″ × 28″.
Driving Wheels: 6′ 7″.
T.E.: 25,320 lb.
Walschaerts valve gear. P.V.

*30453–7   †30448–52
‡30763–92   §30793–30806

Total 54

Classes O1-R1

0-6-0   2F   Class O1

*Introduced 1903. Wainwright rebuild with domed boiler and new cab of Stirling S.E. Class O 0-6-0 (introduced 1878).

†Introduced 1903. Loco. with smaller driving wheels.

Weight: Loco. 41 tons 1 cwt.
Pressure: 150 lb.
Cyls.: 18″ × 26″.

Driving Wheels: $\begin{cases} 5'\ 2''.* \\ 5'\ 1''.† \end{cases}$

T.E.: $\begin{cases} 17,325\ \text{lb.}* \\ 17,610\ \text{lb.}† \end{cases}$

*31065, 31258, 31370, 31425/30/4
†31048

Total 7

0-4-4T   0P   Class O2

*Introduced 1889. Adams L.S.W. design.

†Introduced 1923. Fitted with Westinghouse brake for I.O.W. Bunkers enlarged from 1932.

‡Fitted with Drummond-type boiler.
§Fitted for push-and-pull working.

Weight: $\begin{cases} 46\ \text{tons } 18\ \text{cwt.}*‡ \\ 48\ \text{tons } 8\ \text{cwt.}† \end{cases}$

Pressure: 160 lb.
Cyls.: 17½″ × 24″.
Driving Wheels: 4′ 10″.
T.E.: 17,235 lb.

*30177/9/92/3/9, 30200/12/25/9/32/6
†14/6-8/20-2/4-33
†§35/6
‡30223   ‡§30182/3

Total 33

0-6-0T   Unclass   Class P

Introduced 1909. Wainwright S.E.C. design for push-and-pull work, now used for shunting.

Weight: 28 tons 10 cwt.
Pressure: 160 lb.
Cyls.: 12″ × 18″.
Driving Wheels: 3′ 9½″
T.E.: 7,810 lb.

31027, 31323/5, 31556/8

Total 5

0-6-0   4F   Class Q

Introduced 1938. Maunsell design, later fitted with multiple-jet blastpipe and large-diameter chimney.

Weight: Loco. 49 tons 10 cwt.
Pressure: 200 lb. Su.
Cyls.: 19″ × 26″.
Driving Wheels: 5′ 1″.
T.E.: 26,160 lb.
P.V.

30530-49

Total 20

0-6-0   5F   Class Q1

Introduced 1942. Bulleid "Austerity" design.

Weight: Loco. 51 tons 5 cwt.
Pressure: 230 lb. Su.
Cyls.: 19″ × 26″.
Driving Wheels: 5′ 1″.
T.E.: 30,080 lb.
P.V.

33001-40

Total 40

0-6-0T   2F   Class R1

*Introduced 1888. Stirling S.E. design later rebuilt with domed boiler.

†Introduced 1938. Fitted with Urie type short chimney for Whitstable branch and fitted with or retaining original Stirling-type cab.

Weight: $\begin{cases} 46\ \text{tons } 15\ \text{cwt.}* \\ 46\ \text{tons } 8\ \text{cwt.}† \end{cases}$

Pressure: 160 lb.
Cyls.: 18″ × 26″.

Driving Wheels: $\begin{cases} 5'\ 2''.* \\ 5'\ 1''.† \end{cases}$

T.E.: $\begin{cases} 18,480\ \text{lb.}* \\ 18,780\ \text{lb.}† \end{cases}$

*31047, 31107/28/74, 31337/40
†31010, 31147

Total 8

50

4-6-0   6F   Class S15

*Introduced 1920. Urie L.S.W. design, development of N15 for mixed traffic work.

†Introduced 1927. Maunsell design, with higher pressure, smaller grate, modified footplating and other detail differences. 30833-7 with 6-wheel tenders for Central Section.

‡Introduced 1936. Later locos. with detail differences and reduced weight.

Weight: Loco. $\begin{cases} 79 \text{ tons } 16 \text{ cwt.*} \\ 80 \text{ tons } 14 \text{ cwt.†} \\ 79 \text{ tons } 5 \text{ cwt.‡} \end{cases}$

Pressure: $\begin{cases} 180 \text{ lb. Su.*} \\ 200 \text{ lb. Su.†‡} \end{cases}$

Cyls.: $\begin{cases} (O) 21'' \times 28''.* \\ (O) 20\frac{1}{2}'' \times 28''.†‡ \end{cases}$

Driving Wheels: 5' 7".

T.E.: $\begin{cases} 28,200 \text{ lb.*} \\ 29,855 \text{ lb.†‡} \end{cases}$

Walschaerts valve gear.   P.V.

*30496-30515   †30823-37
‡30838-47

Total 45

4-4-0   3P   Class T9

*Introduced 1899. Drummond L.S.W. design, fitted with superheater and larger cylinders by Urie from 1922.

†Introduced 1899. Locos. with detail differences (originally fitted with firebox watertubes).

‡Introduced 1900. Locos. with wider cab and splashers, without coupling rod splashers and originally fitted with firebox watertubes.

Weight: Loco. $\begin{cases} 51 \text{ tons } 18 \text{ cwt.*} \\ 51 \text{ tons } 16 \text{ cwt.†} \\ 51 \text{ tons } 7 \text{ cwt.‡} \end{cases}$

Pressure: 175 lb. Su.

Cyls.: 19" × 26".

Driving Wheels: 6' 7".

T.E.: 17,675 lb.

*30117/20, 30285/7-9
†30702/6/7/9-12/5/7-9/24/6/7/
    9/32
‡30300/1/10/3/37/8

Total 28

Classes
2-6-0   4P3F   U & U1

*U.   Introduced 1928.   Rebuild of Maunsell S.E.C. Class K (" River ") 2-6-4T (introduced 1917).

†U.   Introduced 1928.   Locos. built as Class U, with smaller splashers and detail alterations.

‡U1.   Introduced 1928.   3-cylinder development of Class U (prototype 31890, rebuilt from 2-6-4T, originally built 1925).

Weight: Loco. $\begin{cases} 63 \text{ tons.*} \\ 62 \text{ tons } 6 \text{ cwt.†} \\ 65 \text{ tons } 6 \text{ cwt.‡} \end{cases}$

Pressure: 200 lb. Su.

Cyls.: $\begin{cases} (O) 19'' \times 28''.*† \\ (3) 16'' \times 28''.‡ \end{cases}$

Driving Wheels: 6' 0".

T.E.: $\begin{cases} 23,865 \text{ lb.*†} \\ 25,385 \text{ lb.‡} \end{cases}$

Walschaerts valve gear.   P.V.

*31790-31809   †31610-39
‡31890-31910

**Total Class U 50
Class U1 21**

0-6-0T   3F   Class USA

Introduced 1942.   U.S. Army Transportation Corps design, purchased by S.R. 1946, and fitted with modified cab and bunker and other detail alterations.

Weight: 46 tons 10 cwt.
Pressure: 210 lb.
Cyls.: (O) 16½" × 24".
Driving Wheels: 4' 6".
T.E.: 21,600 lb.
Walschaerts valve gear.   P.V.
30061-74

Total 14

4-4-0   5P   Class V

*Introduced 1930.   Maunsell design.

†Introduced 1938.   Fitted with multiple-jet blastpipe and large-diameter chimney by Bulleid.

Weight: Loco. 67 tons 2 cwt.
Pressure: 220 lb. Su.
Cyls.: (3) 16½" × 26".
Driving Wheels: 6' 7".
T.E.: 25,135 lb.
Walschaerts valve gear.   P.V

*30902-6/8/10-2/6/22/3/5-8/
    32/5/6
†30900/1/7/9/13-5/7-21/4/29-31/
    3/4/7-9

Total 40

2-6-4T   6F   **Class W**

Introduced 1931. Maunsell design, developed from Class N1 2-6-0.
Weight: 90 tons 14 cwt.
Pressure: 200 lb. Su.
Cyls.: (3) 16½″ × 28″.
Driving Wheels: 5′ 6″.
T.E.: 29,450 lb.
Walschaerts valve gear. P.V.

31911–25   **Total 15**

Classes
4-6-2   7P5F   **WC & BB**

*Introduced 1945. Bulleid "West Country" Class, with Bulleid valve gear.
†Introduced 1946. Bulleid "Battle of Britain" Class, with Bulleid valve gear.
‡Introduced 1948. Locos. with larger tenders.
§Introduced 1957. Rebuilt with Walschaerts valve gear, modified details and air-smoothed casing removed.
Weight: Loco. { 86 tons 0 cwt.*†‡
                { 90 tons 1 cwt.§
Pressure: 250 lb. Su.
Cyls.: (3) 16⅜″ × 24″.
Driving Wheels: 6′ 2″.
T.E.: 27,715 lb.
Bulleid valve gear   P.V.
*34002/6–11/5/8–20/3/4/9–36/8–48   †34049–70
†‡34071–90, 34109/10
*‡34091–34108   §34001/3–5/12–4/6/7/21/2/5–8/37

                 Total 110

0-8-0T   6F   **Class Z**

Introduced 1929. Maunsell design for heavy shunting.
Weight: 71 tons 12 cwt.
Pressure 180 lb.
Cyls.: (3) 16″ × 28″.
Driving Wheels: 4′ 8″.
T.E.: 29,375 lb.
Walschaerts valve gear. P.V.

30950–7   **Total 8**

0-6-0   3F   **Class 700**

Introduced 1897. Drummond L.S.W. design, superheated from 1921.
Weight: Loco. 46 tons 14 cwt.
Pressure: 180 lb. Su.
Cyls.: 19″ × 26″.
Driving Wheels: 5′ 1″.
T.E.: 23 540 lb.

30306/8/9/15–7/25–7/39/46/50/2/5/68, 30687/9–30701

                 Total 29

2-4-0WT   0P   **Class 0298**

Introduced 1874. Beattie L.S.W. design, rebuilt by Adams (1884–92), Urie (1921–2) and Maunsell (1931–5).
Weight: 37 tons 16 cwt.
Pressure: 160 lb.
Cyls.: (O) 16½″ × 20″.
Driving Wheels: 5′ 7″.
T.E.: 11,050 lb.

30585–7   **Total 3**

0-6-0   2F   **Class 0395**

*Introduced 1881. Adams L.S.W. design.
†Introduced 1885. Adams "496" class with longer front overhang.
‡Introduced 1928. Reboilered with ex-L.C. & D. Class M3 4-4-0 boiler.
Weight: Loco. { 37 tons 12 cwt.*‡
                { 38 tons 14 cwt.†‡
Pressure: { 140 lb.*†
           { 150 lb.‡
Driving Wheels: 5′ 1″.
T.E.: { 15,535 lb.*†
      { 16,645 lb.‡

*30575   †30566
*‡30567
                 Total 3

4-4-2T   1P   **Class 0415**

Introduced 1882. Adams L.S.W. design, later reboilered.
Weight: 55 tons 2 cwt.
Pressure: 160 lb.
Cyls.: (O) 17½″ × 24″.
Driving Wheels: 5′ 7″.
T.E.: 14,920 lb.

30582–4   **Total 3**

BRITISH RAILWAYS LOCOMOTIVES
Nos. 30021-35030, 3-36

Named Engines are indicated by an asterisk (*)

No.	Class	No.	Class	No.	Class	No.	Class
30021	M7	30062	U.S.A.	30127	M7	30256	M7
30023	M7	30063	U.S.A.	30128	M7	30258	G6
30024	M7	30064	U.S.A.	30129	M7	30260	G6
30025	M7	30065	U.S.A.	30130	M7	30266	G6
30026	M7	30066	U.S.A.	30131	M7	30270	G6
30027	M7	30067	U.S.A.	30132	M7	30274	G6
30028	M7	30068	U.S.A.	30133	M7	30277	G6
30029	M7	30069	U.S.A.	30160	G6	30285	T9
30030	M7	30070	U.S.A.	30177	O2	30287	T9
30031	M7	30071	U.S.A.	30179	O2	30288	T9
30032	M7	30072	U.S.A.	30182	O2	30289	T9
30033	M7	30073	U.S.A.	30183	O2	30300	T9
30034	M7	30074	U.S.A.	30192	O2	30301	T9
30035	M7	30083	B4	30193	O2	30306	700
30036	M7	30084	B4	30199	O2	30308	700
30039	M7	30086	B4	30200	O2	30309	700
30040	M7	30087	B4	30212	O2	30310	T9
30043	M7	30088	B4	30223	O2	30313	T9
30044	M7	30089	B4	30225	O2	30315	700
30045	M7	30093	B4	30229	O2	30316	700
30046	M7	30096	B4	30232	O2	30317	700
30047	M7	30102	B4	30236	O2	30318	M7
30048	M7	30104	M7	30238	G6	30319	M7
30049	M7	30105	M7	30241	M7	30320	M7
30050	M7	30106	M7	30242	M7	30321	M7
30051	M7	30107	M7	30243	M7	30322	M7
30052	M7	30108	M7	30245	M7	30323	M7
30053	M7	30109	M7	30246	M7	30324	M7
30054	M7	30110	M7	30247	M7	30325	700
30055	M7	30111	M7	30248	M7	30326	700
30056	M7	30112	M7	30249	M7	30327	700
30057	M7	30117	T9	30251	M7	30328	M7
30058	M7	30120	T9	30252	M7	30331	H15
30059	M7	30123	M7	30253	M7	30333	H15
30060	M7	30124	M7	30254	M7	30334	H15
30061	U.S.A.	30125	M7	30255	M7	30335	H15

No.	Class	No.	Class	No.	Class	No.	Class
30337	T9	30495	G16	30545	Q	30718	T9
30338	T9	30496	S15	30546	Q	30719	T9
30339	700	30497	S15	30547	Q	30724	T9
30346	700	30498	S15	30548	Q	30726	T9
30349	G6	30499	S15	30549	Q	30727	T9
30350	700	30500	S15	30566	0395	30729	T9
30352	700	30501	S15	30567	0395	30732	T9
30355	700	30502	S15	30575	0395	30763*	N15
30356	M7	30503	S15	30582	0415	30764*	N15
30357	M7	30504	S15	30583	0415	30765*	N15
30368	700	30505	S15	30584	0415	30766*	N15
30374	M7	30506	S15	30585	0298	30767*	N15
30375	M7	30507	S15	30586	0298	30768*	N15
30376	M7	30508	S15	30587	0298	30769*	N15
30377	M7	30509	S15	30667	M7	30770*	N15
30378	M7	30510	S15	30668	M7	30771*	N15
30379	M7	30511	S15	30669	M7	30772*	N15
30448*	N15	30512	S15	30670	M7	30773*	N15
30449*	N15	30513	S15	30671	M7	30774*	N15
30450*	N15	30514	S15	30673	M7	30775*	N15
30451*	N15	30515	S15	30674	M7	30776*	N15
30452*	N15	30516	H16	30676	M7	30777*	N15
30453*	N15	30517	H16	30687	700	30778*	N15
30454*	N15	30518	H16	30689	700	30779*	N15
30455*	N15	30519	H16	30690	700	30780*	N15
30456*	N15	30520	H16	30691	700	30781*	N15
30457*	N15	30521	H15	30692	700	30782*	N15
30473	H15	30522	H15	30693	700	30783*	N15
30474	H15	30523	H15	30694	700	30784*	N15
30475	H15	30524	H15	30695	700	30785*	N15
30476	H15	30530	Q	30696	700	30786*	N15
30477	H15	30531	Q	30697	700	30787*	N15
30478	H15	30532	Q	30698	700	30788*	N15
30479	M7	30533	Q	30699	700	30789*	N15
30480	M7	30534	Q	30700	700	30790*	N15
30481	M7	30535	Q	30701	700	30791*	N15
30482	H15	30536	Q	30702	T9	30792*	N15
30484	H15	30537	Q	30706	T9	30793*	N15
30486	H15	30538	Q	30707	T9	30794*	N15
30488	H15	30539	Q	30709	T9	30795*	N15
30489	H15	30540	Q	30710	T9	30796*	N15
30491	H15	30541	Q	30711	T9	30797*	N15
30492	G16	30542	Q	30712	T9	30798*	N15
30493	G16	30543	Q	30715	T9	30799*	N15
30494	G16	30544	Q	30717	T9	30800*	N15

No.	Class	No.	Class	No.	Class	No.	Class
30801*	N15	30864*	LN	30953	Z	31242	C
30802*	N15	30865*	LN	30954	Z	31243	C
30803*	N15	30900*	V	30955	Z	31244	C
30804*	N15	30901*	V	30956	Z	31245	C
30805*	N15	30902*	V	30957	Z	31246	DI
30806*	N15	30903*	V	31004	C	31247	DI
30823	S15	30904*	V	31005	H	31252	C
30824	S15	30905*	V	31010	RI	31253	C
30825	S15	30906*	V	31018	C	31255	C
30826	S15	30907*	V	31019	EI	31256	C
30827	S15	30908*	V	31027	P	31258	OI
30828	S15	30909*	V	31033	C	31259	H
30829	S15	30910*	V	31037	C	31261	H
30830	S15	30911*	V	31047	RI	31263	H
30831	S15	30912*	V	31048	OI	31265	H
30832	S15	30913*	V	31054	C	31266	H
30833	S15	30914*	V	31061	C	31267	C
30834	S15	30915*	V	31065	OI	31268	C
30835	S15	30916*	V	31067	EI	31269	H
30836	S15	30917*	V	31063	C	31270	C
30837	S15	30918*	V	31071	C	31271	C
30838	S15	30919*	V	31086	C	31272	C
30839	S15	30920*	V	31102	C	31276	H
30840	S15	30921*	V	31107	RI	31278	H
30841	S15	30922*	V	31112	C	31279	H
30842	S15	30923*	V	31113	C	31280	C
30843	S15	30924*	V	31128	RI	31287	C
30844	S15	30925*	V	31145	DI	31293	C
30845	S15	30926*	V	31147	RI	31295	H
30846	S15	30927*	V	31150	C	31297	C
30847	S15	30928*	V	31161	H	31298	C
30850*	LN	30929*	V	31162	H	31305	H
30851*	LN	30930*	V	31164	H	31306	H
30852*	LN	30931*	V	31165	EI	31307	H
30853*	LN	30932*	V	31174	RI	31308	H
30854*	LN	30933*	V	31177	H	31310	H
30855*	LN	30934*	V	31191	C	31317	C
30856*	LN	30935*	V	31193	H	31319	H
30857*	LN	30936*	V	31218	C	31322	H
30858*	LN	30937*	V	31219	C	31323	P
30859*	LN	30938*	V	31221	C	31324	H
30860*	LN	30939*	V	31223	C	31325	P
30861*	LN	30950	Z	31227	C	31326	H
30862*	LN	30951	Z	31229	C	31327	H
30863*	LN	30952	Z	31239	H	31328	H

No.	Class	No.	Class	No.	Class	No.	Class
31329	H	31521	H	31624	U	31749	DI
31337	RI	31522	H	31625	U	31753	LI
31340	RI	31523	H	31626	U	31754	LI
31370	OI	31530	H	31627	U	31755	LI
31400	N	31533	H	31628	U	31756	LI
31401	N	31540	H	31629	U	31757	LI
31402	N	31542	H	31630	U	31758	LI
31403	N	31543	H	31631	U	31759	LI
31404	N	31544	H	31632	U	31760	L
31405	N	31545	DI	31633	U	31762	L
31406	N	31548	H	31634	U	31763	L
31407	N	31550	H	31635	U	31764	L
31408	N	31551	H	31636	U	31765	L
31409	N	31552	H	31637	U	31766	L
31410	N	31553	H	31638	U	31767	L
31411	N	31554	H	31639	U	31768	L
31412	N	31556	P	31681	C	31770	L
31413	N	31558	P	31682	C	31771	L
31414	N	31573	C	31683	C	31772	L
31425	OI	31575	C	31684	C	31773	L
31430	OI	31576	C	31686	C	31774	L
31434	OI	31578	C	31688	C	31775	L
31461	C	31579	C	31689	C	31776	L
31470	DI	31581	C	31690	C	31777	L
31480	C	31583	C	31691	C	31778	L
31481	C	31584	C	31692	C	31779	L
31487	DI	31585	C	31693	C	31780	L
31489	DI	31588	C	31694	C	31781	L
31492	DI	31589	C	31695	C	31782	LI
31494	DI	31590	C	31714	C	31783	LI
31495	C	31592	C	31715	C	31784	LI
31497	EI	31610	U	31716	C	31785	LI
31498	C	31611	U	31717	C	31786	LI
31500	H	31612	U	31719	C	31787	LI
31503	H	31613	U	31720	C	31788	LI
31505	DI	31614	U	31721	C	31789	LI
31506	EI	31615	U	31722	C	31790	U
31507	EI	31616	U	31723	C	31791	U
31509	DI	31617	U	31724	C	31792	U
31510	C	31618	U	31725	C	31793	U
31512	H	31619	U	31727	DI	31794	U
31517	H	31620	U	31735	DI	31795	U
31518	H	31621	U	31739	DI	31796	U
31519	H	31622	U	31741	DI	31797	U
31520	H	31623	U	31743	DI	31798	U

No.	Class	No.	Class	No.	Class	No.	Class
31799	U	31844	N	31898	UI	32337	K
31800	U	31845	N	31899	UI	32338	K
31801	U	31846	N	31900	UI	32339	K
31802	U	31847	N	31901	UI	32340	K
31803	U	31848	N	31902	UI	32341	K
31804	U	31849	N	31903	UI	32342	K
31805	U	31850	N	31904	UI	32343	K
31806	U	31851	N	31905	UI	32344	K
31807	U	31852	N	31906	UI	32345	K
31808	U	31853	N	31907	UI	32346	K
31809	U	31854	N	31908	UI	32347	K
31810	N	31855	N	31909	UI	32348	K
31811	N	31856	N	31910	UI	32349	K
31812	N	31857	N	31911	W	32350	K
31813	N	31858	N	31912	W	32351	K
31814	N	31859	N	31913	W	32352	K
31815	N	31860	N	31914	W	32353	K
31816	N	31861	N	31915	W	32408	E6
31817	N	31862	N	31916	W	32410	E6
31818	N	31863	N	31917	W	32411	E6X
31819	N	31864	N	31918	W	32413	E6
31820	N	31865	N	31919	W	32415	E6
31821	N	31866	N	31920	W	32416	E6
31822	NI	31867	N	31921	W	32417	E6
31823	N	31868	N	31922	W	32418	E6
31824	N	31869	N	31923	W	32437	C2X
31825	N	31870	N	31924	W	32438	C2X
31826	N	31871	N	31925	W	32440	C2X
31827	N	31872	N	32100	E2	32441	C2X
31828	N	31873	N	32101	E2	32442	C2X
31829	N	31874	N	32102	E2	32443	C2X
31830	N	31875	N	32103	E2	32444	C2X
31831	N	31876	NI	32104	E2	32445	C2X
31832	N	31877	NI	32105	E2	32446	C2X
31833	N	31878	NI	32106	E2	32447	C2X
31834	N	31879	NI	32107	E2	32448	C2X
31835	N	31880	NI	32108	E2	32449	C2X
31836	N	31890	UI	32109	E2	32450	C2X
31837	N	31891	UI	32113	EI	32451	C2X
31838	N	31892	UI	32124	EI/R	32456	E3
31839	N	31893	UI	32135	EI/R	32463	E4
31840	N	31894	UI	32139	EI	32466	E4X
31841	N	31895	UI	32151	EI	32468	E4
31842	N	31896	UI	32165	E3	32469	E4
31843	N	31897	UI	32166	E3	32470	E4

No.	Class	No.	Class	No.	Class	No.	Class
32471	E4	32544	C2X	33008	Q1	34013*	WC
32472	E4	32545	C2X	33009	Q1	34014*	WC
32473	E4	32546	C2X	33010	Q1	34015*	WC
32474	E4	32547	C2X	33011	Q1	34016*	WC
32475	E4	32548	C2X	33012	Q1	34017*	WC
32477	E4X	32549	C2X	33013	Q1	34018*	WC
32479	E4	32550	C2X	33014	Q1	34019*	WC
32480	E4	32551	C2X	33015	Q1	34020*	WC
32484	E4	32552	C2X	33016	Q1	34021*	WC
32486	E4	32553	C2X	33017	Q1	34022*	WC
32487	E4	32554	C2X	33018	Q1	34023*	WC
32491	E4	32556	E4	33019	Q1	34024*	WC
32494	E4	32557	E4	33020	Q1	34025*	WC
32495	E4	32559	E4	33021	Q1	34026*	WC
32497	E4	32560	E4	33022	Q1	34027*	WC
32498	E4	32562	E4	33023	Q1	34028*	WC
32500	E4	32563	E4	33024	Q1	34029*	WC
32503	E4	32564	E4	33025	Q1	34030*	WC
32504	E4	32565	E4	33026	Q1	34031*	WC
32505	E4	32566	E4	33027	Q1	34032*	WC
32506	E4	32577	E4	33028	Q1	34033*	WC
32507	E4	32578	E4	33029	Q1	34034*	WC
32508	E4	32579	E4	33030	Q1	34035*	WC
32509	E4	32580	E4	33031	Q1	34036*	WC
32510	E4	32581	E4	33032	Q1	34037*	WC
32512	E4	32636	A1X	33033	Q1	34038*	WC
32515	E4	32640	A1X	33034	Q1	34039*	WC
32517	E4	32646	A1X	33035	Q1	34040*	WC
32519	E4	32650	A1X	33036	Q1	34041*	WC
32521	C2X	32655	A1X	33037	Q1	34042*	WC
32522	C2X	32661	A1X	33038	Q1	34043*	WC
32523	C2X	32662	A1X	33039	Q1	34044*	WC
32525	C2X	32670	A1X	33040	Q1	34045*	WC
32526	C2X	32677	A1X	34001*	WC	34046*	WC
32527	C2X	32678	A1X	34002*	WC	34047*	WC
32528	C2X	32689	E1	34003*	WC	34048*	WC
32529	C2X	32694	E1	34004*	WC	34049*	BB
32532	C2X	32697	E1/R	34005*	WC	34050*	BB
32534	C2X	33001	Q1	34006*	WC	34051*	BB
32535	C2X	33002	Q1	34007*	WC	34052*	BB
32536	C2X	33003	Q1	34008*	WC	34053*	BB
32538	C2X	33004	Q1	34009*	WC	34054*	BB
32539	C2X	33005	Q1	34010*	WC	34055*	BB
32541	C2X	33006	Q1	34011*	WC	34056*	BB
32543	C2X	33007	Q1	34012*	WC	34057*	BB

Isle of Wight Locomotives

No.	Class	No.	Class
34058*	BB	34103*	WC
34059*	BB	34104*	WC
34060*	BB	34105*	WC
34061*	BB	34106*	WC
34062*	BB	34107*	WC
34063*	BB	34108*	WC
34064*	BB	34109*	BB
34065*	BB	34110*	BB
34066*	BB	35001*	MN
34067*	BB	35002*	MN
34068*	BB	35003*	MN
34069*	BB	35004*	MN
34070*	BB	35005*	MN
34071*	BB	35006*	MN
34072*	BB	35007*	MN
34073*	BB	35008*	MN
34074*	BB	35009*	MN
34075*	BB	35010*	MN
34076*	BB	35011*	MN
34077*	BB	35012*	MN
34078*	BB	35013*	MN
34079*	BB	35014*	MN
34080*	BB	35015*	MN
34081*	BB	35016*	MN
34082*	BB	35017*	MN
34083*	BB	35018*	MN
34084*	BB	35019*	MN
34085*	BB	35020*	MN
34086*	BB	35021*	MN
34087*	BB	35022*	MN
34088*	BB	35023*	MN
34089*	BB	35024*	MN
34090*	BB	35025*	MN
34091*	WC	35026*	MN
34092*	WC	35027*	MN
34093*	WC	35028*	MN
34094*	WC	35029*	MN
34095*	WC	35030*	MN
34096*	WC		
34097*	WC		
34098*	WC		
34099*	WC		
34100*	WC		
34101*	WC		
34102*	WC		

No.	Class	No.	Class
3*	E1	26*	O2
4*	E1	27*	O2
14*	O2	28*	O2
16*	O2	29*	O2
17*	O2	30*	O2
18*	O2	31*	O2
20*	O2	32*	O2
21*	O2	33*	O2
22*	O2	35*	O2
24*	O2	36*	O2
25*	O2		

BRITISH RAILWAYS LOCOMOTIVES
Nos. 26000-35030 and 3-36

NAMED LOCOMOTIVES

CLASS EM1 BO-BO ELECTRIC
26000   Tommy

CLASS N15 " KING ARTHUR " 4-6-0

30448	Sir Tristram	30781	Sir Aglovale
30449	Sir Torre	30782	Sir Brian
30450	Sir Kay	30783	Sir Gillemere
30451	Sir Lamorak	30784	Sir Nerovens
30452	Sir Meliagrance	30785	Sir Mador de la Porte
30453	King Arthur	30786	Sir Lionel
30454	Queen Guinevere	30787	Sir Menadeuke
30455	Sir Launcelot	30788	Sir Urre of the Mount
30456	Sir Galahad	30789	Sir Guy
30457	Sir Bedivere	30790	Sir Villiars
30763	Sir Bors de Ganis	30791	Sir Uwaine
30764	Sir Gawain	30792	Sir Hervis de Revel
30765	Sir Gareth	30793	Sir Ontzlake
30766	Sir Geraint	30794	Sir Ector de Maris
30767	Sir Valence	30795	Sir Dinadan
30768	Sir Balin	30796	Sir Dodinas le Savage
30769	Sir Balan	30797	Sir Blamor de Ganis
30770	Sir Prianius	30798	Sir Hectimere
30771	Sir Sagramore	30799	Sir Ironside
30772	Sir Percivale	30800	Sir Meleaus de Lile
30773	Sir Lavaine	30801	Sir Meliot de Logres
30774	Sir Gaheris	30802	Sir Durnore
30775	Sir Agravaine	30803	Sir Harry le Fise Lake
30776	Sir Galagars	30804	Sir Cador of Cornwall
30777	Sir Lamiel	30805	Sir Constantine
30778	Sir Pelleas	30806	Sir Galleron
30779	Sir Colgrevance		
30780	Sir Persant		

NAMED LOCOMOTIVES—contd.

CLASS LN "LORD NELSON" 4-6-0

30850	Lord Nelson	30858	Lord Duncan
30851	Sir Francis Drake	30859	Lord Hood
30852	Sir Walter Raleigh	30860	Lord Hawke
30853	Sir Richard Grenville	30861	Lord Anson
30854	Howard of Effingham	30862	Lord Collingwood
30855	Robert Blake	30863	Lord Rodney
30856	Lord St. Vincent	30864	Sir Martin Frobisher
30857	Lord Howe	30865	Sir John Hawkins

CLASS V "SCHOOLS" 4-4-0

30900	Eton	30920	Rugby
30901	Winchester	30921	Shrewsbury
30902	Wellington	30922	Marlborough
30903	Charterhouse	30923	Bradfield
30904	Lancing	30924	Haileybury
30905	Tonbridge	30925	Cheltenham
30906	Sherborne	30926	Repton
30907	Dulwich	30927	Clifton
30908	Westminster	30928	Stowe
30909	St. Paul's	30929	Malvern
30910	Merchant Taylors	30930	Radley
30911	Dover	30931	King's Wimbledon
30912	Downside	30932	Blundells
30913	Christ's Hospital	30933	King's Canterbury
30914	Eastbourne	30934	St. Lawrence
30915	Brighton	30935	Sevenoaks
30916	Whitgift	30936	Cranleigh
30917	Ardingly	30937	Epsom
30918	Hurstpierpoint	30938	St. Olave's
30919	Harrow	30939	Leatherhead

CLASSES WC & BB 4-6-2
"WEST COUNTRY" and "BATTLE OF BRITAIN"

34001	Exeter	34011	Tavistock
34002	Salisbury	34012	Launceston
34003	Plymouth	34013	Okehampton
34004	Yeovil	34014	Budleigh Salterton
34005	Barnstaple	34015	Exmouth
34006	Bude	34016	Bodmin
34007	Wadebridge	34017	Ilfracombe
34008	Padstow	34018	Axminster
34009	Lyme Regis	34019	Bideford
34010	Sidmouth	34020	Seaton

34021	Dartmoor	34067	Tangmere
34022	Exmoor	34068	Kenley
34023	Blackmore Vale	34069	Hawkinge
34024	Tamar Valley	34070	Manston
34025	Whimple	34071	601 Squadron
34026	Yes Tor	34072	257 Squadron
34027	Taw Valley	34073	249 Squadron
34028	Eddystone	34074	46 Squadron
34029	Lundy	34075	264 Squadron
34030	Watersmeet	34076	41 Squadron
34031	Torrington	34077	603 Squadron
34032	Camelford	34078	222 Squadron
34033	Chard	34079	141 Squadron
34034	Honiton	34080	74 Squadron
34035	Shaftesbury	34081	92 Squadron
34036	Westward Ho	34082	615 Squadron
34037	Clovelly	34083	605 Squadron
34038	Lynton	34084	253 Squadron
34039	Boscastle	34085	501 Squadron
34040	Crewkerne	34086	219 Squadron
34041	Wilton	34087	145 Squadron
34042	Dorchester	34088	213 Squadron
34043	Combe Martin	34089	602 Squadron
34044	Woolacombe	34090	Sir Eustace Missenden, Southern Railway
34045	Ottery St. Mary		
34046	Braunton	34091	Weymouth
34047	Callington	34092	City of Wells
34048	Crediton	34093	Saunton
34049	Anti-Aircraft Command	34094	Mortehoe
34050	Royal Observer Corps	34095	Brentor
34051	Winston Churchill	34096	Trevone
34052	Lord Dowding	34097	Holsworthy
34053	Sir Keith Park	34098	Templecombe
34054	Lord Beaverbrook	34099	Lynmouth
34055	Fighter Pilot	34100	Appledore
34056	Croydon	34101	Hartland
34057	Biggin Hill	34102	Lapford
34058	Sir Frederick Pile	34103	Calstock
34059	Sir Archibald Sinclair	34104	Bere Alston
34060	25 Squadron	34105	Swanage
34061	73 Squadron	34106	Lydford
34062	17 Squadron	34107	Blandford Forum
34063	229 Squadron	34108	Wincanton
34064	Fighter Command	34109	Sir Trafford Leigh-Mallory
34065	Hurricane		
34066	Spitfire	34110	66 Squadron

NAMED LOCOMOTIVES—*contd.*

CLASS MN " MERCHANT NAVY " 4-6-2

35001	Channel Packet	35015	Rotterdam Lloyd
35002	Union Castle	35016	Elders Fyffes
35003	Royal Mail	35017	Belgian Marine
35004	Cunard White Star	35018	British India Line
35005	Canadian Pacific	35019	French Line CGT
35006	Peninsular & Oriental	35020	Bibby Line
	S.N. Co.	35021	New Zealand Line
35007	Aberdeen	35022	Holland-America Line
	Commonwealth	35023	Holland-Afrika Line
35008	Orient Line	35024	East Asiatic Company
35009	Shaw Savill	35025	Brocklebank Line
35010	Blue Star	35026	Lamport & Holt Line
35011	General Steam	35027	Port Line
	Navigation	35028	Clan Line
35012	United States Line	35029	Ellerman Lines
35013	Blue Funnel	35030	Elder Dempster Lines
35014	Nederland Line		

CLASS E1 0-6-0T

3	Ryde	4	Wroxall

CLASS O2 0-4-4T

14	Fishbourne	27	Merstone
16	Ventnor	28	Ashey
17	Seaview	29	Alverstone
18	Ningwood	30	Shorwell
20	Shanklin	31	Chale
21	Sandown	32	Bonchurch
22	Brading	33	Bembridge
24	Calbourne	35	Freshwater
25	Godshill	36	Carisbrooke
26	Whitweil		

SOUTHERN REGION SERVICE LOCOMOTIVES

No.	Old No.	Class	Station
DS 49	—	—	Broad Clyst
*DS 74	—	Bo-Bo	Durnsford Road Power Station
*DS 75	—	Bo	Waterloo & City
DS 77	0745	C14	Redbridge Sleeper Depot
†DS 377	2635	A1X	Brighton Works
DS 600	—	0-4-0 Diesel	Eastleigh Carriage Works
DS 680	{ L.B.S.C. 654 S.E.C. 751 }	A1	Lancing Carriage Works
DS 681	L.B.S.C. 659	A1X	Lancing Carriage Works
DS 1169	—	—	Folkestone Warren
DS 1173	2217	0-6-0 Diesel	Engineer's Department
DS 3152	30272	G6	Meldon Quarry

* Electric.　　　　　　　　† Repainted 1947 in Stroudley livery.

SOUTHERN RAILWAY LOCOMOTIVE SUPERINTENDENTS AND CHIEF MECHANICAL ENGINEERS OF CONSTITUENT COMPANIES

LONDON & SOUTH WESTERN RAILWAY

J. Woods ...	1835–1841
J. V. Gooch ...	1841–1850
J. Beattie ...	1850–1871
W. G. Beattie ...	1871–1878
W. Adams ...	1878–1895
D. Drummond ...	1895–1912
R. W. Urie...	1912–1922

LONDON, BRIGHTON AND SOUTH COAST RAILWAY

—. Statham ...	? –1845
J. Gray ...	1845–1847
S. Kirtley ...	1847
J. C. Craven	1847–1869
W. Stroudley	1870–1889
R. J. Billinton	1890–1904
D. Earle Marsh	1905–1911
L. B. Billinton	1911–1922

SOUTH EASTERN RAILWAY

B. Cubitt ...	1842–1845
J. Cudworth ...	1845–1876
A. M. Watkin ...	1876
R. Mansell ...	1877–1878
J. Stirling ...	1878–1898

LONDON, CHATHAM AND DOVER RAILWAY

W. Cubitt ...	1853–1860
W. Martley ...	1860–1874
W. Kirtley ...	1874–1898

SOUTH EASTERN AND CHATHAM RAILWAY

H. S. Wainwright ...	1899–1913
R. E. L. Maunsell ...	1913–1922

SOUTHERN RAILWAY

R. E. L. Maunsell ...	1923–1937
O. V. Bulleid ...	1937–1949

Class O2 0-4-4T No. 30182 (push-and-pull fitted) [*G. M. Stubbs*

Class M7 0-4-4T No. 30021 (push-and-pull fitted) [*K. J. M. May*

Class H 0-4-4T No. 31308 (push-and-pull fitted) [*P. H. Groom*

Class 0415 4-4-2T No. 30583   [D. Penney

Class 0298 2-4-0WT No. 30586   [R. E. Vincent

Class T9 4-4-0 No. 30289   [Brian E. Morrison

Class D1 4-4-0 No. 31492   [D. Penney

Class L 4-4-0 No. 31762   [R. C. Riley

Class L1 4-4-0 No. 31754   [R. C. Riley

Class H15 4-6-0 No. 30334 (Maunsell rebuild of Drummond F13) [B. K. B. Green

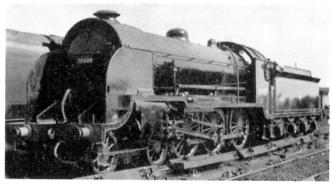

Class H15 4-6-0 (Urie) No. 30489 [G. Wheeler

Class H15 4-6-0 (Maunsell) No. 30476 [B. K. B. Green

Class N15 4-6-0 No. 30790 *Sir Villiars* (with modified cab) [*A. E. Brown*

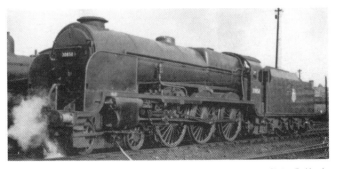

Class LN 4-6-0 No. 30850 *Lord Nelson* [*Brian E. Morrison*

Class V 4-4-0 No. 30908 *Westminster* [*D. Penney*

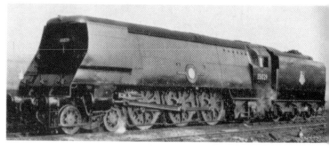

Class MN 4-6-2 No. 35029 *Ellerman Lines*   [*R. J. Buckley*

Rebuilt Class MN 4-6-2 No. 35022 *Holland-America Line*   [*Brian E. Morrison*

Class WC 4-6-2 No. 34010 *Sidmouth*   [*R. K. Evans*

Rebuilt Class WC 4-6-2 No. 34037 *Clovelly*

Class Q 0-6-0 No. 30541

[*R. C. Riley*

Class Q1 0-6-0 No. 33039

[*P. H. Groom*

Class H16 4-6-2T No. 30520　　　　　　　　　　　　[B. K. B. Green

Class Z 0-8-0T No. 30951　　　　　　　　　　　　[P. H. Groom

Class W 2-6-4T No. 31925　　　　　　　　　　　　[P. H. Groom

Class 700 0-6-0 No. 30339 [G. M. Kichenside

Class C 0-6-0 No. 31690 [A. W. Martin

Class C2X 0-6-0 No. 32525 [C. G. Pearson

Class N 2-6-0 No. 31400

[A. R. Carpenter

Class U 2-6-0 No. 31625

Class U1 2-6-0 No. 31907

[C. P. Boocock

Class A1X 0-6-0T No. 32646   [W. M. J. Jackson

Class E1 0-6-0T No. 32151   [R. A. Panting

Class E1/R 0-6-2T No. 32697   [C. P. Boocock

Class E2 0-6-0T No. 32107   *[P. H. Groom*

Class E4 0-6-2T No. 32503   *[R. E. Vincent*

Class E6 0-6-2T No. 32410   *[R. C. Riley*

BRITISH RAILWAYS LOCOMOTIVES
Nos. 40000-59999

The code given in bold type to the right of each Class heading,
e.g. " 2P " denotes its British Railways power classification.
The numbers of locomotives in service have been checked to July 7th, 1958.

2-6-2T   3

Introduced 1930. Fowler L.M.S. design
  with parallel boiler.
*Introduced 1930. Condensing locos.
  for working to Moorgate, London.
Weight: {70 tons 10 cwt.
       {71 tons 16 cwt.*
Pressure: 200 lb. Su.
Cyls.: (O) 17½″ × 26″.
Driving Wheels: 5′ 3″.
T.E.: 21,485 lb.
Walschaerts valve gear. P.V.

40001	40019	40037*	40054
40002	40020	40038*	40055
40003	40021	40039*	40056
40004	40022*	40040*	40057
40005	40023*	40041	40058
40006	40024*	40042	40059
40007	40025*	40043	40060
40008	40026*	40044	40061
40009	40027*	40045	40062
40010	40028*	40046	40063
40011	40029*	40047	40064
40012	40030*	40048	40065
40013	40031*	40049	40066
40014	40032*	40050	40067
40015	40033*	40051	40068
40016	40034*	40052	40069
40017	40035*	40053	40070
40018	40036*		

Total 70

2-6-2T   3

Introduced 1935. Stanier L.M.S. taper
  boiler development of Fowler design
  (above).
*Introduced 1941. Rebuilt with larger
  boiler.
Weight: {71 tons 5 cwt.
       {72 tons 10 cwt.*
Pressure: 200 lb. Su.
Cyls.: (O) 17½″ × 26″.
Driving Wheels: 5′ 3″.

T.E.: 21,485 lb.
Walschaerts valve gear. P.V.

40071	40106	40141	40176
40072	40107	40142	40177
40073	40108	40143	40178
40074	40109	40144	40179
40075	40110	40145	40180
40076	40111	40146	40181
40077	40112	40147	40182
40078	40113	40148*	40183
40079	40114	40149	40184
40080	40115	40150	40185
40081	40116	40151	40186
40082	40117	40152	40187
40083	40118	40153	40188
40084	40119	40154	40189
40085	40120	40155	40190
40086	40121	40156	40191
40087	40122	40157	40192
40088	40123	40158	40193
40089	40124	40159	40194
40090	40125	40160	40195
40091	40126	40161	40196
40092	40127	40162	40197
40093	40128	40163*	40198
40094	40129	40164	40199
40095	40130	40165	40200
40096	40131	40166	40201
40097	40132	40167*	40202
40098	40133	40168	40203*
40099	40134	40169*	40204
40100	40135	40170	40205
40101	40136	40171	40206
40102	40137	40172	40207
40103	40138	40173	40208
40104	40139	40174	40209
40105	40140	40175	

Total 139

4-4-0   2P

Introduced 1912. Fowler rebuild of
Johnson locos. with superheater and
piston valves.
Weight: Loco. 53 tons 7 cwt.
Pressure: 160 lb. Su.
Cyls.: $20\frac{1}{2}'' \times 26''$.
Driving Wheels: $7'\ 0\frac{1}{2}''$.
T.E.: 17,585 lb.
P.V.

40332	40439	40493	40538
40396	40443	40501	40540
40402	40452	40502	40542
40411	40453	40504	40543
40412	40454	40511	40548
40413	40461	40513	40550
40416	40487	40534	40552
40420	40489	40536	40553
40421	40491	40537	40557

Total 36

4-4-0   2P

Introduced 1928. Post-grouping devel-
opment of Midland design, with
modified dimensions and reduced
boiler mountings.
*Introduced 1928. Locos. built for S. &
D.J.R. (taken into L.M.S. stock, 1930).
†Fitted experimentally in 1933 with
Dabeg feed-water heater.
Weight: Loco. 54 tons 1 cwt.
Pressure: 180 lb. Su.
Cyls.: $19'' \times 26''$.
Driving Wheels: $6'\ 9''$.
T.E.: 17,730 lb.
P.V.

40563	40575	40587	40600
40564	40576	40588	40601
40565	40577	40589	40602
40566	40578	40590	40603
40567	40579	40592	40604
40568	40580	40593	40605
40569	40581	40594	40606
40570	40582	40595	40607
40571	40583	40596	40608
40572	40584	40597	40609
40573	40585	40598	40610
40574	40586	40599	40611

40612	40634*	40657	40680
40613	40635*	40658	40681
40614	40636	40659	40682
40615	40637	40660	40683
40616	40638	40661	40684
40617	40640	40663	40685
40618	40641	40664	40686
40619	40642	40665	40687
40620	40643	40666	40688
40621	40644	40667	40689
40622	40645	40668	40690
40623	40646	40669	40691
40624	40647	40670	40692
40625	40648	40671	40693
40626	40649	40672	40694
40627	40650	40673	40695
40628	40651	40674	40696
40629	40652	40675	40697
40630	40653†	40677	40698
40631	40654	40678	40699
40632	40655	40679	40700
40633*†	40656		

Total 134

4-4-0 (3-Cyl. Compd.)   4P

Introduced 1924. Post-grouping
development of Johnson Midland
compound with modified dimensions
and (with some exceptions) reduced
boiler mountings.
Weight: Loco. 61 tons 14 cwt.
Pressure: 200 lb. Su.
Cyls.: $\begin{cases} \text{L.P. (2) } 21'' \times 26''. \\ \text{H.P. (1) } 19'' \times 26''. \end{cases}$
Driving Wheels: $6'\ 9''$.
T.E. (of L.P. cyls. at
80% boiler pressure): 22,650 lb.
P.V. (H.P. cyl. only).

40907	41083	41120	41162
40925	41090	41121	41163
40931	41094	41122	41164
40936	41100	41123	41165
41049	41101	41143	41167
41062	41102	41156	41168
41063	41113	41157	41173
41068	41119	41158	41193
41078			

Total 33

2-6-2T 2

Introduced 1946. Ivatt L.M.S. taper boiler design.

Weight: 63 tons 5 cwt.

Pressure: 200 lb. Su.

Cyls.: $\begin{cases} \text{(O)} \ 16'' \times 24''. \\ \text{(O)} \ 16\frac{1}{2}'' \times 24''.* \end{cases}$

Driving Wheels: 5' 0".

T.E.: $\begin{cases} 17,410 \text{ lb.} \\ 18,510 \text{ lb.}* \end{cases}$

Walschaerts valve gear. P.V.

41200	41233	41266	41298*
41201	41234	41267	41299*
41202	41235	41268	41300*
41203	41236	41269	41301*
41204	41237	41270	41302*
41205	41238	41271	41303*
41206	41239	41272	41304*
41207	41240	41273	41305*
41208	41241	41274	41306*
41209	41242	41275	41307*
41210	41243	41276	41308*
41211	41244	41277	41309*
41212	41245	41278	41310*
41213	41246	41279	41311*
41214	41247	41280	41312*
41215	41248	41281	41313*
41216	41249	41282	41314*
41217	41250	41283	41315*
41218	41251	41284	41316*
41219	41252	41285	41317*
41220	41253	41286	41318*
41221	41254	41287	41319*
41222	41255	41288	41320*
41223	41256	41289	41321*
41224	41257	41290*	41322*
41225	41258	41291*	41323*
41226	41259	41292*	41324*
41227	41260	41293*	41325*
41228	41261	41294*	41326*
41229	41262	41295*	41327*
41230	41263	41296*	41328*
41231	41264	41297*	41329*
41232	41265		

Total 130

0-4-0T 0F

Introduced 1907. Deeley Midland design.

Weight: 32 tons 16 cwt.

Pressure: 160 lb.

Cyls.: (O) 15" × 22".

Driving Wheels: 3' 9¾".

T.E.: 14,635 lb.

Walschaerts valve gear.

41528	41531	41533	41536
41529	41532	41535	41537

Total 8

0-6-0T 1F

Introduced 1878. Johnson Midland design.

*Rebuilt with Belpaire firebox.

Weight: 39 tons 11 cwt.

Pressure: $\begin{cases} 150 \text{ lb.} \\ 140 \text{ lb.}* \end{cases}$

Cyls.: 17" × 24".

Driving Wheels: 4' 7".

T.E.: $\begin{cases} 16,080 \text{ lb.} \\ 15,005 \text{ lb.}* \end{cases}$

41661*	41739*	41797*	41855*
41702*	41754*	41804*	41857*
41708*	41763*	41835	41875*
41712*	41769*	41844*	41878*
41726*	41773*	41847*	41879*
41734*	41795*		

Total 22

0-4-4T 2P

Introduced 1932. Stanier L.M.S. design. Push-and-pull fitted.

Weight: 58 tons 1 cwt.

Pressure: 160 lb.

Cyls.: 18" × 26".

Driving Wheels: 5' 7".

T.E.: 17,100 lb.

41900	41903	41906	41908
41901	41904	41907	41909
41902	41905		

Total 10

4-4-2T 3P

Introduced 1923. Midland and L.M.S. development of Whitelegg L.T. & S. " 79 " Class.
Weight: 71 tons 10 cwt.
Pressure: 170 lb.
Cyls.: (O) 19″ × 26″.
Driving Wheels: 6′ 6″.
T.E.: 17,390 lb.

41928	41945	41949	41975
41936	41946	41950	41977
41939	41947	41969	41978
41941	41948		

Total 14

0-6-2T 3F

Introduced 1903. Whitelegg L.T. & S. " 69 " Class (Nos. 41990–3 built 1912 taken directly into M.R. stock).
Weight: 64 tons 13 cwt.
Pressure: 170 lb.
Cyls.: 18″ × 26″.
Driving Wheels: 5′ 3″.
T.E.: 19,320 lb.

41981	41984	41987	41992
41982	41985	41990	41993
41983	41986	41991	

Total 11

2-6-4T 4

*Introduced 1927. Fowler L.M.S. parallel boiler design.
†Introduced 1933. As earlier engines, but with side-window cab and doors.
‡Introduced 1934. Stanier taper-boiler 3-cylinder design for L.T. & S.
§Introduced 1935. Stanier taper-boiler 2-cylinder design.
¶Introduced 1945. Fairburn development of Stanier design with shorter wheelbase and detail alterations.

Weight:
{ 86 tons 5 cwt.*†
{ 92 tons 5 cwt.‡
{ 87 tons 17 cwt.§
{ 85 tons 5 cwt.¶

Pressure (all types): 200 lb. Su.
Cyls.:
{ (O) 19″ × 26″.*†
{ (3) 16″ × 26″.‡
{ (O) 19¾″ × 26″.§¶

Driving Wheels (all types): 5′ 9″.
T.E.:
{ 23,125 lb.*†
{ 24,600 lb.‡
{ 24,670 lb.§¶

Walschaerts valve gear. P.V.

¶FAIRBURN LOCOS.

42050	42095	42140	42185
42051	42096	42141	42186
42052	42097	42142	42187
42053	42098	42143	42188
42054	42099	42144	42189
42055	42100	42145	42190
42056	42101	42146	42191
42057	42102	42147	42192
42058	42103	42148	42193
42059	42104	42149	42194
42060	42105	42150	42195
42061	42106	42151	42196
42062	42107	42152	42197
42063	42108	42153	42198
42064	42109	42154	42199
42065	42110	42155	42200
42066	42111	42156	42201
42067	42112	42157	42202
42068	42113	42158	42203
42069	42114	42159	42204
42070	42115	42160	42205
42071	42116	42161	42206
42072	42117	42162	42207
42073	42118	42163	42208
42074	42119	42164	42209
42075	42120	42165	42210
42076	42121	42166	42211
42077	42122	42167	42212
42078	42123	42168	42213
42079	42124	42169	42214
42080	42125	42170	42215
42081	42126	42171	42216
42082	42127	42172	42217
42083	42128	42173	42218
42084	42129	42174	42219
42085	42130	42175	42220
42086	42131	42176	42221
42087	42132	42177	42222
42088	42133	42178	42223
42089	42134	42179	42224
42090	42135	42180	42225
42091	42136	42181	42226
42092	42137	42182	42227
42093	42138	42183	42228
42094	42139	42184	42229

42230	42248	42266	42284
42231	42249	42267	42285
42232	42250	42268	42286
42233	42251	42269	42287
42234	42252	42270	42288
42235	42253	42271	42289
42236	42254	42272	42290
42237	42255	42273	42291
42238	42256	42274	42292
42239	42257	42275	42293
42240	42258	42276	42294
42241	42259	42277	42295
42242	42260	42278	42296
42243	42261	42279	42297
42244	42262	42280	42298
42245	42263	42281	42299
42246	42264	42282	
42247	42265	42283	

*FOWLER LOCOS.

42300	42324	42348	42372
42301	42325	42349	42373
42302	42326	42350	42374
42303	42327	42351	42375
42304	42328	42352	42376
42305	42329	42353	42377
42306	42330	42354	42378
42307	42331	42355	42379
42308	42332	42356	42380
42309	42333	42357	42381
42310	42334	42358	42382
42311	42335	42359	42383
42312	42336	42360	42384
42313	42337	42361	42385
42314	42338	42362	42386
42315	42339	42363	42387
42316	42340	42364	42388
42317	42341	42365	42389
42318	42342	42366	42390
42319	42343	42367	42391
42320	42344	42368	42392
42321	42345	42369	42393
42322	42346	42370	42394
42323	42347	42371	

†FOWLER LOCOS. WITH SIDE-WINDOW CAB

42395	42403	42411	42418
42396	42404	42412	42419
42397	42405	42413	42420
42398	42406	42414	42421
42399	42407	42415	42422
42400	42408	42416	42423
42401	42409	42417	42424
42402	42410		

§STANIER 2-CYL. LOCOS.

42425	42443	42461	42479
42426	42444	42462	42480
42427	42445	42463	42481
42428	42446	42464	42482
42429	42447	42465	42483
42430	42448	42466	42484
42431	42449	42467	42485
42432	42450	42468	42486
42433	42451	42469	42487
42434	42452	42470	42488
42435	42453	42471	42489
42436	42454	42472	42490
42437	42455	42473	42491
42438	42456	42474	42492
42439	42457	42475	42493
42440	42458	42476	42494
42441	42459	42477	
42442	42460	42478	

‡STANIER 3-CYL. LOCOS.

42500	42510	42519	42528
42501	42511	42520	42529
42502	42512	42521	42530
42503	42513	42522	42531
42504	42514	42523	42532
42505	42515	42524	42533
42506	42516	42525	42534
42507	42517	42526	42535
42508	42518	42527	42536
42509			

§STANIER 2-CYL. LOCOS.

42537	42571	42605	42639
42538	42572	42606	42640
42539	42573	42607	42641
42540	42574	42608	42642
42541	42575	42609	42643
42542	42576	42610	42644
42543	42577	42611	42645
42544	42578	42612	42646
42545	42579	42613	42647
42546	42580	42614	42648
42547	42581	42615	42649
42548	42582	42616	42650
42549	42583	42617	42651
42550	42584	42618	42652
42551	42585	42619	42653
42552	42586	42620	42654
42553	42587	42621	42655
42554	42588	42622	42656
42555	42589	42623	42657
42556	42590	42624	42658
42557	42591	42625	42659
42558	42592	42626	42660
42559	42593	42627	42661
42560	42594	42628	42662
42561	42595	42629	42663
42562	42596	42630	42664
42563	42597	42631	42665
42564	42598	42632	42666
42565	42599	42633	42667
42566	42600	42634	42668
42567	42601	42635	42669
42568	42602	42636	42670
42569	42603	42637	42671
42570	42604	42638	42672

¶FAIRBURN LOCOS.

42673	42680	42687	42694
42674	42681	42688	42695
42675	42682	42689	42696
42676	42683	42690	42697
42677	42684	42691	42698
42678	42685	42692	42699
42679	42686	42693	

2-6-0   6P5F

Introduced 1926. Hughes L.M.S. design built under Fowler's direction. Walschaerts valve gear. P.V.
*Introduced 1953. Locos. rebuilt experimentally with Lentz R.C. poppet valves in 1931; rebuilt with Reidinger rotary poppet valve gear in 1953.
Weight: Loco. 66 tons 0 cwt.
Pressure: 180 lb. Su.
Cyls. :(O) 21″ × 26″.
Driving Wheels: 5′ 6″.
T.E.: 26,580 lb.

42700	42735	42770	42805
42701	42736	42771	42806
42702	42737	42772	42807
42703	42738	42773	42808
42704	42739	42774	42809
42705	42740	42775	42810
42706	42741	42776	42811
42707	42742	42777	42812
42708	42743	42778	42813
42709	42744	42779	42814
42710	42745	42780	42815
42711	42746	42781	42816
42712	42747	42782	42817
42713	42748	42783	42818*
42714	42749	42784	42819
42715	42750	42785	42820
42716	42751	42786	42821
42717	42752	42787	42822*
42718	42753	42788	42823
42719	42754	42789	42824*
42720	42755	42790	42825*
42721	42756	42791	42826
42722	42757	42792	42827
42723	42758	42793	42828
42724	42759	42794	42829*
42725	42760	42795	42830
42726	42761	42796	42831
42727	42762	42797	42832
42728	42763	42798	42833
42729	42764	42799	42834
42730	42765	42800	42835
42731	42766	42801	42836
42732	42767	42802	42837
42733	42768	42803	42838
42734	42769	42804	42839

Total 645

42840	42867	42894	42920
42841	42868	42895	42921
42842	42869	42896	42922
42843	42870	42897	42923
42844	42871	42898	42924
42845	42872	42899	42925
42846	42873	42900	42926
42847	42874	42901	42927
42848	42875	42902	42928
42849	42876	42903	42929
42850	42877	42904	42930
42851	42878	42905	42931
42852	42879	42906	42932
42853	42880	42907	42933
42854	42881	42908	42934
42855	42882	42909	42935
42856	42883	42910	42936
42857	42884	42911	42937
42858	42885	42912	42938
42859	42886	42913	42939
42860	42887	42914	42940
42861	42888	42915	42941
42862	42889	42916	42942
42863	42890	42917	42943
42864	42891	42918	42944
42865	42892	42919	
42866	42893		**Total 245**

2-6-0   6P5F

Introduced 1933. Stanier L.M.S. taper boiler design, some with safety valves mounted on the top feed.
Weight: Loco. 69 tons 2 cwt.
Pressure: 225 lb. Su.
Cyls.: (O) 18″ × 28″.
Driving Wheels: 5′ 6″.
T.E.: 26,290 lb.
Walschaerts valve gear. P.V.

42945	42955	42965	42975
42946	42956	42966	42976
42947	42957	42967	42977
42948	42958	42968	42978
42949	42959	42969	42979
42950	42960	42970	42980
42951	42961	42971	42981
42952	42962	42972	42982
42953	42963	42973	42983
42954	42964	42974	42984
			Total 40

2-6-0   4

Introduced 1947. Ivatt L.M.S. taper boiler design with double chimney. Later engines introduced with single chimney, with which earlier engines are being rebuilt.
Weight: Loco. 59 tons 2 cwt.
Pressure: 225 lb. Su.
Cyls.: (O) 17½″ × 26″.
Driving Wheels: 5′ 3″.
T.E.: 24,170 lb.
Walschaerts valve gear. P.V.

43000	43036	43072	43108
43001	43037	43073	43109
43002	43038	43074	43110
43003	43039	43075	43111
43004	43040	43076	43112
43005	43041	43077	43113
43006	43042	43078	43114
43007	43043	43079	43115
43008	43044	43080	43116
43009	43045	43081	43117
43010	43046	43082	43118
43011	43047	43083	43119
43012	43048	43084	43120
43013	43049	43085	43121
43014	43050	43086	43122
43015	43051	43087	43123
43016	43052	43088	43124
43017	43053	43089	43125
43018	43054	43090	43126
43019	43055	43091	43127
43020	43056	43092	43128
43021	43057	43093	43129
43022	43058	43094	43130
43023	43059	43095	43131
43024	43060	43096	43132
43025	43061	43097	43133
43026	43062	43098	43134
43027	43063	43099	43135
43028	43064	43100	43136
43029	43065	43101	43137
43030	43066	43102	43138
43031	43067	43103	43139
43032	43068	43104	43140
43033	43069	43105	43141
43034	43070	43106	43142
43035	43071	43107	43143

43144	43149	43154	43158
43145	43150	43155	43159
43146	43151	43156	43160
43147	43152	43157	43161
43148	43153		

Total 162

0-6-0   3F

Introduced 1885. Johnson Midland locos., rebuilt from 1916 by Fowler with Belpaire firebox.
*Introduced 1885. Johnson Midland locos., rebuilt from 1920 by Fowler with Belpaire firebox.
†Introduced 1896. Locos. built for S. & D.J. (taken into L.M.S. stock 1930).
Weight: Loco. 43 tons 17 cwt.
Pressure: 175 lb.
Cyls.: 18″ × 26″.

Driving Wheels: $\begin{cases} 5' \ 3''. \\ 5' \ 3''.† \\ 4' \ 11''.* \end{cases}$

T.E.: $\begin{cases} 19{,}890 \ \text{lb.} \\ 19{,}890 \ \text{lb.}† \\ 21{,}240 \ \text{lb.}* \end{cases}$

43174*	43225	43267	43326
43178*	43231	43268	43327
43180*	43233	43271	43329
43183*	43234	43274	43330
43185*	43235	43277	43333
43186*	43237	43278	43335
43187*	43240	43282	43337
43188*	43241	43284	43339
43189*	43242	43287	43340
43192	43243	43292	43342
43194†	43244	43294	43344
43200	43245	43295	43355
43203	43247	43300	43357
43205	43248†	43301	43359
43207	43249	43305	43361
43210	43250	43306	43368
43211†	43251	43307	43369
43212	43253	43308	43370
43213	43254	43309	43371
43214	43256	43314	43373
43216†	43257	43315	43374
43218†	43258	43318	43378
43219	43261	43321	43379
43222	43263	43324	43381
43223	43266	43325	43386

43387	43496	43605	43679
43388	43499	43608	43680
43389	43502	43612	43681
43394	43506	43615	43682
43395	43507	43618	43687
43398	43509	43619	43693
43399	43510	43620	43705
43400	43514	43621	43709
43405	43515	43622	43711
43406	43520	43623	43712
43410	43521	43624	43714
43411	43522	43627	43715
43419	43523	43629	43721
43427	43529	43630	43727
43428	43531	43634	43728
43429	43538	43637	43729
43431	43548	43638	43731
43433	43553	43639	43734
43435	43558	43644	43735
43436	43562	43645	43737
43440	43565	43650	43745
43441	43570	43651	43749
43444	43572	43652	43750*
43446	43574	43657	43751
43449	43578	43658	43753
43453	43579	43660	43754
43456	43580	43664	43756
43457	43583	43665	43759
43459	43584	43668	43760
43464	43585	43669	43762
43468	43586	43673	43763
43474	43587	43674	43766
43482	43593	43675	43771
43484	43594	43678	43773
43490	43599		

Total 238

0-6-0   3F

Introduced 1906. Deeley Midland design. Rebuilt by Fowler with Belpaire firebox.
Weight: Loco. 46 tons 3 cwt.
Pressure: 175 lb.
Cyls.: 18½″ × 26″.
Driving Wheels: 5′ 3″.
T.E.: 21,010 lb.

43778	43793	43812	43826
43784	43799	43814	43828
43785	43800	43815	43829
43787	43808	43822	43832
43789	43809	43825	

Total 19

0-6-0　　　　　4F

Introduced 1911. Fowler superheated Midland design.
Weight: Loco. 48 tons 15 cwt.
Pressure: 175 lb. Su.
Cyls.: 20″ × 26″.
Driving Wheels: 5′ 3″.
T.E.: 24,555 lb.
P.V.

43836	43876	43917	43951
43839	43877	43918	43952
43840	43878	43919	43953
43841	43880	43920	43954
43842	43881	43921	43955
43843	43882	43922	43957
43844	43883	43923	43958
43845	43884	43924	43960
43846	43885	43925	43961
43848	43886	43926	43962
43849	43887	43928	43963
43850	43888	43929	43964
43853	43890	43930	43965
43854	43893	43931	43966
43855	43896	43932	43967
43856	43897	43933	43968
43858	43899	43934	43969
43859	43900	43935	43970
43860	43902	43937	43971
43861	43903	43938	43972
43863	43904	43939	43973
43864	43905	43940	43975
43865	43906	43942	43976
43866	43907	43944	43977
43868	43908	43945	43979
43869	43910	43946	43981
43870	43911	43947	43982
43871	43913	43948	43983
43872	43914	43949	43984
43873	43915	43950	43985

43986	43997	44007	44016
43987	43998	44008	44018
43988	43999	44009	44019
43989	44000	44010	44020
43990	44001	44011	44021
43991	44002	44012	44022
43994	44003	44013	44023
43995	44004	44014	44025
43996	44005	44015	44026

Total 156

0-6-0　　　　　4F

Introduced 1924. Post-grouping development of Midland design with reduced boiler mountings.
*Introduced 1922. Locos. built for S. & D.J.R. to M.R. design (taken into L.M.S. stock 1930).
Weight: Loco. 48 tons 15 cwt.
Pressure: 175 lb. Su.
Cyls.: 20″ × 26″.
Driving Wheels: 5′ 3″.
T.E.: 24,555 lb.
P.V.

44027	44048	44069	44090
44028	44049	44070	44091
44029	44050	44071	44092
44030	44051	44072	44093
44031	44052	44073	44094
44032	44053	44074	44095
44033	44054	44075	44096
44034	44055	44076	44097
44035	44056	44077	44098
44036	44057	44078	44099
44037	44058	44079	44100
44038	44059	44080	44101
44039	44060	44081	44102
44040	44061	44082	44103
44041	44062	44083	44104
44042	44063	44084	44105
44043	44064	44085	44106
44044	44065	44086	44107
44045	44066	44087	44108
44046	44067	44088	44109
44047	44068	44089	44110

44111	44158	44205	44252	44299	44346	44393	44440
44112	44159	44206	44253	44300	44347	44394	44441
44113	44160	44207	44254	44301	44348	44395	44442
44114	44161	44208	44255	44302	44349	44396	44443
44115	44162	44209	44256	44303	44350	44397	44444
44116	44163	44210	44257	44304	44351	44398	44445
44117	44164	44211	44258	44305	44352	44399	44446
44118	44165	44212	44259	44306	44353	44400	44447
44119	44166	44213	44260	44307	44354	44401	44448
44120	44167	44214	44261	44308	44355	44402	44449
44121	44168	44215	44262	44309	44356	44403	44450
44122	44169	44216	44263	44310	44357	44404	44451
44123	44170	44217	44264	44311	44358	44405	44452
44124	44171	44218	44265	44312	44359	44406	44453
44125	44172	44219	44266	44313	44360	44407	44454
44126	44173	44220	44267	44314	44361	44408	44455
44127	44174	44221	44268	44315	44362	44409	44456
44128	44175	44222	44269	44316	44363	44410	44457
44129	44176	44223	44270	44317	44364	44411	44458
44130	44177	44224	44271	44318	44365	44412	44459
44131	44178	44225	44272	44319	44366	44413	44460
44132	44179	44226	44273	44320	44367	44414	44461
44133	44180	44227	44274	44321	44368	44415	44462
44134	44181	44228	44275	44322	44369	44416	44463
44135	44182	44229	44276	44323	44370	44417	44464
44136	44183	44230	44277	44324	44371	44418	44465
44137	44184	44231	44278	44325	44372	44419	44466
44138	44185	44232	44279	44326	44373	44420	44467
44139	44186	44233	44280	44327	44374	44421	44468
44140	44187	44234	44281	44328	44375	44422	44469
44141	44188	44235	44282	44329	44376	44423	44470
44142	44189	44236	44283	44330	44377	44424	44471
44143	44190	44237	44284	44331	44378	44425	44472
44144	44191	44238	44285	44332	44379	44426	44473
44145	44192	44239	44286	44333	44380	44427	44474
44146	44193	44240	44287	44334	44381	44428	44475
44147	44194	44241	44288	44335	44382	44429	44476
44148	44195	44242	44289	44336	44383	44430	44477
44149	44196	44243	44290	44337	44384	44431	44478
44150	44197	44244	44291	44338	44385	44432	44479
44151	44198	44245	44292	44339	44386	44433	44480
44152	44199	44246	44293	44340	44387	44434	44481
44153	44200	44247	44294	44341	44388	44435	44482
44154	44201	44248	44295	44342	44389	44436	44483
44155	44202	44249	44296	44343	44390	44437	44484
44156	44203	44250	44297	44344	44391	44438	44485
44157	44204	44251	44298	44345	44392	44439	44486

44487	44517	44547	44577
44488	44518	44548	44578
44489	44519	44549	44579
44490	44520	44550	44580
44491	44521	44551	44581
44492	44522	44552	44582
44493	44523	44553	44583
44494	44524	44554	44584
44495	44525	44555	44585
44496	44526	44556	44586
44497	44527	44557*	44587
44498	44528	44558*	44588
44499	44529	44559*	44589
44500	44530	44560*	44590
44501	44531	44561*	44591
44502	44532	44562	44592
44503	44533	44563	44593
44504	44534	44564	44594
44505	44535	44565	44595
44506	44536	44566	44596
44507	44537	44567	44597
44508	44538	44568	44598
44509	44539	44569	44599
44510	44540	44570	44600
44511	44541	44571	44601
44512	44542	44572	44602
44513	44543	44573	44603
44514	44544	44574	44604
44515	44545	44575	44605
44516	44546	44576	44606

Total 580

4-6-0   5

Introduced 1934. Stanier L.M.S. taper boiler design.

Experimental locomotives:—

1. Introduced 1947. Stephenson link motion (outside), Timken roller bearings.
2. Introduced 1948. Caprotti valve gear.
3. Introduced 1948. Caprotti valve gear, Timken roller bearings.
4. Introduced 1948. Caprotti valve gear, Timken roller bearings, double chimney.
5. Introduced 1947. Timken roller bearings.
6. Introduced 1947. Timken roller bearings, double chimney.
7. Introduced 1949. Fitted with steel firebox.
8. Introduced 1950. Skefko roller bearings.
9. Introduced 1950. Timken roller bearings on driving coupled axle only.
10. Introduced 1950. Skefko roller bearings on driving coupled axle only.
11. Introduced 1951. Caprotti valve gear, Skefko roller bearings.

Weight: Loco.
{ 72 tons 2 cwt.
75 tons 6 cwt. (1, 5, 6, 8, 9, 10).
74 tons 0 cwt. (2, 3, 4, 11).
72 tons 2 cwt. (7). }

Pressure: 225 lb. Su.
Cyls.: (O) $18\frac{1}{4}'' \times 28''$.
Driving Wheels: 6' 0".
T.E.: 25,455 lb.

Walschaerts valve gear and P.V. except where otherwise shown.

44658	44684[8]	44710	44736
44659	44685[8]	44711	44737
44660	44686[11]	44712	44738[2]
44661	44687[11]	44713	44739[2]
44662	44688[9]	44714	44740[2]
44663	44689[9]	44715	44741[2]
44664	44690[9]	44716	44742[2]
44665	44691[9]	44717	44743[2]
44666	44692[9]	44718[7]	44744[2]
44667	44693[9]	44719[7]	44745[2]
44668[10]	44694[9]	44720[7]	44746[2]
44669[10]	44695[9]	44721[7]	44747[2]
44670[10]	44696[9]	44722[7]	44748[3]
44671[10]	44697[9]	44723[7]	44749[3]
44672[10]	44698	44724[7]	44750[3]
44673[10]	44699	44725[7]	44751[3]
44674[10]	44700	44726[7]	44752[3]
44675[10]	44701	44727[7]	44753[3]
44676[10]	44702	44728	44754[3]
44677[10]	44703	44729	44755[4]
44678[8]	44704	44730	44756[4]
44679[8]	44705	44731	44757[4]
44680[8]	44706	44732	44758[5]
44681[8]	44707	44733	44759[5]
44682[8]	44708	44734	44760[5]
44683[8]	44709	44735	44761[5]

44762⁵	44809	44856	44903	44950	44997	45044	45091
44763⁵	44810	44857	44904	44951	44998	45045	45092
44764⁵	44811	44858	44905	44952	44999	45046	45093
44765⁶	44812	44859	44906	44953	45000	45047	45094
44766⁶	44813	44860	44907	44954	45001	45048	45095
44767¹	44814	44861	44908	44955	45002	45049	45096
44768	44815	44862	44909	44956	45003	45050	45097
44769	44816	44863	44910	44957	45004	45051	45098
44770	44817	44864	44911	44958	45005	45052	45099
44771	44818	44865	44912	44959	45006	45053	45100
44772	44819	44866	44913	44960	45007	45054	45101
44773	44820	44867	44914	44961	45008	45055	45102
44774	44821	44868	44915	44962	45009	45056	45103
44775	44822	44869	44916	44963	45010	45057	45104
44776	44823	44870	44917	44964	45011	45058	45105
44777	44824	44871	44918	44965	45012	45059	45106
44778	44825	44872	44919	44966	45013	45060	45107
44779	44826	44873	44920	44967	45014	45061	45108
44780	44827	44874	44921	44968	45015	45062	45109
44781	44828	44875	44922	44969	45016	45063	45110
44782	44829	44876	44923	44970	45017	45064	45111
44783	44830	44877	44924	44971	45018	45065	45112
44784	44831	44878	44925	44972	45019	45066	45113
44785	44832	44879	44926	44973	45020	45067	45114
44786	44833	44880	44927	44974	45021	45068	45115
44787	44834	44881	44928	44975	45022	45069	45116
44788	44835	44882	44929	44976	45023	45070	45117
44789	44836	44883	44930	44977	45024	45071	45118
44790	44837	44884	44931	44978	45025	45072	45119
44791	44838	44885	44932	44979	45026	45073	45120
44792	44839	44886	44933	44980	45027	45074	45121
44793	44840	44887	44934	44981	45028	45075	45122
44794	44841	44888	44935	44982	45029	45076	45123
44795	44842	44889	44936	44983	45030	45077	45124
44796	44843	44890	44937	44984	45031	45078	45125
44797	44844	44891	44938	44985	45032	45079	45126
44798	44845	44892	44939	44986	45033	45080	45127
44799	44846	44893	44940	44987	45034	45081	45128
44800	44847	44894	44941	44988	45035	45082	45129
44801	44848	44895	44942	44989	45036	45083	45130
44802	44849	44896	44943	44990	45037	45084	45131
44803	44850	44897	44944	44991	45038	45085	45132
44804	44851	44898	44945	44992	45039	45086	45133
44805	44852	44899	44946	44993	45040	45087	45134
44806	44853	44900	44947	44994	45041	45088	45135
44807	44854	44901	44948	44995	45042	45089	45136
44808	44855	44902	44949	44996	45043	45090	45137

45138	45179	45220	45261	45302	45349	45396	45443
45139	45180	45221	45262	45303	45350	45397	45444
45140	45181	45222	45263	45304	45351	45398	45445
45141	45182	45223	45264	45305	45352	45399	45446
45142	45183	45224	45265	45306	45353	45400	45447
45143	45184	45225	45266	45307	45354	45401	45448
45144	45185	45226	45267	45308	45355	45402	45449
45145	45186	45227	45268	45309	45356	45403	45450
45146	45187	45228	45269	45310	45357	45404	45451
45147	45188	45229	45270	45311	45358	45405	45452
45148	45189	45230	45271	45312	45359	45406	45453
45149	45190	45231	45272	45313	45360	45407	45454
45150	45191	45232	45273	45314	45361	45408	45455
45151	45192	45233	45274	45315	45362	45409	45456
45152	45193	45234	45275	45316	45363	45410	45457
45153	45194	45235	45276	45317	45364	45411	45458
45154*	45195	45236	45277	45318	45365	45412	45459
45155	45196	45237	45278	45319	45366	45413	45460
45156*	45197	45238	45279	45320	45367	45414	45461
45157*	45198	45239	45280	45321	45368	45415	45462
45158*	45199	45240	45281	45322	45369	45416	45463
45159	45200	45241	45282	45323	45370	45417	45464
45160	45201	45242	45283	45324	45371	45418	45465
45161	45202	45243	45284	45325	45372	45419	45466
45162	45203	45244	45285	45326	45373	45420	45467
45163	45204	45245	45286	45327	45374	45421	45468
45164	45205	45246	45287	45328	45375	45422	45469
45165	45206	45247	45288	45329	45376	45423	45470
45166	45207	45248	45289	45330	45377	45424	45471
45167	45208	45249	45290	45331	45378	45425	45472
45168	45209	45250	45291	45332	45379	45426	45473
45169	45210	45251	45292	45333	45380	45427	45474
45170	45211	45252	45293	45334	45381	45428	45475
45171	45212	45253	45294	45335	45382	45429	45476
45172	45213	45254	45295	45336	45383	45430	45477
45173	45214	45255	45296	45337	45384	45431	45478
45174	45215	45256	45297	45338	45385	45432	45479
45175	45216	45257	45298	45339	45386	45433	45480
45176	45217	45258	45299	45340	45387	45434	45481
45177	45218	45259	45300	45341	45388	45435	45482
45178	45219	45260	45301	45342	45389	45436	45483
				45343	45390	45437	45484
				45344	45391	45438	45485
				45345	45392	45439	45486
				45346	45393	45440	45487
				45347	45394	45441	45488
				45348	45395	45442	45489

* NAMES :

45154	Lanarkshire Yeomanry
45156	Ayrshire Yeomanry
45157	The Glasgow Highlander
45158	Glasgow Yeomanry

45490	45493	45496	45498
45491	45494	45497	45499
45492	45495		

Total 842

" Patriot " Class

4-6-0   6P5F & 7P

*6P5F. Introduced 1930. Fowler 3-cyl. rebuild of L.N.W. " Claughton " Class (introduced 1912), retaining original wheels and other details.

Remainder. Introduced 1933. New locos. to Fowler design (45502–41 were officially considered as rebuilds).

†7P. Introduced 1946. Ivatt rebuild of Fowler locos. with larger taper boiler, new cylinders and double chimney.

Weight: Loco. $\begin{cases} 80 \text{ tons } 15 \text{ cwt.} \\ 80 \text{ tons } 15 \text{ cwt.*} \\ 82 \text{ tons } 0 \text{ cwt.†} \end{cases}$

Pressure: $\begin{cases} 200 \text{ lb. Su.} \\ 200 \text{ lb. Su.*} \\ 250 \text{ lb. Su.†} \end{cases}$

Cyls.: $\begin{cases} (3) \ 18'' \times 26''. \\ (3) \ 18'' \times 26''.* \\ (3) \ 17'' \times 26''.† \end{cases}$

Driving Wheels: 6' 9".

T.E.: $\begin{cases} 26,520 \text{ lb.} \\ 26,520 \text{ lb.*} \\ 29,570 \text{ lb.†} \end{cases}$

Walschaerts valve gear. P.V.

45500*	Patriot
45501*	St. Dunstan's
45502	Royal Naval Division
45503	The Royal Leicestershire Regiment
45504	Royal Signals
45505	The Royal Army Ordnance Corps
45506	The Royal Pioneer Corps
45507	Royal Tank Corps
45508	
45509	The Derbyshire Yeomanry

45510	
45511	Isle of Man
45512†	Bunsen
45513	
45514†	Holyhead
45515	Caernarvon
45516	The Bedfordshire and Hertfordshire Regiment
45517	
45518	Bradshaw
45519	Lady Godiva
45520	Llandudno
45521†	Rhyl
45522†	Prestatyn
45523†	Bangor
45524	Blackpool
45525†	Colwyn Bay
45526†	Morecambe and Heysham
45527†	Southport
45528†	
45529†	Stephenson
45530†	Sir Frank Ree
45531†	Sir Frederick Harrison
45532†	Illustrious
45533	Lord Rathmore
45534†	E. Tootal Broadhurst
45535†	Sir Herbert Walker K.C.B.
45536†	Private W. Wood, V.C.
45537	Private E. Sykes, V.C.
45538	Giggleswick
45539	E. C. Trench
45540†	Sir Robert Turnbull
45541	Duke of Sutherland
45542	
45543	Home Guard
45544	
45545†	Planet
45546	Fleetwood
45547	
45548	Lytham St. Annes
45549	
45550	
45551	

Total 52

" Jubilee " Class

4-6-0   6P5F & 7P

6P5F. Introduced 1934. Stanier L.M.S. taper boiler development of the " Patriot " class.

*7P. Introduced 1942. Rebuilt with larger boiler and double chimney.

Weight: Loco. $\begin{cases} 79 \text{ tons } 11 \text{ cwt.} \\ 82 \text{ tons } 0 \text{ cwt.*} \end{cases}$

Pressure: $\begin{cases} 225 \text{ lb. Su.} \\ 250 \text{ lb. Su.*} \end{cases}$

Cyls.: (3) 17″ × 26″.

Driving Wheels: 6′ 9″.

T.E.: $\begin{cases} 26,610 \text{ lb.} \\ 29,570 \text{ lb.*} \end{cases}$

Walschaerts valve gear. P.V.

45552	Silver Jubilee
45553	Canada
45554	Ontario
45555	Quebec
45556	Nova Scotia
45557	New Brunswick
45558	Manitoba
45559	British Columbia
45560	Prince Edward Island
45561	Saskatchewan
45562	Alberta
45563	Australia
45564	New South Wales
45565	Victoria
45566	Queensland
45567	South Australia
45568	Western Australia
45569	Tasmania
45570	New Zealand
45571	South Africa
45572	Eire
45573	Newfoundland
45574	India
45575	Madras
45576	Bombay
45577	Bengal
45578	United Provinces
45579	Punjab
45580	Burma
45581	Bihar and Orissa
45582	Central Provinces
45583	Assam
45584	North West Frontier
45585	Hyderabad
45586	Mysore
45587	Baroda
45588	Kashmir
45589	Gwalior
45590	Travancore
45591	Udaipur
45592	Indore
45593	Kolhapur
45594	Bhopal
45595	Southern Rhodesia
45596	Bahamas
45597	Barbados
45598	Basutoland
45599	Bechuanaland
45600	Bermuda
45601	British Guiana
45602	British Honduras
45603	Solomon Islands
45604	Ceylon
45605	Cyprus
45606	Falkland Islands
45607	Fiji
45608	Gibraltar
45609	Gilbert and Ellice Islands
45610	
45611	Hong Kong
45612	Jamaica
45613	Kenya
45614	Leeward Islands
45615	Malay States
45616	Malta G.C.
45617	Mauritius
45618	New Hebrides
45619	Nigeria
45620	North Borneo
45621	Northern Rhodesia
45622	Nyasaland
45623	Palestine
45624	St. Helena
45625	Sarawak
45626	Seychelles
45627	Sierra Leone

45628	Somaliland
45629	Straits Settlements
45630	Swaziland
45631	Tanganyika
45632	Tonga
45633	Aden
45634	Trinidad
45635	Tobago
45636	Uganda
45638	Zanzibar
45639	Raleigh
45640	Frobisher
45641	Sandwich
45642	Boscawen
45643	Rodney
45644	Howe
45645	Collingwood
45646	Napier
45647	Sturdee
45648	Wemyss
45649	Hawkins
45650	Blake
45651	Shovell
45652	Hawke
45653	Barham
45654	Hood
45655	Keith
45656	Cochrane
45657	Tyrwhitt
45658	Keyes
45659	Drake
45660	Rooke
45661	Vernon
45662	Kempenfelt
45663	Jervis
45664	Nelson
45665	Lord Rutherford of Nelson
45666	Cornwallis
45667	Jellicoe
45668	Madden
45669	Fisher
45670	Howard of Effingham
45671	Prince Rupert
45672	Anson
45673	Keppel
45674	Duncan
45675	Hardy
45676	Codrington
45677	Beatty
45678	De Robeck
45679	Armada
45680	Camperdown
45681	Aboukir
45682	Trafalgar
45683	Hogue
45684	Jutland
45685	Barfleur
45686	St. Vincent
45687	Neptune
45688	Polyphemus
45689	Ajax
45690	Leander
45691	Orion
45692	Cyclops
45693	Agamemnon
45694	Bellerophon
45695	Minotaur
45696	Arethusa
45697	Achilles
45698	Mars
45699	Galatea
45700	Amethyst
45701	Conqueror
45702	Colossus
45703	Thunderer
45704	Leviathan
45705	Seahorse
45706	Express
45707	Valiant
45708	Resolution
45709	Implacable
45710	Irresistible
45711	Courageous
45712	Victory
45713	Renown
45714	Revenge
45715	Invincible
45716	Swiftsure
45717	Dauntless
45718	Dreadnought
45719	Glorious
45720	Indomitable
45721	Impregnable

45722	Defence
45723	Fearless
45724	Warspite
45725	Repulse
45726	Vindictive
45727	Inflexible
45728	Defiance
45729	Furious
45730	Ocean
45731	Perseverance
45732	Sanspareil
45733	Novelty
45734	Meteor
45735*	Comet
45736*	Phoenix
45737	Atlas
45738	Samson
45739	Ulster
45740	Munster
45741	Leinster
45742	Connaught

Total 190

"Royal Scot" Class
4-6-0   7P

Introduced 1943. Stanier rebuild of Fowler locos. (introduced 1927) with taper boiler, new cylinders and double chimney.

*Introduced 1935. Stanier taper boiler rebuild with simple cylinders of experimental high pressure compound loco. No. 6399 *Fury*. (Introduced 1929.)

Weight: Loco. $\begin{cases} 83 \text{ tons.} \\ 84 \text{ tons 1 cwt.*} \end{cases}$

Pressure: 250 lb. Su.

Cyls.: (3) 18″ × 26″.

Driving Wheels: 6′ 9″.

T.E.: 33,150 lb.

Walschaerts valve gear. P.V.

46100	Royal Scot
46101	Royal Scots Grey
46102	Black Watch
46103	Royal Scots Fusilier
46104	Scottish Borderer
46105	Cameron Highlander
46106	Gordon Highlander
46107	Argyll and Sutherland Highlander
46108	Seaforth Highlander
46109	Royal Engineer
46110	Grenadier Guardsman
46111	Royal Fusilier
46112	Sherwood Forester
46113	Cameronian
46114	Coldstream Guardsman
46115	Scots Guardsman
46116	Irish Guardsman
46117	Welsh Guardsman
46118	Royal Welch Fusilier
46119	Lancashire Fusilier
46120	Royal Inniskilling Fusilier
46121	Highland Light Infantry, City of Glasgow Regiment
46122	Royal Ulster Rifleman
46123	Royal Irish Fusilier
46124	London Scottish
46125	3rd Carabinier
46126	Royal Army Service Corps
46127	Old Contemptibles
46128	The Lovat Scouts
46129	The Scottish Horse
46130	The West Yorkshire Regiment
46131	The Royal Warwickshire Regiment
46132	The King's Regiment Liverpool
46133	The Green Howards
46134	The Cheshire Regiment
46135	The East Lancashire Regiment
46136	The Border Regiment
46137	The Prince of Wales's Volunteers (South Lancashire)
46138	The London Irish Rifleman
46139	The Welch Regiment

46140	The King's Royal Rifle Corps
46141	The North Staffordshire Regiment
46142	The York & Lancaster Regiment
46143	The South Staffordshire Regiment
46144	Honourable Artillery Company
46145	The Duke of Wellington's Regt. (West Riding)
46146	The Rifle Brigade
46147	The Northamptonshire Regiment
46148	The Manchester Regiment
46149	The Middlesex Regiment
46150	The Life Guardsman
46151	The Royal Horse Guardsman
46152	The King's Dragoon Guardsman
46153	The Royal Dragoon
46154	The Hussar
46155	The Lancer
46156	The South Wales Borderer
46157	The Royal Artilleryman
46158	The Loyal Regiment
46159	The Royal Air Force
46160	Queen Victoria's Rifleman
46161	King's Own
46162	Queen's Westminster Rifleman
46163	Civil Service Rifleman
46164	The Artists' Rifleman
46165	The Ranger (12th London Regt.)
46166	London Rifle Brigade
46167	The Hertfordshire Regiment
46168	The Girl Guide
46169	The Boy Scout
46170*	British Legion

Total 71

" Princess " Class
4-6-2   8P

*Introduced 1933. Stanier L.M.S. taper boiler design.

Remainder. Introduced 1935. Development of original design with alterations to valve gear, boiler and other details.

Weight: Loco. 104 tons 10 cwt.

Pressure: 250 lb. Su.

Cyls.: (4) $16\frac{1}{4}'' \times 28''$.

Driving Wheels: 6' 6".

T.E.: 40,285 lb.

Walschaerts valve gear (inside valves operated by rocking shafts on No. 46205; remainder have four sets of valve gear). P.V.

46200*	The Princess Royal
46201*	Princess Elizabeth
46203	Princess Margaret Rose
46204	Princess Louise
46205	Princess Victoria
46206	Princess Marie Louise
46207	Princess Arthur of Connaught
46208	Princess Helena Victoria
46209	Princess Beatrice
46210	Lady Patricia
46211	Queen Maud
46212	Duchess of Kent

Total 12

" Coronation " Class
4-6-2   8P

Introduced 1937. Stanier L.M.S. enlargement of " Princess Royal " class. All Nos. 46230–4/49–55 originally streamlined. (Streamlining removed from 1946.)

*Introduced 1947. Ivatt development with roller bearings and detail alterations.

Weight: Loco. { 105 tons 5 cwt.
{ 106 tons 8 cwt.*

Pressure: 250 lb. Su.
Cyls.: (4) $16\frac{1}{2}" \times 28"$.
Driving Wheels: 6' 9".
T.E.: 40,000 lb.
Walschaerts valve gear and rocking shafts. P.V.

46220	Coronation
46221	Queen Elizabeth
46222	Queen Mary
46223	Princess Alice
46224	Princess Alexandra
46225	Duchess of Gloucester
46226	Duchess of Norfolk
46227	Duchess of Devonshire
46228	Duchess of Rutland
46229	Duchess of Hamilton
46230	Duchess of Buccleuch
46231	Duchess of Atholl
46232	Duchess of Montrose
46233	Duchess of Sutherland
46234	Duchess of Abercorn
46235	City of Birmingham
46236	City of Bradford
46237	City of Bristol
46238	City of Carlisle
46239	City of Chester
46240	City of Coventry
46241	City of Edinburgh
46242	City of Glasgow
46243	City of Lancaster
46244	King George VI
46245	City of London
46246	City of Manchester
46247	City of Liverpool
46248	City of Leeds
46249	City of Sheffield
46250	City of Lichfield
46251	City of Nottingham
46252	City of Leicester
46253	City of St. Albans
46254	City of Stoke-on-Trent
46255	City of Hereford
46256*	Sir William A. Stanier, F.R.S.
46257*	City of Salford

Total 38

2-6-0　　　　　　　　2

Introduced 1946. Ivatt L.M.S. **taper** boiler design.
Weight: Loco. 47 tons 2 cwt.
Pressure: 200 lb. Su.
Cyls.: $\begin{cases} \text{(O) } 16" \times 24". \\ \text{(O) } 16\frac{1}{2}" \times 24".* \end{cases}$
Driving Wheels: 5' 0".
T.E.: $\begin{cases} 17,410 \text{ lb.} \\ 18,510 \text{ lb.*} \end{cases}$
Walschaerts valve gear.　P.V.

46400	46434	46468*	46498*
46401	46435	46469*	46499*
46402	46436	46470*	46500*
46403	46437	46471*	46501*
46404	46438	46472*	46502*
46405	46439	46473*	46503*
46406	46440	46474*	46504*
46407	46441	46475*	46505*
46408	46442	46476*	46506*
46409	46443	46477*	46507*
46410	46444	46478*	46508*
46411	46445	46479*	46509*
46412	46446	46480*	46510*
46413	46447	46481*	46511*
46414	46448	46482*	46512*
46415	46449	46483*	46513*
46416	46450	46484*	46514*
46417	46451	46485*	46515*
46418	46452	46486*	46516*
46419	46453	46487*	46517*
46420	46454	46488*	46518*
46421	46455	46489*	46519*
46422	46456	46490*	46520*
46423	46457	46491*	46521*
46424	46458	46492*	46522*
46425	46459	46493*	46523*
46426	46460	46494*	46524*
46427	46461	46495*	46525*
46428	46462	46496*	46526*
46429	46463	46497*	46527*
46430	46464		
46431	46465*		
46432	46466*		
46433	46467*		

Total 128

0-4-0ST 0F

Introduced 1932. Kitson design prepared to Stanier's requirements for L.M.S.

*Introduced 1953. Extended side tanks and coal space.

Weight: $\begin{cases} 33 \text{ tons 0 cwt.} \\ 34 \text{ tons 0 cwt.*} \end{cases}$
Pressure: 160 lb.
Cyls.: (O) $15\frac{1}{2}'' \times 30''$.
Driving Wheels: 3' 10".
T.E.: 14,205 lb.

47000	47003	47006*	47008*
47001	47004	47007*	47009*
47002	47005*		

Total 10

0-6-0T 2F

Introduced 1928. Fowler L.M.S. short-wheelbase dock tanks.
Weight: 43 tons 12 cwt.
Pressure: 160 lb.
Cyls.: (O) $17'' \times 22''$.
Driving Wheels: 3' 11".
T.E.: 18,400 lb.
Walschaerts valve gear.

47160	47163	47166	47168
47161	47164	47167	47169
47162	47165		

Total 10

0-4-0T Sentinel

Geared Sentinel locos.

Introduced 1929. Single-speed locos. for S. & D.J. (taken into L.M.S. stock 1930).

Weight: 27 tons 15 cwt.
Pressure: 275 lb. Su.
Cyls.: (4) $6\frac{3}{4}'' \times 9''$.
Driving Wheels: 3' $1\frac{1}{4}''$.
T.E.: 15,500 lb.
Poppet valves.

47190   47191

Total 2

0-6-0T 3F

Introduced 1899. Johnson large Midland design, rebuilt with Belpaire firebox from 1919; fitted with condensing apparatus for London area.

*Introduced 1899. Non-condensing locos.
Weight: 48 tons 15 cwt.
Pressure: 160 lb.
Cyls.: $18'' \times 26''$.
Driving Wheels: 4' 7".
T.E.: 20,835 lb.

47200	47212	47226	47247
47201*	47213	47228	47248*
47202	47214	47229	47249
47203	47216	47230*	47250*
47204	47217	47231*	47251
47205	47218	47235*	47254*
47207	47219	47236*	47255*
47208	47221	47238*	47257*
47209	47223	47239*	47259*
47210	47224	47241	
47211	47225	47246*	

Total 42

0-6-0T 3F

Introduced 1924. Post-grouping development of Midland design with detail alterations.

*Introduced 1929. Locos. built for S. & D.J. (taken into L.M.S. stock 1930).

†Push-and-pull fitted.
Weight: 49 tons 10 cwt.
Pressure: 160 lb.
Cyls.: $18'' \times 26''$.
Driving Wheels: 4' 7".
T.E.: 20,835 lb.

47260	47273	47286	47299
47261	47274	47287	47300
47262	47275	47288	47301
47263	47276	47289	47302
47264	47277	47290	47303
47265	47278	47291	47304
47266	47279	47292	47305
47267	47280	47293	47306
47268	47281	47294	47307
47269	47282	47295	47308
47270	47283	47296	47309
47271	47284	47297	47310*
47272	47285	47298	47311*

47312*	47359	47406	47453	47501	47546	47592S	47638
47313*	47360	47407	47454	47502	47547	47593	47639
47314*	47361	47408	47455	47503	47548	47594	47640
47315*	47362	47409	47457	47504	47549	47595	47641
47316*	47363	47410	47458	47505	47550	47596	47642
47317	47364	47411	47459	47506	47551	47597	47643
47318	47365	47412	47460	47507	47552	47598	47644
47319	47366	47413	47461	47508	47554	47599	47645
47320	47367	47414	47462	47509	47555	47600	47646
47321	47368	47415	47463	47510	47556	47601	47647
47322	47369	47416	47464	47511	47557	47602	47648
47323	47370	47417	47465	47512	47558	47603	47649
47324	47371	47418	47466	47513	47559	47604	47650
47325	47372	47419	47467	47514	47560	47605	47651
47326	47373	47420	47468	47515	47561	47606	47652
47327	47374	47421	47469	47516	47562	47607	47653
47328	47375	47422	47470	47517	47563	47608	47654
47329	47376	47423	47471	47518	47564	47609	47655†
47330	47377	47424	47472	47519	47565	47610	47656
47331	47378	47425	47473	47520	47566	47611	47657
47332	47379	47426	47474	47521	47567	47612	47658
47333	47380	47427	47475	47522	47568	47614	47659
47334	47381	47428	47476	47523	47569	47615	47660
47335	47382	47429	47477†	47524	47570	47616	47661
47336	47383	47430	47478†	47525	47571	47618	47662
47337	47384	47431	47479†	47526	47572	47619	47664
47338	47385	47432	47480†	47527	47573	47620	47665
47339	47386	47433	47481†	47528	47574	47621	47666
47340	47387	47434	47482	47529	47575	47622	47667
47341	47388	47435	47483	47530	47576	47623	47668
47342	47389	47436	47484	47531	47577	47624	47669
47343	47390	47437	47485	47532	47578	47625	47670
47344	47391	47438	47486	47533	47579	47626	47671
47345	47392	47439	47487	47534	47580	47627	47672
47346	47393	47440	47488	47535	47581	47628	47673
47347	47394	47441	47489	47536	47582	47629	47674
47348	47395	47442	47490	47537	47583	47630	47675
47349	47396	47443	47491	47538	47584	47631	47676
47350	47397	47444	47492	47539	47585	47632	47677
47351	47398	47445	47493	47540	47586	47633	47678
47352	47399	47446	47494	47541	47587	47634	47679
47353	47400	47447	47495	47542	47588	47635	47680
47354	47401	47448	47496	47543	47589	47636	47681†
47355	47402	47449	47497	47544	47590	47637	
47356	47403	47450	47498	47545	47591		
47357	47404	47451	47499				
47358	47405	47452	47500				**Total 417**

97

48000-48391

2-8-0   8F

Introduced 1935. Stanier L.M.S. taper
  boiler design.
Weight: Loco. 72 tons 2 cwt.
Pressure: 225 lb. Su.
Cyls.: (O) 18½″ × 28″.
Driving Wheels: 4′ 8½″.
T.E.: 32,440 lb.
Walschaerts valve gear.   P.V.

				48181	48248	48295	48345
				48182	48249	48296	48346
				48183	48250	48297	48347
				48184	48251	48301	48348
				48185	48252	48302	48349
				48186	48253	48303	48350
				48187	48254	48304	48351
				48188	48255	48305	48352
				48189	48256	48306	48353
				48190	48257	48307	48354
48000	48063	48107	48144	48191	48258	48308	48355
48001	48064	48108	48145	48192	48259	48309	48356
48002	48065	48109	48146	48193	48260	48310	48357
48003	48067	48110	48147	48194	48261	48311	48358
48004	48069	48111	48148	48195	48262	48312	48359
48005	48070	48112	48149	48196	48263	48313	48360
48006	48073	48113	48150	48197	48264	48314	48361
48007	48074	48114	48151	48198	48265	48315	48362
48008	48075	48115	48152	48199	48266	48316	48363
48009	48076	48116	48153	48200	48267	48317	48364
48010	48077	48117	48154	48201	48268	48318	48365
48011	48078	48118	48155	48202	48269	48319	48366
48012	48079	48119	48156	48203	48270	48320	48367
48016	48080	48120	48157	48204	48271	48321	48368
48017	48081	48121	48158	48205	48272	48322	48369
48018	48082	48122	48159	48206	48273	48323	48370
48020	48083	48123	48160	48207	48274	48324	48371
48024	48084	48124	48161	48208	48275	48325	48372
48026	48085	48125	48162	48209	48276	48326	48373
48027	48088	48126	48163	48210	48277	48327	48374
48029	48089	48127	48164	48211	48278	48328	48375
48033	48090	48128	48165	48212	48279	48329	48376
48035	48092	48129	48166	48213	48280	48330	48377
48036	48093	48130	48167	48214	48281	48331	48378
48037	48094	48131	48168	48215	48282	48332	48379
48039	48095	48132	48169	48216	48283	48333	48380
48045	48096	48133	48170	48217	48284	48334	48381
48046	48097	48134	48171	48218	48285	48335	48382
48050	48098 .	48135	48172	48219	48286	48336	48383
48053	48099	48136	48173	48220	48287	48337	48384
48054	48100	48137	48174	48221	48288	48338	48385
48055	48101	48138	48175	48222	48289	48339	48386
48056	48102	48139	48176	48223	48290	48340	48387
48057	48103	48140	48177	48224	48291	48341	48388
48060	48104	48141	48178	48225	48292	48342	48389
48061	48105	48142	48179	48246	48293	48343	48390
48062	48106	48143	48180	48247	48294	48344	48391

48392	48439	48500	48547	48634	48670	48706	48742
48393	48440	48501	48548	48635	48671	48707	48743
48394	48441	48502	48549	48636	48672	48708	48744
48395	48442	48503	48550	48637	48673	48709	48745
48396	48443	48504	48551	48638	48674	48710	48746
48397	48444	48505	48552	48639	48675	48711	48747
48398	48445	48506	48553	48640	48676	48712	48748
48399	48446	48507	48554	48641	48677	48713	48749
48400	48447	48508	48555	48642	48678	48714	48750
48401	48448	48509	48556	48643	48679	48715	48751
48402	48449	48510	48557	48644	48680	48716	48752
48403	48450	48511	48558	48645	48681	48717	48753
48404	48451	48512	48559	48646	48682	48718	48754
48405	48452	48513	48600	48647	48683	48719	48755
48406	48453	48514	48601	48648	48684	48720	48756
48407	48454	48515	48602	48649	48685	48721	48757
48408	48455	48516	48603	48650	48686	48722	48758
48409	48456	48517	48604	48651	48687	48723	48759
48410	48457	48518	48605	48652	48688	48724	48760
48411	48458	48519	48606	48653	48689	48725	48761
48412	48459	48520	48607	48654	48690	48726	48762
48413	48460	48521	48608	48655	48691	48727	48763
48414	48461	48522	48609	48656	48692	48728	48764
48415	48462	48523	48610	48657	48693	48729	48765
48416	48463	48524	48611	48658	48694	48730	48766
48417	48464	48525	48612	48659	48695	48731	48767
48418	48465	48526	48613	48660	48696	48732	48768
48419	48466	48527	48614	48661	48697	48733	48769
48420	48467	48528	48615	48662	48698	48734	48770
48421	48468	48529	48616	48663	48699	48735	48771
48422	48469	48530	48617	48664	48700	48736	48772
48423	48470	48531	48618	48665	48701	48737	48773
48424	48471	48532	48619	48666	48702	48738	48774
48425	48472	48533	48620	48667	48703	48739	48775
48426	48473	48534	48621	48668	48704	48740	
48427	48474	48535	48622	48669	48705	48741	
48428	48475	48536	48623				
48429	48476	48537	48624				
48430	48477	48538	48625				
48431	48478	48539	48626				
48432	48479	48540	48627				
48433	48490	48541	48628				
48434	48491	48542	48629				
48435	48492	48543	48630				
48436	48493	48544	48631				
48437	48494	48545	48632				
48438	48495	48546	48633				

Total 666

0-8-0   **7F**

Introduced 1936. L.N.W. G2a Class.
Bowen-Cooke G1 superheated design
of 1912, rebuilt with G2 boiler and
Belpaire firebox.
Weight: Loco. 62 tons 0 cwt.
Pressure: 175 lb. Su.
Cyls.: $20\frac{1}{2}'' \times 24''$.
Driving Wheels: 4' $5\frac{1}{2}''$.
T.E.: 28,045 lb.
Joy valve gear. P.V.

48895	49082	49173	49301
48898	49087	49177	49304
48905	49093	49180	49306
48915	49094	49181	49308
48922	49099	49191	49310
48926	49104	49196	49311
48927	49105	49198	49313
48930	49106	49199	49314
48932	49109	49200	49315
48942	49112	49203	49321
48943	49113	49209	49323
48945	49114	49210	49327
48950	49115	49216	49328
48951	49116	49224	49330
48953	49117	49226	49335
48964	49119	49228	49340
49002	49120	49229	49342
49007	49121	49234	49343
49008	49122	49240	49344
49009	49125	49243	49348
49010	49126	49245	49350
49018	49129	49246	49352
49020	49130	49249	49355
49021	49132	49252	49357
49023	49134	49262	49361
49025	49137	49266	49366
49027	49139	49267	49368
49034	49141	49268	49373
49037	49142	49270	49375
49044	49143	49275	49377
49045	49144	49276	49378
49048	49147	49277	49381
49049	49149	49278	49382
49061	49150	49281	49386
49063	49153	49287	49387
49064	49154	49288	49391
49070	49155	49289	49392
49077	49157	49293	49394
49078	49158		
49079	49160		
49081	49164		

Total 158

0-8-0   7F

Introduced 1921. Development of L.N.W. G2 Class. Bowen-Cooke G1 superheated design of 1912 with higher pressure boiler. Many later rebuilt with Belpaire firebox.
Weight: Loco. 62 tons 0 cwt.
Pressure: 175 lb. Su.
Cyls.: $20\frac{1}{2}'' \times 24''$.
Driving Wheels: 4' 5½".
T.E.: 28,045 lb.
Joy valve gear.   P.V.

49395	49410	49425	49440
49396	49411	49426	49441
49397	49412	49427	49442
49398	49413	49428	49443
49399	49414	49429	49444
49400	49415	49430	49445
49401	49416	49431	49446
49402	49417	49432	49447
49403	49418	49433	49448
49404	49419	49434	49449
49405	49420	49435	49450
49406	49421	49436	49451
49407	49422	49437	49452
49408	49423	49438	49453
49409	49424	49439	49454

Total 60

0-8-0   7F

Introduced 1929. Fowler L.M.S. design, developed from L.N.W. G2.
Weight: Loco. 60 tons 15 cwt.
Pressure: 200 lb. Su.
Cyls.: $19\frac{1}{2}'' \times 26''$.
Driving Wheels: 4' 8½".
T.E.: 29,745 lb.
Walschaerts valve gear.   P.V.

49505	49544	49598	49640
49508	49578	49618	49662
49509	49582	49624	49667
49511	49586	49627	49668
49515	49592	49637	49674

Total 20

2-4-2T   2P

Introduced 1889. Aspinall L. & Y. Class 5 with 2 tons coal capacity.
*Introduced 1890. Locos. built or rebuilt with smaller cylinders.
†Introduced 1898. Locos. with longer tanks and 4 tons coal capacity.

¶Introduced 1910. Locos. rebuilt with Belpaire firebox and extended smokebox.

Weight: $\begin{cases} 55 \text{ tons } 19 \text{ cwt.} \\ 55 \text{ tons } 19 \text{ cwt.*} \\ 59 \text{ tons } 3 \text{ cwt.†¶} \end{cases}$

Pressure: 180 lb.

Cyls.: $\begin{cases} 17\frac{1}{2}'' \times 26''.* \\ 18'' \times 26''. \text{ (Remainder)} \end{cases}$

Driving Wheels: 5' 8".

T.E.: $\begin{cases} 18,360 \text{ lb.*} \\ 18,955 \text{ lb. (Remainder)} \end{cases}$

Joy valve gear.

50643*	50712	50777¶	50831†
50644	50721	50781	50850†¶
50646	50725	50795*	50855*†
50647	50746	50818	50865*†
50705	50757		

Total 18

0-4-0ST 0F

Introduced 1891. Aspinall L. & Y. Class 21.
Weight: 21 tons 5 cwt.
Pressure: 160 lb.
Cyls.: (O) 13" × 18".
Driving Wheels: 3' 0⅜".
T.E.: 11,335 lb.

51204	51221	51231	51244
51206	51222	51232	51246
51207	51227	51235	51253
51217	51229	51237	
51218	51230	51241	

Total 18

0-6-0ST 2F

Introduced 1891. Aspinall rebuild of L. & Y. Barton Wright Class 23 0-6-0. Originally introduced 1877.
Weight: 43 tons 17 cwt.
Pressure: 140 lb.
Cyls.: 17½" × 26".
Driving Wheels: 4' 6".
T.E.: 17,545 lb.

See also page 58.

51316	51336	51358	51397
51319	51343	51371	51404

51408	51424	51446S	51486
51412S	51429S	51453	51496
51413	51441	51457	51497
51415	51444S	51458	51498
51419	51445	51484	51524
51423			

Total 34

0-6-0T 1F

Introduced 1897. Aspinall L. & Y. Class 24 dock tanks.
Weight: 50 tons 0 cwt.
Pressure: 140 lb.
Cyls.: (O) 17" × 24".
Driving Wheels: 4' 0".
T.E.: 15,285 lb.
Allan straight link valve gear.

51537	51544	51546

Total 3

0-6-0 2F

Introduced 1887. Barton Wright L. & Y. Class 25.
Weight: Loco. 39 tons 1 cwt.
Pressure: 140 lb.
Cyls.: 17½" × 26".
Driving Wheels: 4' 6".
T.E.: 17,545 lb.

52044

Total 1

0-6-0 3F

Introduced 1889. Aspinall L. & Y. Class 27. Nos. 52515–27 built superheated with roundtop firebox and extended smokebox, later rebuilt with saturated boiler and short smokebox.

*Introduced 1911. Rebuilt with Belpaire firebox and extended smokebox.

Weight: Loco. 42 tons 3 cwt.

Pressure: 180 lb.
Cyls.: 18" × 26".

Driving Wheels: 5' 1".

T.E.: $\begin{cases} 21,130 \text{ lb.} \\ 21,130 \text{ lb.*} \end{cases}$

Joy valve gear.

52089	52095	52119	52129
52093S	52108	52121	52133

101

52135*	52232	52319	52431*
52139	52237	52322	52432
52140*	52240	52341	52438*
52141	52244	52345S	52441S
52154*	52248	52348	52443
52161*	52252	52350	52445*
52162*S	52260	52351	52452
52171	52268	52355	52455
52179	52269	52360*	52456
52182	52270	52378	52458
52183	52271	52389	52459S
52201*	52275	52393	52461
52207S	52278	52400*	52464S
52212S	52289	52410	52466
52216	52290	52411	52515
52218S	52305	52413*	52523
52225	52311	52415	52526
52230	52312*S	52429	52527

Total 80

2-8-0   7F

Introduced 1914. Fowler design for
S. & D.J.
(All taken into L.M.S. stock, 1930.)
Weight: Loco. 64 tons 15 cwt.
Pressure: 190 lb. Su.
Cyls.: (O) 21″ × 28″.
Driving Wheels: 4′ 8½″.
T.E.: 35,295 lb.
Walschaerts valve gear.   P.V.

53800	53803	53806	53809
53801	53804	53807	53810
53802	53805	53808	

Total 11

4-4-0   3P

Introduced 1915. Superheated rebuild
of McIntosh Caledonian "Dunalastair
IV" or "140" class (originally
introduced 1904).
Weight: Loco. 61 tons 5 cwt.
Pressure: 180 lb. Su.
Cyls.: 20½″ × 26″.
Driving Wheels: 6′ 6″.
T.E.: 20,915 lb.   P.V.

54439   **Total 1**

4-4-0   3P

Introduced 1916. Pickersgill Caledonian
"113" and "928" classes.
Weight: Loco. 61 tons 5 cwt.
Pressure: 180 lb. Su.
Cyls.: 20″ × 26″.
Driving Wheels: 6′ 6″.
T.E.: 20,400 lb.
P.V.

54461	54465	54469	54473
54462	54466	54470	54474
54463	54467	54471	54475
54464	54468	54472	54476

Total 16

4-4-0   3P

Introduced 1920. Pickersgill Caledonian
"72" class.
Weight: Loco. 61 tons 5 cwt.
Pressure: 180 lb. Su.
Cyls.: 20½″ × 26″.
Driving Wheels: 6′ 6″.
T.E.: 21,435 lb.
P.V.

54477	54486	54494	54502
54478	54487	54495	54503
54479	54488	54496	54504
54480	54489	54497	54505
54482	54490	54498	54506
54483	54491	54499	54507
54484	54492	54500	54508
54485	54493	54501	

Total 31

0-4-4T   2P

*Introduced 1895. McIntosh Cale-
donian "19" class, with railed coal
bunker.
Remainder. Introduced 1897. McIntosh
"92" class, developed from "29"
class with larger tanks and highsided
coal bunker (both classes originally
fitted for condensing on Glasgow
Central Low Level lines).
Weight: $\begin{cases} 53 \text{ tons } 16 \text{ cwt.}^* \\ 53 \text{ tons } 19 \text{ cwt.} \end{cases}$

Pressure: 180 lb.
Cyls.: 18″ × 26″.
Driving Wheels: 5′ 9″.
T.E.: 18,680 lb.

55124*   55126

Total 2

0-4-4T   2P

Introduced 1900. McIntosh Caledonian
"439" or "Standard Passenger"
class.
*Introduced 1915. Pickersgill locos.
with detail alterations.

Weight: $\begin{cases} 53 \text{ tons } 19 \text{ cwt.} \\ 57 \text{ tons } 12 \text{ cwt.*} \end{cases}$

Pressure: 180 lb.
Cyls.: 18″ × 26″.
Driving Wheels: 5′ 9″.
T.E.: 18,680 lb.

55160	55199	55212	55225
55164	55200	55214	55226
55165	55201	55215	55227*
55167	55202	55216	55228*
55169	55203	55217	55229*
55173	55204	55218	55230*
55176	55206	55219	55231*
55178	55207	55220	55232*
55185	55208	55221	55233*
55189	55209	55222	55234*
55195	55210	55223	55235*
55198	55211	55224	55236*

Total 48

0-4-4T   2P

Introduced 1922. Pickersgill Caledonian
"431" class (developed from "439"
class) with cast-iron front buffer
beam for banking.

Weight: 57 tons 17 cwt.
Pressure: 180 lb.
Cyls.: 18½″ × 26″.
Driving Wheels: 5′ 9″.
T.E.: 19,200 lb.

55237   55238   55239   55240

Total 4

0-4-4T   2P

Introduced 1925. Post-Grouping devel-
opment of Caledonian "439" class.
Weight: 59 tons 12 cwt.
Pressure: 180 lb.
Cyls.: 18½″ × 26″.
Driving Wheels: 5′ 9″.
T.E.: 19,200 lb.

55260	55263	55266	55268
55261	55264	55267	55269
55262	55265		

Total 10

0-4-0ST   0F

Introduced 1885. Drummond and
McIntosh Caledonian "Pugs."
Weight: 27 tons 7 cwt.
Pressure: 160 lb.
Cyls.: (O) 14″ × 20″.
Driving Wheels: 3′ 8″.
T.E.: 12,115 lb.

56011	56029	56032S	56038
56025S	56031	56035	56039
56027S			

Total 9

0-6-0T   2F

Introduced 1911. McIntosh Caledonian
dock shunters, "498" class.
Weight: 47 tons 15 cwt.
Pressure: 160 lb.
Cyls.: (O) 17″ × 22″.
Driving Wheels: 4′ 0″.
T.E.: 18,015 lb.

56151	56157	56163	56169
56152	56158	56164	56170
56153	56159	56165	56171
56154	56160	56166	56172
56155	56161	56167	56173
56156	56162	56168	

Total 23

0-6-0T   3F

Introduced 1895. McIntosh Caledonian
"29" and "782" classes (56232–9
originally condensing).
Weight: 47 tons 15 cwt.
Pressure: 160 lb.
Cyls.: 18″ × 26″.
Driving Wheels: 4′ 6″.
T.E.: 21,215 lb.

56232	56278	56310	56344
56235	56279	56311	56345
56236	56281	56312	56347
56238	56283	56313	56348
56239	56285	56316	56349
56240	56286	56318	56352
56241	56287	56321	56353
56242	56288	56322	56356
56245	56289	56323	56359
56246	56290	56324	56360
56247	56291	56325	56361
56251	56292	56326	56362
56252	56293	56327	56363
56253	56295	56328	56364
56255	56296	56331	56365
56256	56298	56332	56367
56259	56300	56333	56368
56260	56301	56335	56370
56262	56302	56336	56371
56264	56304	56337	56372
56265	56305	56338	56373
56266	56306	56340	56374
56267	56308	56341	56375
56269	56309	56343	56376
56272			

Total 97

57274	57326	57365	57419
57275	57328	57366	57424
57276	57329	57367	57426
57278	57331	57369	57429
57279	57335	57370	57431
57284	57336	57373	57432
57285	57338	57375	57434
57287	57339	57377	57435
57288	57340	57378	57436
57291	57341	57383	57437
57292	57345	57384	57441
57295	57347	57385	57443
57296	57348	57386	57444
57299	57349	57389	57445
57300	57350	57392	57446
57302	57353	57398	57447
57303	57354	57404	57448
57307	57355	57405	57451
57309	57356	57407	57461
57311	57357	57411	57462
57314	57359	57413	57463
57317	57360	57414	57465
57319	57361	57416	57470
57321	57362	57417	57472
57324	57363	57418	57473
57325	57364		

Total 138

0-6-0   2F

Introduced 1883. Drummond Caledonian "Standard Goods"; later additions by Lambie and McIntosh.
*Some rebuilt with L.M.S. boiler.
Weight: Loco. { 41 tons 6 cwt.
                42 tons 4 cwt.*
Pressure: 180 lb.
Cyls.: 18″ × 26″.
Driving Wheels: 5′ 0″.
T.E.: 21,480 lb.

57232	57243	57253	57264
57233	57244	57254	57265
57236	57245	57256	57266
57237	57246	57257	57267
57238	57247	57258	57268
57239	57249	57259	57269
57240	57250	57261	57270
57241	57251	57262	57271
57242	57252	57263	57273

0-6-0   3F

Introduced 1899. McIntosh Caledonian "812" (Nos. 57550–57623) and "652" (remainder) classes.
Weight: Loco. 45 tons 14 cwt.
Pressure: 180 lb.
Cyls.: 18½″ × 26″.
Driving Wheels: 5′ 0″.
T.E.: 22,690 lb.

57550	57562	57572	57586
57552	57563	57575	57587
57553	57564	57576	57590
57554	57565	57577	57591
57555	57566	57579	57592
57557	57568	57580	57593
57558	57569	57581	57594
57559	57570	57583	57595
57560	57571	57585	57596

57597	57609	57621	57633
57599	57611	57622	57634
57600	57612	57623	57635
57601	57613	57625	57637
57602	57614	57626	57638
57603	57615	57627	57640
57604	57617	57628	57642
57605	57618	57630	57643
57607	57619	57631	57644
57608	57620	57632	57645

Total 76

0-6-0   3F

Introduced 1918. Pickersgill Caledonian "294" class (superheated) and "670" classes.
Weight: Loco. 50 tons 13 cwt.
Pressure: 180 lb. Su.
Cyls.: $18\frac{1}{2}'' \times 26''$.
Driving Wheels: 5' 0".
T.E.: 22,690 lb.
P.V.

57650	57661	57670	57682
57651	57663	57671	57684
57652	57665	57672	57686
57653	57666	57673	57688
57654	57667	57674	57689
57655	57668	57679	57690
57658	57669	57681	57691
57659			

Total 29

0-4-4T   1P

*Introduced 1889. Johnson Midland design of 1881 with larger cylinders and higher boiler pressure. All rebuilt with Belpaire firebox.
†Introduced 1895. Final Johnson 0-4-4T design, with higher-pitched boiler and larger tanks, later rebuilt with Belpaire firebox.
Push-and-pull fitted.
Weight: 53 tons 4 cwt.
Pressure: 150 lb.
Cyls.: $\begin{cases} 18'' \times 24''.^* \\ 17'' \times 24''.† \end{cases}$
Driving Wheels: 5' 4".
T.E.: $\begin{cases} 18,225 \text{ lb.}^* \\ 16,255 \text{ lb.}† \end{cases}$

58065*	58066*	58085†	58086†

Total 4

0-6-0   2F

*Introduced 1875. Johnson Midland 4' 11" design with round top firebox.
†Introduced 1917. Johnson 4' 11" design rebuilt with Belpaire firebox.
§Introduced 1917. Johnson Midland 5' 3" design rebuilt with Belpaire firebox.
Weight: Loco. Various—
37 tons 12 cwt. to 40 tons 3 cwt.
Pressure: 160 lb.
Cyls.: $18'' \times 26''$.
Driving Wheels: $\begin{cases} 4' \ 11''.^* \\ 4' \ 11''.† \\ 5' \ 3''.§ \end{cases}$
T.E.: $\begin{cases} 19,420 \text{ lb.}^* \\ 19,420 \text{ lb.}† \\ 18,185 \text{ lb.}§ \end{cases}$

58115†	58153†	58182†	58220§
58116†	58157†	58183†	58221§
58118†	58158†	58185†	58225§
58119†	58160†	58186†	58228§
58120†	58163†	58190§	58246*
58122†	58165†	58191§	58260§
58123†	58166†	58192§	58261§
58124†	58167†	58197§	58271§
58128†	58168†	58198§	58279§
58130†	58169†	58199§	58281§
58131†	58170†	58204§	58283§
58132†	58171†	58209§	58287§
58135†	58173†	58213§	58291§
58137†	58174†	58214§	58293§
58138†	58175†	58215§	58295§
58143†	58177†	58217§	58298§
58144†	58178†	58218§	58305§
58146†	58181†	58219§	58308§
58148†			

Total 73

0-6-0T   2F

Introduced 1879. Park North London design.
Weight: 45 tons 10 cw
Pressure: 160 lb.
Cyls.: (O) $17'' \times 24''$.
Driving Wheels: 4' 4"
T.E.: 18,140 lb.

58850

Total 1

0-6-2T   2F

Introduced 1882. Webb L.N.W. "Coal Tanks."

Weight: 43 tons 15 cwt.
Pressure: 150 lb.
Cyls.: 17" × 24".
Driving Wheels: 4' 5½".
T.E.: 16,530 lb.

58926   **Total 1**

4-2-2

Introduced 1886. Neilson & Co. design for the Caledonian Railway incorporating Drummond details.

Weight: Engine and Tender: 75 tons.
Pressure: 150 lb.
Cyls.: 18" × 26".
Driving Wheels: 7' 0".
T.E.: 12,785 lb.

123   **Total 1**

Withdrawn as L.M.S. No. 14010 in 1935. Returned to service 1958.

SERVICE LOCOS.

0-4-0   Diesel

E.D.1	E.D.4	E.D.6
E.D.2	E.D.5	E.D.7
E.D.3		

0-4-0 (3'0" gauge)   Diesel

E.D.10.

0-6-0ST   2F

Introduced 1870. Webb version of Ramsbottom "Special Tank."

Weight: 34 tons 10 cwt.
Pressure: 140 lb.
Cyls.: 17" × 24".
Driving Wheels: 4' 5½".
T.E.: 17,005 lb.

C.D.3 Wolverton Carriage Works
C.D.6   "   "   "
C.D.7   "   "   "
C.D.8 *Earlestown*, Wolverton C.W.

0-6-0ST   2F

For details see page 53, 51316 etc.

11304	11324	11368	11394
11305			

                         Total 5

CHIEF MECHANICAL ENGINEERS

BRITISH RAILWAYS (L.M. Region)

H. G. Ivatt ... 1948–1951

L.M.S.

George Hughes	1923–1925	Sir William Stanier ... 1932–1944
Sir Henry Fowler	1925–1931	Charles E. Fairburn ... 1944–1945
E. H. J. Lemon	1931–1932	H. G. Ivatt 1945–1947
(Sir Ernest Lemon)		

LOCOMOTIVE SUPERINTENDENTS AND C.M.E.'S—L.M.S. CONSTITUENT COMPANIES

CALEDONIAN RAILWAY

Robert Sinclair	
(First loco. engineer)*	1847–1856
Benjamin Connor	1856–1876
George Brittain ...	1876–1882
Dugald Drummond ...	1882–1890
Hugh Smellie ...	1890
J. Lambie	1890–1895
J. F. McIntosh ...	1895–1914
William Pickersgill ...	1914–1923

FURNESS RAILWAY

R. Mason	1890–1897
W. F. Pettigrew	1897–1918
D. J. Rutherford	1918–1923

GLASGOW AND SOUTH WESTERN RAILWAY

Patrick Stirling ...	1853–1866
James Stirling	1866–1878
Hugh Smellie	1878–1890
James Manson	1890–1912
Peter Drummond ...	1912–1918
R. H. Whitelegg	1918–1923

HIGHLAND RAILWAY

William Stroudley	
(First loco. engineer) ...	1866–1869
David Jones	1869–1896
Peter Drummond	1896–1911
F. G. Smith	1912–1915
C. Cumming	1915–1923

L. & Y.R.

Sir John Hawkshaw (Consultant),*	
Hurst and Jenkins successively to 1868	
W. Hurst	1868–1876
W. Barton Wright ...	1876–1886
John A. F. Aspinall ...	1886–1899
H. A. Hoy	1899–1904
George Hughes	1904–1921

The L. & Y. amalgamated with L.N.W.R. as from January 1st, 1922.

L.N.W.R.

Francis Trevithick and J. E. McConnell, first loco. engineers, 1846, with Alexander Allan largely responsible for design at Crewe.*

John Ramsbottom	1857–1871
Francis William Webb ...	1871–1903
George Whale	1903–1909
Charles John	
Bowen-Cooke	1909–1920
Capt. Hewitt Pearson	
Montague Beames ...	1920–1921
George Hughes	1922

L.T. & S.R.

Thomas Whitelegg ...	1880–1910
Robert Harben Whitelegg	1910–1912

(L.T. & S.R. absorbed by M.R., control of locos. transferred to Derby as from August, 1912.)

---

* Exclusive of previous service with constituent company.

LOCOMOTIVE SUPERINTENDENTS
AND C.M.E.'S (continued)

MARYPORT & CARLISLE

Hugh Smellie	... ...	1870–1878
J. Campbell	...	1878–
William Coulthard	...	* –1904
J. B. Adamson	... ...	1904–1923

MIDLAND RAILWAY

Matthew Kirtley (First loco. engineer)	... ...	1844–1873
Samuel Waite Johnson	...	1873–1903
Richard Mountford Deeley		1903–1909
Henry Fowler	... ...	1909–1923

SOMERSET AND DORSET JOINT RAILWAY

Until leased by Mid. and L. & S. W. (as from 1st November, 1875) locomotives were bought from outside builders, principally George England of Hatcham Iron Works, S.E. After the above date, Derby and its various Loco. Supts. and C.M.E.'s have acted for S. & D.J. aided by a resident Loco. Supt. stationed at Highbridge Works.

NORTH STAFFORDSHIRE RAILWAY

L. Clare	... ...	1876–1882
L. Longbottom	... ...	1882–1902
J. H. Adams	... ...	1902–1915
J. A. Hookham	... ...	1915–1923

W. Angus was Loco. Supt. at Stoke prior to 1876. No earlier records can be traced.

WIRRAL

Eric G. Barker	... ...	1892–1902
T. B. Hunter	... ...	1903–1923

Barker of the Wirral Railway is noteworthy for originating the 4-4-4 tank type in this country (1896).

NORTH LONDON RAILWAY

(Worked by L. & N.W. by agreement dated December, 1908.)

William Adams	... ...	1853–1873
J. C. Park	... ...	1873–1893
Henry J. Pryce	... ...	1893–1908

* Date of actual entry into office not known.

HISTORIC LOCOMOTIVES PRESERVED IN STORE

Type	Originating Company	Pre-Grouping No.	L.M.S. No.	Name	Place of Preservation
4-2-2	M.R.	118	(673)	—	Derby
2-4-0	M.R.	158A	—	—	Derby
*4-4-0	M.R.	(1000)	(1000)	—	Crewe
4-4-2T	L.T. & S.	80	(2148)	Thundersley	Derby
2-2-2	L.N.W.	(49)	—	Columbine	York Museum
2-2-2	L.N.W.	3020	—	Cornwall	Crewe
2-4-0	L.N.W.	790	(5031)	Hardwicke	Crewe
0-4-0ST	L.N.W.	1439	—	—	Crewe
†0-4-0T	L.N.W.	—	—	Pet	Crewe
2-4-2T	L. & Y.	1008	(10621)	—	Horwich
0-4-0	F.R.	3	—	Coppernob	Horwich
0-4-2	Liverpool & Manchester	—	—	Lion	Crewe
4-6-0	H.R.	103	(17916)	—	St. Rollox
‡4-4-0	H.R.	(2)	(14398)	Ben Alder	Boat of Garten

The unbracketed numbers are the ones at present carried by the locos.
* Present number 41000.
† 18 in. gauge works shunter.
‡ Present number 54398.

Class 3 (Fowler) 2-6-2T No. 40001 [R. J. Buckley

Class 3 (Fowler) 2-6-2T No. 40017 (push-and-pull fitted) [B. K. B. Green

Class 3 (Stanier) 2-6-2T No. 40109 [B. K. B. Green

Class 2P (Midland) 4-4-0 No. 40537

[K. R. Pirt

Class 2P (L.M.S.) 4-4-0 No. 40688

[W. S. Sellar

Class 4P 4-4-0 No. 41193

[R. J. Buckley

Class 4 (Fowler; side-window cab) 2-6-4T No. 42399   [*P. H. Groom*

Class 4 (Stanier 3-cylinder) 2-6-4T No. 42523   [*P. J. Sharpe*

Class 4 (Fairburn) 2-6-4T No. 42096   *G. Clarke*

Class 2 (Ivatt) 2-6-2T No. 41293   [B. K. B. Green

Class 2 (Riddles) 2-6-2T No. 84000   [B. K. B. Green

Class 4 (Riddles) 2-6-4T No. 80032   [L. Elsey

Class 6P5F (Hughes-Fowler) 2-6-0 No. 42785 [*P. H. Groom*

Class 6P5F (Hughes-Fowler) 2-6-0 No. 42322 (with Reidinger rotary poppet valve gear)
[*J. Cupit*

Class 6P5F (Stanier) 2-6-0 No. 42979 [*B. K. B. Green*

Class 2 (Ivatt) 2-6-0 No. 46501 [J. Cupit

Class 4 (Ivatt) 2-6-0 No. 43154 [B. K. B. Green

Class 4 (Riddles) 2-6-0 No. 76038 [K. R. Pirt

Class 7F 0-8-0 No. 49446

[J. Davenport

Class 7F (Fowler) 0-8-0 No. 49511

[M. Brown

Class 7F 2-8-0 No. 53806

A. R. Carpenter

Class 5 4-6-0 No. 45154 *Lanarkshire Yeomanry* [L. King

Class 6P5F 4-6-0 No. 45590 *Travancore* [G. Wheeler

Class 6P5F 4-6-0 No. 45520 *Llandudno* [B. K. B. Green

Class 8F 2-8-0 No. 48207

[A. E. Brown

Class 8P 4-6-2 No. 46210 *Lady Patricia* (with dome and top feed combined)

[B. K. B. Green

Class 8P 4-6-2 No. 46205 *Princess Victoria* (with derived motion for inside cylinders)

[G. Browne

Class 7P 4-6-0 No. 46100 *Royal Scot*　　　　　　　　　　　[F. R. Sherlock

Class 8P 4-6-2 No. 46250 *City of Lichfield*　　　　　　　　　[G. Wheeler

Class 8P 4-6-2 No. 46257 *City of Salford* (with modified front-end and rear bogie details)
　　　　　　　　　　　　　　　　　　　　　　　　　　[G. Wheeler

Class 2F 0-6-0 No. 58246 (with 4' 11" driving wheels; last engine of class to retain round-top firebox) [P. H. Groom

Class 2F 0-6-0 No. 58260 (with 5' 3" driving wheels)

Class 2F 0-6-0 No. 58153 (with 4' 11" driving wheels and Deeley cab) [P. H. Groom

Class 3F 0-6-0 No. 43832   [A. R. Carpenter

Class 4F 0-6-0 No. 44159   [J. A. Young

Class 2F (Drummond) 0-6-0 No. 57279   [P. J. Robinson

Class 3F 0-6-0 No. 52319   [P. Cookson

Class 3F 0-6-0 No. 52400 (with Belpaire firebox and extended smokebox)
                                            [C. P. Boocock

Class 2F 0-6-0 No. 52044   [A. Cox

Class 3P 4-4-0 No. 54507   [David A. Anderson

Class 2P 0-4-4T No. 55265   [B. K. B. Green

Class 2P 2-4-2T No. 50721   [T. C. Lawrence

Class 0F 0-4-0T No. 41529   [K. R. Pirt

Class 1F 0-6-0T No. 41804   [B. K. B. Green

Class 3F (Midland) 0-6-0T No. 47248 (fitted with condensing apparatus)
                                             [C. P. Boocock

Left: Class 0F
0-4-0ST No. 47004
[R. K. Evans

Centre: Class 2F
0-6-0T No. 47166
[B. K. B. Green

Bottom: Class 2F
0-6-0T No. 58850
[B. K. B. Green

Right: Class 2F
0-6-0T No. 56157
[*Brian E. Morrison*

Centre: Class 1F
0-6-0T No. 51537
[*T. K. Widd*

Bottom: Class 2F
0-6-0ST No. 51412
[*P. J. Sharpe*

Class 0F 0-4-0ST No. 51222   [*R. K. Evans*

Sentinel 0-4-0T No. 47190   [*R. C. Riley*

Class 0F 0-4-0ST No. 56025   *W. S. Sellar*

NUMERICAL LIST OF ENGINES

The code given in smaller bold type at the head of each class,
e.g. " 4MT " denotes its British Railways power classification.

The numbers of locomotives in service have been checked to August 23rd, 1958.

4-6-2   8P6F   Class A4

Introduced 1935. Gresley streamlined
design with corridor tender (except
those marked †).
*Inside cylinder reduced to 17".
‡Double blast pipe and chimney.
Weight: Loco.   102 tons 19 cwt.
Tender { 64 tons 19 cwt.
        60 tons 7 cwt.†
Pressure: 250 lb. Su.
Cyls.: { (3) 18¼" × 26".
      (2) 18¼" × 26" (1) 17" × 26".*
Driving Wheels: 6' 8".
T.E.: { 35,455 lb.
     33,616 lb.*
Walschaerts valve gear and derived
motion. P.V.

60001†‡Sir Ronald Matthews
60002†‡Sir Murrough Wilson
60003‡ Andrew K. McCosh
60004‡ William Whitelaw
60005‡ Sir Charles Newton
60006†‡Sir Ralph Wedgwood
60007‡ Sir Nigel Gresley
60008† Dwight D. Eisenhower
60009‡ Union of South Africa
60010‡ Dominion of Canada
60011‡ Empire of India
60012*†‡Commonwealth of
         Australia
60013‡ Dominion of New
         Zealand
60014‡ Silver Link
60015‡ Quicksilver
60016†‡Silver King
60017‡ Silver Fox
60018†‡Sparrow Hawk
60019†‡Bittern
60020*†‡Guillemot
60021‡ Wild Swan
60022‡ Mallard
60023†‡Golden Eagle
60024‡ Kingfisher
60025 Falcon

60026†‡Miles Beevor
60027‡ Merlin
60028‡ Walter K. Whigham
60029 Woodcock
60030‡ Golden Fleece
60031*‡Golden Plover
60032 Gannet
60033‡ Seagull
60034‡ Lord Faringdon

Total 34

4-6-2   7P6F   Class A3

Introduced 1927. Development of
Gresley G.N. 180 lb. Pacific (intro-
duced 1922, L.N.E.R. A1, later A10)
with 220 lb. pressure (prototype and
others rebuilt from A10). Some have
G.N.-type tender† with coal rails,
remainder L.N.E.R. pattern.
*Double blast pipe and chimney.
Weight: Loco.   96 tons 5 cwt.
Tender { 56 tons 6 cwt.†
        57 tons 18 cwt.
Pressure: 220 lb. Su.
Cyls.: (3) 19" × 26".
Driving Wheels: 6' 8".
T.E.: 32,910 lb.
Walschaerts valve gear and derived
motion. P.V.

60035 Windsor Lad
60036 Colombo
60037 Hyperion
60038 Firdaussi
60039 Sandwich
60040 Cameronian
60041 Salmon Trout
60042 Singapore
60043 Brown Jack
60044 Melton
60045 Lemberg
60046* Diamond Jubilee
60047 Donovan
60048 Doncaster
60049 Galtee More
60050 Persimmon

60051	Blink Bonny
60052	Prince Palatine
60053	Sansovino
60054	Prince of Wales
60055*	Woolwinder
60056	Centenary
60057	Ormonde
60058	Blair Athol
60059*	Tracery
60060	The Tetrarch
60061	Pretty Polly
60062	Minoru
60063	Isinglass
60064	Tagalie
60065	Knight of Thistle
60066	Merry Hampton
60067	Ladas
60068	Sir Visto
60069	Sceptre
60070	Gladiateur
60071*	Tranquil
60072	Sunstar
60073*	St. Gatien
60074	Harvester
60075	St. Frusquin
60076	Galopin
60077	The White Knight
60078	Night Hawk
60079	Bayardo
60080	Dick Turpin
60081	Shotover
60082	Neil Gow
60083	Sir Hugo
60084*	Trigo
60085	Manna
60086	Gainsborough
60087*	Blenheim
60088	Book Law
60089	Felstead
60090*	Grand Parade
60091	Captain Cuttle
60092	Fairway
60093	Coronach
60094	Colorado
60095	Flamingo
60096*	Papyrus
60097*	Humorist

60098	Spion Kop
60099*	Call Boy
60100	Spearmint
60101	Cicero
60102	Sir Frederick Banbury
60103	Flying Scotsman
60104	Solario
60105	Victor Wild
60106	Flying Fox
60107	Royal Lancer
60108	Gay Crusader
60109	Hermit
60110	Robert the Devil
60111	Enterprise
60112*	St. Simon

Total 78

4-6-2   8P6F   Class A1

A1/1* Introduced 1945. Thompson rebuild of A10.
A1 Peppercorn development of A1/1 for new construction.
A1† Fitted with roller bearings.
Weight: Loco. { 101 tons.*
{ 104 tons 2 cwt.
Tender 60 tons 7 cwt.
Pressure: 250 lb. Su.
Cyls.: (3) 19″ × 26″.
Driving Wheels: 6′ 8″.
T.E.: 37,400 lb.
Walschaerts valve gear. P.V.

60113*	Great Northern
60114	W. P. Allen
60115	Meg Merrilies
60116	Hal o' the Wynd
60117	Bois Roussel
60118	Archibald Sturrock
60119	Patrick Stirling
60120	Kittiwake
60121	Silurian
60122	Curlew
60123	H. A. Ivatt
60124	Kenilworth
60125	Scottish Union
60126	Sir Vincent Raven
60127	Wilson Worsdell
60128	Bongrace
60129	Guy Mannering
60130	Kestrel

60131	Osprey
60132	Marmion
60133	Pommern
60134	Foxhunter
60135	Madge Wildfire
60136	Alcazar
60137	Redgauntlet
60138	Boswell
60139	Sea Eagle
60140	Balmoral
60141	Abbotsford
60142	Edward Fletcher
60143	Sir Walter Scott
60144	King's Courier
60145	Saint Mungo
60146	Peregrine
60147	North Eastern
60148	Aboyeur
60149	Amadis
60150	Willbrook
60151	Midlothian
60152	Holyrood
60153†	Flamboyant
60154†	Bon Accord
60155†	Borderer
60156†	Great Central
60157†	Great Eastern
60158	Aberdonian
60159	Bonnie Dundee
60160	Auld Reekie
60161	North British
60162	Saint Johnstoun

Total 50

4-6-2 _(A2/1: 7P6F) ^{8P7F} Class A2

A2/2* Introduced 1943. Original Thompson Pacific, rebuilt from Gresley Class P2 2-8-2 (introduced 1934).
Weight: Loco. 101 tons 10 cwt.
Pressure: 225 lb. Su.
Cyls.: (3) 20″ × 26″.
Driving Wheels: 6′ 2″.
T.E.: 40,320 lb.

A2/1† Introduced 1944. Development of Class A2/2, incorporating Class V2 2-6-2 boiler.
Weight: Loco. 98 tons.
Pressure: 225 lb. Su.
Cyls.: (3) 19″ × 26″.
Driving Wheels: 6′ 2″.   T.E.: 36,385 lb.

A2/3‡ Introduced 1946. Development of Class A2/2 for new construction.
Weight: Loco. 101 tons 10 cwt.
Pressure: 250 lb. Su.
Cyls.: (3) 19″ × 26″.
Driving Wheels: 6′ 2″.
T.E.: 40,430 lb.

A2§ Introduced 1947. Peppercorn development of Class A2/2 with shorter wheelbase. (No. 60539 built with double blast pipe.)

A2** Rebuilt with double blast pipe and multiple valve regulator.
Weight: Loco. 101 tons.
Pressure: 250 lb. Su.
Cyls.: (3) 19″ × 26″.
Driving Wheels: 6′ 2″.
T.E.: 40,430 lb.
Tender weight (all parts): 60 tons 7 cwt.
Walschaerts valve gear. P.V.

60500‡	Edward Thompson
60501*	Cock o' the North
60502*	Earl Marischal
60503*	Lord President
60504*	Mons Meg
60505*	Thane of Fife
60506*	Wolf of Badenoch
60507†	Highland Chieftain
60508†	Duke of Rothesay
60509†	Waverley
60510†	Robert the Bruce
60511‡	Airborne
60512‡	Steady Aim
60513‡	Dante
60514‡	Chamossaire
60515‡	Sun Stream
60516‡	Hycilla
60517‡	Ocean Swell
60518‡	Tehran
60519‡	Honeyway
60520‡	Owen Tudor
60521‡	Watling Street
60522‡	Straight Deal
60523‡	Sun Castle
60524‡	Herringbone
60525§	A. H. Peppercorn
60526**	Sugar Palm
60527§	Sun Chariot
60528§	Tudor Minstrel
60529**	Pearl Diver
60530§	Sayajirao

60531§ Bahram	60812
60532**Blue Peter	60813
60533**Happy Knight	60814
60534§ Irish Elegance	60815
60535§ Hornet's Beauty	60816
60536§ Trimbush	60817
60537§ Bachelor's Button	60818
60538**Velocity	60819
60539§ Bronzino	60820

Total

Class A2 15 Class A2/2 6
Class A2/1 4 Class A2/3 15

4-6-4   εP7F   Class W1

Introduced 1937. Rebuilt from Gresley experimental high-pressure 4-cyl. compound with water-tube boiler, introduced 1929.
Weight: Loco. 107 tons 17 cwt.
         Tender 60 tons 7 cwt.
Pressure: 250 lb. Su.
Cyls.: (3) 19″ × 26″.
Driving Wheels: 6′ 8″.
T.E.: 37,400 lb.
Walschaerts valve gear and derived motion. P.V.

60700   **Total 1**

2-6-2   7P6F   Class V2

Introduced 1936. Gresley design.
Weight: Loco. 93 tons 2 cwt.
         Tender 52 tons.
Pressure: 220 lb. Su.
Cyls.: (3) 18¼″ × 26″.
Driving Wheels: 6′ 2″.
T.E.: 33,730 lb.
Walschaerts valve gear and derived motion. P.V.

60800	Green Arrow
60801	
60802	
60803	
60804	
60805	
60806	
60807	
60808	
60809	The Snapper, The East Yorkshire Regiment, The Duke of York's Own
60810	
60811	

60821	
60822	
60823	
60824	
60825	
60826	
60827	
60828	
60829	
60830	
60831	
60832	
60833	
60834	
60835	The Green Howard, Alexandra, Princess of Wales's Own Yorkshire Regiment
60836	
60837	
60838	
60839	
60840	
60841	
60842	
60843	
60844	
60845	
60846	
60847	St. Peter's School York, A.D. 627
60848	
60849	
60850	
60851	
60852	
60853	
60854	

60855	60974	60977	60980	60983
60856	60975	60978	60981	
60857	60976	60979	60982	
60858			
60859			

Total 184

60860	Durham School
60861	
60862	

4-6-0   5MT   Class B1

Introduced 1942. Thompson design.
Weight: Loco. 71 tons 3 cwt.
         Tender 52 tons.
Pressure: 225 lb. Su.
Cyls.: (O) 20″ × 26″.
Driving Wheels: 6′ 2″.
T.E.: 26,880 lb.
Walschaerts valve gear. P.V.

60863	
60864	
60865	
60866	
60867	
60868	
60869	
60870	
60871	
60872	King's Own Yorkshire Light Infantry
60873	Coldstreamer

60874	60897		
60875	60898	60920	60942
60876	60899	60921	60943
60877	60900	60922	60944
60878	60901	60923	60945
60879	60902	60924	60946
60880	60903	60925	60947
60881	60904	60926	60948
60882	60905	60927	60949
60883	60906	60928	60950
60884	60907	60929	60951
60885	60908	60930	60952
60886	60909	60931	60953
60887	60910	60932	60954
60888	60911	60933	60955
60889	60912	60934	60956
60890	60913	60935	60957
60891	60914	60936	60958
60892	60915	60937	60959
60893	60916	60938	60960
60894	60917	60939	60961
60895	60918	60940	60962
60896	60919	60941	60963

60964 The Durham Light Infantry		
60965	60968	60971
60966	60969	60972
60967	60970	60973

61000	Springbok
61001	Eland
61002	Impala
61003	Gazelle
61004	Oryx
61005	Bongo
61006	Blackbuck
61007	Klipspringer
61008	Kudu
61009	Hartebeeste
61010	Wildebeeste
61011	Waterbuck
61012	Puku
61013	Topi
61014	Oribi
61015	Duiker
61016	Inyala
61017	Bushbuck
61018	Gnu
61019	Nilghal
61020	Gemsbok
61021	Reitbok
61022	Sassaby
61023	Hirola
61024	Addax
61025	Pallah
61026	Ourebi
61027	Madoqua
61023	Umseke
61029	Chamois
61030	Nyala
61031	Reedbuck

61032 Stembok				61190
61033 Dibatag				61191
61034 Chiru				61192
61035 Pronghorn				61193
61036 Ralph Assheton				61194
61037 Jairou				61195
61038 Blacktail				61196
61039 Steinbok				61197
61040 Roedeer				61198
61041	61079	61116	61153	61199
61042	61080	61117	61154	61200
61043	61081	61118	61155	61201
61044	61082	61119	61156	61202
61045	61083	61120	61157	61203
61046	61084	61121	61158	61204
61047	61085	61122	61159	61205
61048	61086	61123	61160	61206
61049	61087	61124	61161	61207
61050	61088	61125	61162	61208
61051	61089	61126	61163	61209
61052	61090	61127	61164	61210
61053	61091	61128	61165	61211
61054	61092	61129	61166	61212
61055	61093	61130	61167	61213
61056	61094	61131	61168	61214
61058	61095	61132	61169	61215 William Henton Carver
61059	61096	61133	61170	61216
61060	61097	61134	61171	61217
61061	61098	61135	61172	61218
61062	61099	61136	61173	61219
61063	61100	61137	61174	61220
61064	61101	61138	61175	61221 Sir Alexander Erskine-Hill
61065	61102	61139	61176	61222
61066	61103	61140	61177	61223
61067	61104	61141	61178	61224
61068	61105	61142	61179	61225
61069	61106	61143	61180	61226
61070	61107	61144	61181	61227
61071	61108	61145	61182	61228
61072	61109	61146	61183	61229
61073	61110	61147	61184	61230
61074	61111	61148	61185	61231
61075	61112	61149	61186	61232
61076	61113	61150	61187	61233
61077	61114	61151	61188	61234
61078	61115	61152		61235
61189 Sir William Gray				

61236			
61237	Geoffrey H. Kitson		
61238	Leslie Runciman		
61239			
61240	Harry Hinchcliffe		
61241	Viscount Ridley		
61242	Alexander Reith Gray		
61243	Sir Harold Mitchell		
61244	Strang Steel		
61245	Murray of Elibank		
61246	Lord Balfour of Burleigh		
61247	Lord Burghley		
61248	Geoffrey Gibbs		
61249	FitzHerbert Wright		
61250	A. Harold Bibby		
61251	Oliver Bury		

61252	61283	61314	61345
61253	61284	61315	61346
61254	61285	61316	61347
61255	61286	61317	61348
61256	61287	61318	61349
61257	61288	61319	61350
61258	61289	61320	61351
61259	61290	61321	61352
61260	61291	61322	61353
61261	61292	61323	61354
61262	61293	61324	61355
61263	61294	61325	61356
61264	61295	61326	61357
61265	61296	61327	61358
61266	61297	61328	61359
61267	61298	61329	61360
61268	61299	61330	61361
61269	61300	61331	61362
61270	61301	61332	61363
61271	61302	61333	61364
61272	61303	61334	61365
61273	61304	61335	61366
61274	61305	61336	61367
61275	61306	61337	61368
61276	61307	61338	61369
61277	61308	61339	61370
61278	61309	61340	61371
61279	61310	61341	61372
61280	61311	61342	61373
61281	61312	61343	61374
61282	61313	61344	61375

61376	61377		61378
61379	Mayflower		
61380	61388	61396	61404
61381	61389	61397	61405
61382	61390	61398	61406
61383	61391	61399	61407
61384	61392	61400	61408
61385	61393	61401	61409
61386	61394	61402	
61387	61395	61403	

Total 409

4-6-0   5MT   Class B16

B16/1 Introduced 1920. Raven N.E. design with Stephenson valve gear.
B16/2* Introduced 1937. Gresley rebuild of B16/1 with Walschaerts valve gear and derived motion for inside cylinder.
B16/3† Introduced 1944. Thompson rebuild of B16/1 with individual sets of Walschaerts valve gear for each cylinder.

Weight: Loco. $\begin{cases} 77 \text{ tons } 14 \text{ cwt.} \\ 79 \text{ tons } 4 \text{ cwt.*} \\ 78 \text{ tons } 19 \text{ cwt.†} \end{cases}$
Tender 46 tons 12 cwt.
Pressure: 180 lb. Su.
Cyls.: (3) $18\frac{1}{2}'' \times 26''$.
Driving Wheels: 5′ 8″.
T.E.: 30,030 lb.   P.V.

61410	61427	61444†	61461†
61411	61428	61445	61462
61412	61429	61446	61463†
61413	61430	61447	61464†
61414	61431	61448†	61465
61415	61432	61449†	61466
61416	61433	61450	61467†
61417†	61434†	61451	61468†
61418†	61435*	61452	61469
61419	61436	61453†	61470
61420†	61437*	61454†	61471
61421*	61438†	61455*	61472†
61422	61439†	61456	61473
61423	61440	61457*	61475*
61424	61441	61458	61476†
61425	61442	61459	61477
61426	61443	61460	61478

Total: Class B16/1 44
Class B16/3 17 Class B16/2 7

4-6-0   4P3F   **Class B12**

B12/3 Introduced 1932. Gresley re-build of Holden G.E. design of 1911 with large boiler, round-topped firebox and long-travel valves.
(B12/2 was a development of B12 1 with Lentz valves, since rebuilt to B12/3.)

Weight: Loco.   69 tons 10 cwt.
        Tender 39 tons 6 cwt.
Pressure: 180 lb. Su.
Cyls.: 20″ × 28″.
Driving Wheels: 6′ 6″.
T.E.: 21,970 lb.
P.V.

61514	61549	61566	61575
61530	61553	61567	61576
61533	61554	61568	61577
61535	61558	61571	61580
61546	61561	61572	
61547	61564	61573	

Total 22

4-6-0   4MT (B2 and B17/6: 5P4F)   **Classes B2 & B17**

B17/1[1] Introduced 1928. Gresley design for G.E. section with G.E.-type tender.

B17/6[2] Introduced 1947. B17/1 fitted with 100A (B1-type) boiler.

B17/4[3] Introduced 1936. Locos. with L.N.E.R. 4,200-gallon tender.

B17/6[4] Introduced 1943. B17/4 fitted with 100A (B1-type) boiler.

B17/6[5] Rebuild of streamlined B17/5 introduced in 1937. Rebuilt with 100A boiler and de-streamlined in 1951.

Weight: Loco.   77 tons 5 cwt.
        Tender $\begin{cases} 39 \text{ tons } 6 \text{ cwt.}^{12} \\ 52 \text{ tons.}^{345} \end{cases}$

Pressure: $\begin{cases} 180 \text{ lb.}^{12} \\ 225 \text{ lb.}^{345} \end{cases}$ Su,

Cyls.: (3) 17½″ × 26″.
Driving Wheels: 6′ 8″.
T.E.: $\begin{cases} 22,485 \text{ lb.}^{12} \\ 28,555 \text{ lb.}^{345} \end{cases}$

Walschaerts valve gear and derived motion. P.V.

B2[6] Introduced 1945. Thompson 2-cyl. rebuild of B17, with 100A boiler and N.E. tender.

B2[7] Introduced 1945, with L.N.E.R. tender.

Weight: Loco.   73 tons 10 cwt.
        Tender $\begin{cases} 46 \text{ tons } 12 \text{ cwt.}^{6} \\ 52 \text{ tons.}^{7} \end{cases}$

Pressure: 225 lb. Su.
Cyls.: (O) 20″ × 26″.
Driving Wheels: 6′ 8″.
T.E.: 24,865 lb.
Walschaerts valve gear. P.V.

61603[6]	Framlingham
61606[2]	Audley End
61607[6]	Blickling
61608[2]	Gunton
61610[2]	Honingham Hall
61611[2]	Raynham Hall
61612[2]	Houghton Hall
61613[2]	Woodbastwick Hall
61614[6]	Castle Hedingham
61615[7]	Culford Hall
61616[6]	Fallodon
61618[2]	Wynyard Park
61619[2]	Welbeck Abbey
61620[2]	Clumber
61621[2]	Hatfield House
61622[2]	Alnwick Castle
61623[2]	Lambton Castle
61625[1]	Raby Castle
61626[2]	Brancepeth Castle
61627[2]	Aske Hall
61629[1]	Naworth Castle
61631[2]	Serlby Hall
61632[2]	Belvoir Castle
61633[2]	Kimbolton Castle
61635[2]	Milton
61636[2]	Harlaxton Manor
61637[2]	Thorpe Hall
61639[6]	Norwich City
61640[2]	Somerleyton Hall
61641[2]	Gayton Hall
61642[2]	Kilverstone Hall
61644[6]	Earlham Hall
61645[2]	The Suffolk Regiment
61646[2]	Gilwell Park
61647[2]	Helmingham Hall
61648[4]	Arsenal
61649[4]	Sheffield United

61650⁴	Grimsby Town		
61651⁴	Derby County		
61652³	Darlington		
61653⁴	Huddersfield Town		
61654⁴	Sunderland		
61655⁴	Middlesbrough		
61656⁴	Leeds United		
61657⁴	Doncaster Rovers		
61658⁴	The Essex Regiment		
61659⁵	East Anglian		
61660³	Hull City		
61661⁴	Sheffield Wednesday		
61662⁴	Manchester United		
61663⁴	Everton		
61664⁴	Liverpool		
61665⁴	Leicester City		
61666⁴	Nottingham Forest		
61668⁴	Bradford City		
61669⁴	Barnsley		
61670⁵	City of London		
61671⁷	Royal Sovereign		
61672⁴	West Ham United		

Total

Class B2 9 Class B17/4 2
Class B17/1 3 Class B17/6 45

2-6-0 4MT Class K2

K2/2 Introduced 1914. Gresley G.N. design.

K2/1* Introduced 1931. Rebuilt from small-boilered K1 (introduced 1912).

†K2/2 with side-window cab.

‡K2/1 with side-window cab.

Weight: Loco. 64 tons 8 cwt.
  Tender 43 tons 2 cwt.
Pressure: 180 lb. Su.
Cyls.: (O) 20″ × 26″.
Driving Wheels: 5′ 8″.
T.E.: 23,400 lb.
Walschaerts valve gear. P.V.

61721‡	61738	61743	61749
61723*	61739	61745	61750
61728*	61740	61746	61751
61730	61741†	61747	61752
61731	61742	61748	61753

IMPORTANT NOTE
A careful reading of the notes on page 2 is essential to understand the use of reference marks in this book.

61754	61757	61760	61763
61755†	61758†	61761	
61756	61759	61762	

61764†	Loch Arkaig
61766	
61767	
61768	
61769†	
61770†	
61771	
61772†	Loch Lochy
61773	
61776†	
61777	
61778	
61779†	
61780	
61781†	Loch Morar
61782†	Loch Eil
61783†	Loch Shiel
61784†	
61785†	
61786†	
61787†	Loch Quoich
61788†	Loch Rannoch
61789†	Loch Laidon
61790†	Loch Lomond
61791†	Loch Laggan
61792†	
61793†	
61794†	Loch Oich

Total
Class K2/1 3   Class K2/2 55

2-6-0 5P6F Classes K3 & K5

K3/2 Introduced 1924. Development of Gresley G.N. design, built to L.N.E.R. loading gauge.

135

K3/3* Introduced 1929. Differ in details only, such as springs, from K3/2.
‡K3/3 fitted with G.N. tender.
(K3/1 were G.N. locos. (introduced 1920), with G.N. cabs, and K3/4, K3/5 and K3/6 were variations of K3/2 differing in weight and details. These locos. have now been modified to K3/2.)

Weight: Loco. 72 tons 12 cwt.
Tender $\begin{cases} 52 \text{ tons.} \\ 43 \text{ tons } 2 \text{ cwt.} ‡ \end{cases}$
Pressure: 180 lb. Su.
Cyls.: (3) $18\frac{1}{2}" \times 26"$.
Driving Wheels: 5' 8".
T.E.: 30,030 lb.
Walschaerts valve gear and derived motion. P.V.

K5† Introduced 1945. Thompson 2-cyl. rebuild of K3.
Weight: Loco. 71 tons 5 cwt.
Tender 52 tons.
Pressure: 225 lb. Su.
Cyls.: (O) 20" × 26".
Driving Wheels: 5' 8".
T.E.: 29,250 lb.
Walschaerts valve gear. P.V.

61800	61826	61852	61878*
61801	61827	61853	61879*
61802	61828	61854‡	61880*
61803	61829	61855‡	61881*
61804	61830	61856‡	61882*
61805	61831	61857‡	61883*
61806	61832	61858‡	61884*
61807	61833	61859‡	61885*
61808	61834	61860	61886*
61809	61835	61861	61887*
61810	61836	61862	61888*
61811	61837	61863†	61889*
61812‡	61838	61864	61890
61813	61839	61865	61891
61814	61840	61866	61892
61815	61841‡	61867	61893
61816	61842	61868	61894
61817	61843	61869	61895
61818	61844	61870*	61896
61819	61845	61871*	61897
61820	61846	61872*	61898
61821	61847	61873*	61899
61822	61848	61874*	61900
61823	61849	61875*	61901
61824	61850	61876*	61902
61825	61851	61877*	61903

61904	61927	61949	61971
61905	61928	61950	61972
61906	61929	61951	61973
61907	61930	61952	61974
61908	61931	61953	61975
61909	61932	61954	61976
61910	61933	61955	61977
61911	61934	61956	61978
61912	61935	61957	61979
61913	61936	61958	61980
61914	61937	61959	61981
61915	61938	61960	61982
61916	61939	61961	61983
61917	61940	61962	61984
61918	61941	61963	61985
61919	61942	61964	61986
61920	61943	61965	61987
61921	61944	61966	61988
61922	61945	61967	61989
61923	61946	61968	61990
61924	61947	61969	61991
61925	61948	61970	61992
61926			

Total
Class K3/2 172   Class K5 1
Class K3/3 20

Classes
2-6-0 5P6F **K1 & K4**

K4* Introduced 1937. Gresley locos. for West Highland line.
Weight: Loco. 68 tons 8 cwt.
Tender 44 tons 4 cwt.
Pressure: 200 lb. Su.
Cyls.: (3) $18\frac{1}{2}" \times 26"$.
Driving Wheels: 5' 2".
T.E.: 36,600 lb.
Walschaerts valve gear and derived motion. P.V.

K1/1† Introduced 1945. Thompson 2-cyl. loco. Rebuilt from K4.

K1 Introduced 1949. Peppercorn development of Thompson K1/1 (No. 61997) for new construction, with increased length.
Weight: Loco. 66 tons 17 cwt.
Tender 44 tons 4 cwt.
Pressure: 225 lb. Su.
Cyls.: (O) 20" × 26".
Driving Wheels: 5' 2".
T.E.: 32,080 lb.
Walschaerts valve gear. **P.V.**

61993* Loch Long
61994* The Great Marquess
61995* Cameron of Lochiel
61996* Lord of the Isles
61997† MacCailin Mor
61998* Macleod of Macleod

62001	62019	62037	62055
62002	62020	62038	62056
62003	62021	62039	62057
62004	62022	62040	62058
62005	62023	62041	62059
62006	62024	62042	62060
62007	62025	62043	62061
62008	62026	62044	62062
62009	62027	62045	62063
62010	62028	62046	62064
62011	62029	62047	62065
62012	62030	62048	62066
62013	62031	62049	62067
62014	62032	62050	62068
62015	62033	62051	62069
62016	62034	62052	62070
62017	62035	62053	
62018	62036	62054	

Total

Class K1 70   Class K4 5
Class K1/1 1

4-4-0 3P Class D30

D30/2 Introduced 1914. Development of D30/1, introduced 1912 (Reid N.B. "Scott" class) with detail differences.
Weight: Loco. 57 tons 16 cwt.
Tender 46 tons 13 cwt.
Pressure: 165 lb. Su.
Cyls.: 20" × 26".
Driving Wheels: 6' 6".
T.E.: 18,700 lb.
P.V.

62418	The Pirate
62421	Laird o' Monkbarns
62422	Caleb Balderstone
62425	Ellangowan
62426	Cuddie Headrigg
62427	Dumbiedykes
62428	The Talisman
62431	Kenilworth
62432	Quentin Durward
62436	Lord Glenvarloch
62439	Father Ambrose
62440	Wandering Willie
62441	Black Duncan

Total 13

4-4-0 3P Class D34

Introduced 1913. Reid N.B. "Glen" class.
Weight: Loco. 57 tons 4 cwt.
Tender 46 tons 13 cwt.
Pressure: 165 lb. Su.

HISTORIC LOCOMOTIVES PRESERVED IN STORE

Type	Originating Company	Pre-Grouping No.	L.N.E.R. No.	Name	Place of Preservation
4-2-2	G.N.R.	1	—	—	York Museum
4-4-2	G.N.R.	990	(3990)	Henry Oakley	York Museum
4-4-2	G.N.R.	251	(3251)	—	York Museum
2-2-4T	N.E.R.	66	66	Aerolite	York Museum
2-4-0	N.E.R.	910	910	—	York Museum
2-4-0	N.E.R.	1463	1463	—	York Museum
4-4-0	N.E.R.	1621	1621	—	York Museum
4-4-0	G.N.S.	49	(6849)	Gordon Highlander	Inverurie Works

The unbracketed numbers are the ones at present carried by the locos.

Cyls.: 20″ × 26″.
Driving Wheels: 6′ 0″.
T.E.: 20,260 lb.
P.V.

62467	Glenfinnan
62468	Glen Orchy
62469	Glen Douglas
62470	Glen Roy
62471	Glen Falloch
62472	Glen Nevis
62474	Glen Croe
62475	Glen Beasdale
62477	Glen Dochart
62478	Glen Quoich
62479	Glen Sheil
62480	Glen Fruin
62482	Glen Mamie
62483	Glen Garry
62484	Glen Lyon
62485	Glen Murran
62487	Glen Arklet
62488	Glen Aladale
62489	Glen Dessary
62490	Glen Fintaig
62492	Glen Garvin
62493	Glen Gloy
62494	Glen Gour
62495	Glen Luss
62496	Glen Loy
62497	Glen Mallie
62498	Glen Moidart

Total 27

4-4-0   3P1F   Class D16

D16/3¹ Introduced 1933. Gresley rebuild of D15 with larger boiler, round-topped firebox and modified footplating. D15 was Belpaire firebox development of original J. Holden (G.E.) " Claud Hamilton " class.

D16/3² Introduced 1933. Rebuild of D15 with larger boiler, round-topped firebox, modified footplate and 8″ piston valves.

D16/3³ Introduced 1936. Rebuild of D15 with larger boiler, round-topped firebox, modified footplating and 9¼″ piston valves.

D16/3⁴ Introduced 1938. Rebuild of D16/2 with round-topped firebox,

but retaining original footplating and slide valves.

Weight: Loco. 55 tons 18 cwt.
        Tender 39 tons 5 cwt.
Pressure: 180 lb. Su.
Cyls.: 19″ × 26″.
Driving Wheels: 7′ 0″.
T.E.: 17,095 lb.

62511¹	62534¹	62571¹	62606⁴
62513¹	62540¹	62582¹	62610¹
62517¹	62543⁴	62588²	62612⁴
62518¹	62544⁴	62589⁴	62613⁴
62524¹	62545¹	62597¹	62615⁴
62529¹	62566¹	62599³	62618⁴
62530¹	62570⁴	62604¹	

Total 27

4-4-0   3P2F   Class D11

D11/1* Introduced 1920. Robinson G.C. " Large Director "development of D10 (introduced 1913).

D11/2 Introduced 1924. Post-grouping locos. built to Scottish loading gauge. From 1938 the class has been rebuilt with long-travel valves.

Weight: Loco. 61 tons 3 cwt.
        Tender 48 tons 6 cwt.
Pressure: 180 lb. Su.
Cyls.: 20″ × 26″.
Driving Wheels: 6′ 9″.
T.E.: 19,645 lb.
P.V.

62660*	Butler-Henderson
62661*	Gerard Powys Dewhurst
62662*	Prince of Wales
62663*	Prince Albert
62664*	Princess Mary
62665*	Mons
62666*	Zeebrugge
62667*	Somme
62668*	Jutland
62669*	Ypres
62670*	Marne
62671	Bailie MacWheeble
62672	Baron of Bradwardine
62673	Evan Dhu
62674	Flora MacIvor
62675	Colonel Gardiner
62676	Jonathan Oldbuck

62677	Edie Ochiltree
62678	Luckie Mucklebackit
62679	Lord Glenallan
62680	Lucy Ashton
62681	Captain Craigengelt
62682	Haystoun of Bucklaw
62683	Hobbie Elliott
62684	Wizard of the Moor
62685	Malcolm Graeme
62686	The Fiery Cross
62687	Lord James of Douglas
62688	Ellen Douglas
62689	Maid of Lorn
62690	The Lady of the Lake
62691	Laird of Balmawhapple
62692	Allan-Bane
62693	Roderick Dhu
62694	James Fitzjames

Total
Class D11/1 11 Class D11/2 24

4-4-0   4P   Class D49

D49/1* Introduced 1927. Gresley design with piston valves. Walschaerts valve gear and derived motion.

D49/2† Introduced 1928. Development of D49/1 with Lentz Rotary Cam poppet valves.

D49/3‡ Introduced 1949. Fitted with Reidinger R.R. Rotary valve gear.
(D49/3 comprised locos. 62720–5 as built with Lentz Oscillating Cam poppet valves. From 1938 these locos. were converted to D49/1. 62751–75 have larger valves than the earlier D49/2, and were at first classified D49/4).
[1]Fitted with G.C. tender.
[2]Fitted with N.E. tender.
[3]The remainder have L.N.E.R. tenders.

Weight: Loco. { 66 tons.*†
{ 64 tons 10 cwt.‡

Tender { 48 tons 6 cwt.[1]
{ 44 tons 2 cwt.[2]
{ 52 tons.[3]

Pressure: 180 lb. Su.
Cyls.: (3) 17″ × 26″.
Driving Wheels: 6′ 8″.
T.E.: 21,555 lb.

62700*[1]	Yorkshire
62701*[1]	Derbyshire
62702*[1]	Oxfordshire
62704*[1]	Stirlingshire
62705*[1]	Lanarkshire
62707*[1]	Lancashire
62708*[1]	Argyllshire
62709*[1]	Berwickshire
62710*[1]	Lincolnshire
62711*[1]	Dumbartonshire
62712*[1]	Morayshire
62714*[1]	Perthshire
62715*[1]	Roxburghshire
62716*[1]	Kincardineshire
62717*[1]	Banffshire
62718*[1]	Kinross-shire
62719*[1]	Peebles-shire
62720*[1]	Cambridgeshire
62721*[1]	Warwickshire
62722*[1]	Huntingdonshire
62723*[2]	Nottinghamshire
62725*[1]	Inverness-shire
62727†[2]	The Quorn
62728*[1]	Cheshire
62729*[1]	Rutlandshire
62730*[1]	Berkshire
62731*[1]	Selkirkshire
62732*[1]	Dumfries-shire
62733*[1]	Northumberland
62734*[2]	Cumberland
62735*[2]	Westmorland
62738†[3]	The Zetland
62739†[3]	The Badsworth
62740†[3]	The Bedale
62741†[3]	The Blankney
62742†[3]	The Braes of Derwent
62743†[3]	The Cleveland
62744†[3]	The Holderness
62745†[3]	The Hurworth
62747†[3]	The Percy
62750†[3]	The Pytchley
62751†[3]	The Albrighton
62753†[3]	The Belvoir
62754†[3]	The Berkeley
62755†[3]	The Bilsdale
62759†[3]	The Craven
62760†[3]	The Cotswold

62762†³ The Fernie
62763‡³ The Fitzwilliam
62764‡³ The Garth
62765†³ The Goathland
62766†³ The Grafton
62767†³ The Grove
62769†³ The Oakley
62770†³ The Puckeridge
62771†³ The Rufford
62772†³ The Sinnington
62774†³ The Staintondale
62775‡³ The Tynedale

Total
Class D49/1 30 Class D49/2 29

2-4-0   IMT   Class E4

Introduced 1891. J. Holden G.E. design.
Weight: Loco.   40 tons 6 cwt.
        Tender 30 tons 13 cwt.
Pressure: 160 lb.
Cyls.: 17½″ × 24″.
Driving Wheels: 5′ 8″.
T.E.: 14,700 lb.

62785

Total 1

0-8-0   6F   Class Q6

Introduced 1913. Raven N.E. design.
*Some locos. are fitted with tender
from withdrawn B15 locos.
Weight: Loco.   65 tons 18 cwt.
        Tender { 44 tons 2 cwt.
                44 tons.*
Pressure: 180 lb. Su.
Cyls.: (O) 20″ × 26″.
Driving Wheels: 4′ 7½″.
T.E.: 28,800 lb.
P.V.

63340	63343	63346	63349
63341	63344	63347	63350
63342	63345	63348	63351

63352	63379	63406	63433
63353	63380	63407	63434
63354	63381	63408	63435
63355	63382	63409	63436
63356	63383	63410	63437
63357	63384	63411	63438
63358	63385	63412	63439
63359	63386	63413	63440
63360	63387	63414	63441
63361	63388	63415	63442
63362	63389	63416	63443
63363	63390	63417	63444
63364	63391	63418	63445
63365	63392	63419	63446
63366	63393	63420	63447
63367	63394	63421	63448
63368	63395	63422	63449
63369	63396	63423	63450
63370	63397	63424	63451
63371	63398	63425	63452
63372	63399	63426	63453
63373	63400	63427	63454
63374	63401	63428	63455
63375	63402	63429	63456
63376	63403	63430	63457
63377	63404	63431	63458
63378	63405	63432	63459

Total 120

0-8-0   8F   Class Q7

Introduced 1919. Raven N.E. design.
Weight: Loco.   71 tons 12 cwt.
        Tender 44 tons 2 cwt.
Pressure: 180 lb. Su.
Cyls.: (3) 18½″ × 26″.
Driving Wheels: 4′ 7¼″
T.E.: 36,965 lb.
P.V.

63460	63464	63468	63472
63461	63465	63469	63473
63462	63466	63470	63474
63463	63467	63471	

Total 15

Classes
O1 & O4

2-8-0 8F (O1)
7F (O4)

O4/1¹ Introduced 1911. Robinson G.C. design with small boiler, Belpaire firebox, steam and vacuum brakes and water scoop.

O4/3² Introduced 1917. R.O.D. locos. with steam brake only and no scoop.

O4/2³ Introduced 1925. O4/3 with cabs and boiler mountings reduced.

O4/5⁴ Introduced 1932. Rebuilt with shortened O2-type boiler and separate smokebox saddle.

O4/6⁵ Introduced 1924. Rebuilt from O5 retaining higher cab (63914–20 with side windows).

O4/7⁶ Introduced 1939. Rebuilt with shortened O2-type boiler, retaining G.C. smokebox.

O4/8⁷ Introduced 1944. Rebuilt with 100A (B1) boiler, retaining original cylinders.

(O4/4 were rebuilds with O2 boilers, since rebuilt again; O5 was a G.C. development of O4 with larger boiler and Belpaire firebox.)

Weight: Loco.
73 tons 4 cwt.¹
73 tons 4 cwt.²
73 tons 4 cwt.³
74 tons 13 cwt.⁴
73 tons 4 cwt.⁵
73 tons 17 cwt.⁶
72 tons 10 cwt.⁷

Tender
48 cwt. 6 cwt.
(with scoop)
47 tons 6 cwt.
(without scoop)

Pressure: 180 lb. Su.
Cyls.: (O) 21″ × 26″.
Driving Wheels: 4′ 8″.
T.E.: 31,325 lb.
P.V.

O1⁸ Introduced 1944. Thompson rebuild with 100A boiler, Walschaerts valve gear and new cylinders.
Weight: Loco. 73 tons 6 cwt.
Tender as O4.
Pressure: 225 lb. Su.
Cyls.: (O) 20″ × 26″.
Driving Wheels: 4′ 8″.
T.E.: 35,520 lb.
Walschaerts valve gear. P.V.

63570⁶	63575⁷	63581¹	63586¹
63571⁸	63576¹	63582⁶	63587¹
63572¹	63577¹	63583¹	63588⁶
63573⁷	63578⁸	63584¹	63589⁸
63574¹	63579⁸	63585¹	63590⁸

63591⁸	63639⁷	63686²	63733²
63592⁸	63640¹	63687⁸	63734⁷
63593¹	63641⁷	63688⁷	63735²
63594⁸	63642⁸	63689⁸	63736¹
63595⁶	63643⁶	63690³	63737²
63596⁸	63644⁷	63691⁷	63738⁷
63597¹	63645⁷	63692¹	63739⁷
63598¹	63646⁸	63693¹	63740⁸
63599¹	63647⁷	63694²	63741⁷
63600⁶	63648³	63695²	63742⁷
63601¹	63649²	63696²	63743¹
63602¹	63650⁸	63697⁷	63744²
63603⁶	63651⁷	63698¹	63745⁴
63604⁷	63652⁸	63699⁶	63746⁸
63605¹	63653⁷	63700¹	63747⁶
63606⁷	63654¹	63701²	63748⁸
63607⁷	63655⁷	63702²	63749⁶
63608¹	63656²	63703⁷	63750⁷
63609¹	63657⁴	63704⁷	63751²
63610⁸	63658¹	63705⁷	63752⁸
63611¹	63659²	63706⁷	63753²
63612⁷	63660¹	63707¹	63754⁷
63613⁷	63661⁶	63708⁶	63755⁸
63614¹	63662⁶	63709⁷	63756²
63615⁶	63663⁸	63710¹	63757¹
63616⁶	63664¹	63711⁸	63758⁶
63617¹	63665²	63712⁸	63759²
63618¹	63666²	63713²	63760⁸
63619⁸	63667²	63714²	63761⁶
63620¹	63668²	63715⁷	63762¹
63621¹	63669⁶	63716²	63763⁷
63622¹	63670⁸	63717⁷	63764²
63623¹	63671¹	63718⁷	63765⁷
63624⁷	63672⁷	63719¹	63766²
63625¹	63673⁶	63720⁷	63767²
63626¹	63674⁷	63721⁷	63768⁸
63628⁷	63675⁷	63722¹	63769²
63629²	63676⁸	63723¹	63770⁶
63630⁸	63677¹	63724³	63771²
63631⁷	63678⁸	63725⁸	63772⁸
63632¹	63679²	63726⁷	63773⁸
63633⁷	63680³	63727¹	63774²
63634⁶	63681²	63728⁷	63775⁵
63635¹	63682³	63729²	63776⁷
63636⁷	63683⁷	63730⁷	63777⁸
63637²	63684¹	63731⁸	63779²
63638²	63685²	63732⁷	63780⁸

141

63781⁷	63813²	63852⁷	63884⁷
63782²	63816⁷	63853⁷	63885⁷
63783²	63817⁸	63854⁸	63886⁸
63784⁸	63818⁷	63855²	63887⁸
63785⁷	63819⁷	63856⁸	63888⁷
63786⁸	63821²	63857⁷	63889²
63787²	63822²	63858⁷	63890⁸
63788⁷	63823⁷	63859²	63891⁶
63789⁸	63824⁶	63860⁶	63893⁷
63790²	63827⁷	63861²	63894⁶
63791⁷	63828⁷	63862⁷	63895⁷
63792⁸	63829⁷	63863⁸	63896⁵
63793⁷	63832⁷	63864⁷	63897⁷
63794⁷	63833²	63865⁸	63898⁷
63795⁸	63835²	63867⁸	63899⁷
63796⁸	63836⁷	63868⁸	63900²
63797¹	63837⁸	63869⁸	63901⁸
63798²	63838⁸	63870²	63902⁵
63799¹	63839⁶	63872⁸	63904⁵
63800⁷	63840⁷	63873⁷	63905⁵
63801⁷	63841⁷	63874⁸	63906⁵
63802⁷	63842²	63876⁶	63907⁵
63803⁸	63843⁶	63877⁷	63908⁵
63804²	63845²	63878⁷	63911⁵
63805⁷	63846²	63879⁸	63912⁵
63806⁸	63847⁸	63880⁶	63913⁵
63807⁷	63848⁶	63881²	63914⁷
63808⁸	63850⁷	63882⁷	63915⁷
63812²	63851⁴	63883²	63917⁵
			63920⁵

Total

Class O1	58	Class O4/5	2
Class O4/1	46	Class O4/6	11
Class O4/2	5	Class O4/7	33
Class O4/3	74	Class O4/8	95

O2/3 Introduced 1932. Development of O2/2 with side-window cab and reduced boiler mountings.

O2/4‡ Introduced 1943. Rebuilt with 100A (B1 type) boiler and smokebox extended backwards (63924 retaining G.N. tender).

Weight: Loco. { 75 tons 16 cwt.*†
78 tons 13 cwt.
74 tons 2 cwt.‡
Tender { 43 tons 2 cwt. (63922–46)
52 tons (63947–87).

Pressure: 180 lb. Su.
Cyls.: (3) 18½" × 26".
Driving Wheels: 4' 8".
T.E.: 36,740 lb.
Walschaerts valve gear and derived motion. P.V.

63922*	63939†	63956	63973
63923*	63940†	63957	63974
63924‡	63941†	63958	63975
63925*	63942†	63959	63976
63926*	63943†	63960	63977
63927*	63944†	63961	63978
63928*	63945‡	63962‡	63979
63929*	63946†	63963	63980
63930*	63947	63964	63981
63931*	63948	63965	63982‡
63932‡	63949‡	63966‡	63983‡
63933‡	63950‡	63967	63984
63934‡	63951	63968	63985
63935‡	63952	63969	63986
63936†	63953	63970	63987
63937†	63954	63971	
63938†	63955	63972	

Total

Class O2/1	9	Class O2/3	35
Class O2/2	11	Class O2/4	11

2-8-0   8F   Class O2

O2 1* Introduced 1921. Development of experimental Gresley G.N. 3-cyl. loco. (L.N.E.R. 3921). Subsequently rebuilt with side-window cab, and reduced boiler mountings.

O2/2† Introduced 1924. Development of O2/1 with detail differences.

0-6-0   2P3F   Class J6

Introduced 1911. Gresley G.N. design.
Weight: Loco. 50 tons 10 cwt.
Tender 43 tons 2 cwt.
Pressure: 170 lb. Su.
Cyls.: 19" × 26".
Driving Wheels: 5' 2".
T.E.: 21,875 lb.
P.V.

64170	64197	64228	64256
64171	64198	64229	64257
64172	64201	64231	64258
64173	64202	64232	64259
64174	64203	64233	64260
64175	64205	64234	64261
64176	64206	64235	64262
64177	64207	64236	64265
64178	64208	64237	64266
64179	64209	64238	64268
64180	64210	64239	64269
64181	64213	64240	64270
64182	64214	64241	64271
64183	64215	64245	64272
64184	64216	64246	64273
64185	64217	64247	64274
64188	64218	64248	64276
64189	64219	64249	64277
64190	64222	64250	64278
64191	64223	64251	64279
64192	64224	64253	
64196	64226	64254	

Total 86

64280	64329	64377	64420*
64281	64331	64379*	64421
64283*	64332*	64381	64422
64284*	64333*	64382	64423
64287	64336	64383	64425
64288	64337	64384	64427*
64292	64338	64385	64428
64294	64341	64386*	64429
64297	64343	64387	64430
64298	64345	64388	64433
64302	64346*	64389	64434
64304*	64348	64392	64435
64305	64351	64393*	64437
64306	64352*	64394*	64438
64308	64354*	64395*	64439*
64310	64355	64396	64440
64311	64357	64397	64441*
64313	64359*	64402*	64442*
64314*	64361	64403	64443
64315	64362*	64404	64444
64316*	64363	64405	64445
64317*	64364*	64406*	64446
64318*	64365	64407	64447
64319	64368	64409	64450*
64321	64371	64416	64451
64324*	64373*	64417*	64452
64325	64375*	64418*	
64328	64376	64419	

Total
Class J11/3 33
Class J11 (other parts) 77

0-6-0   2P3F   Class J11

Introduced 1901. Robinson G.C. design. Parts 1 and 4 have 3,250-gallon tenders; Parts 2 and 5, 4,000-gallon. Parts 1 and 2 have high boiler mountings; Parts 4 and 5 low. All of Parts 4 and 5 are superheated, and some of Parts 1 and 2. There are frequent changes between parts.

J11/3* Introduced 1942. Rebuilt with long-travel piston valves and boiler higher pitched.

Weight: Loco. $\begin{cases} 51 \text{ tons } 19 \text{ cwt. (Sat.)} \\ 52 \text{ tons } 2 \text{ cwt. (Su.)} \\ 53 \text{ tons } 6 \text{ cwt.*} \end{cases}$

Tender $\begin{cases} 44 \text{ tons } 3 \text{ cwt. (3,250 gall.)} \\ 48 \text{ tons } 6 \text{ cwt. (4,000 gall.)} \end{cases}$

Pressure: 180 lb. SS.
Cyls.: $18\frac{1}{2}'' \times 26''$.
Driving Wheels: 5' 2".
T.E.: 21,960 lb.

0-6-0   3F   Class J35

J35/5* Introduced 1906. Reid N.B. design with piston valves.

J35/4 Introduced 1908. Slide valves. (Parts 1, 2 and 3 were variations of Parts 4 and 5 before superheating.)

Weight: Loco. $\begin{cases} 51 \text{ tons.*} \\ 50 \text{ tons } 15 \text{ cwt.} \end{cases}$

Tender $\begin{cases} 38 \text{ tons } 1 \text{ cwt.*} \\ 37 \text{ tons } 15 \text{ cwt.} \end{cases}$

Pressure: 180 lb. Su.
Cyls.: $18\frac{1}{4}'' \times 26''$.
Driving Wheels: 5' 0".
T.E.: 22,080 lb.

143

Class J17 0-6-0 No. 65526   [R. C. Riley

Class J19 0-6-0 No. 64671   [R. C. Riley

Class J20/I 0-6-0 No. 64691   [K. R. Pirt

64460*	64482	64500	64519
64461*	64483	64501	64520
64462*	64484	64502	64521
64463*	64485	64504	64522
64466*	64486	64505	64523
64468*	64487	64506	64524
64470*	64488	64507	64525
64471*	64489	64509	64527
64472*	64490	64510	64528
64473*	64491	64511	64529
64474*	64492	64512	64530
64475*	64493	64513	64531
64476*	64494	64514	64532
64477*	64496	64515	64533
64478	64497	64516	64534
64479	64498	64517	64535
64480	64499	64518	

Total
Class J35/4 53   Class J35/5 14

0-6-0   5F   Class J37

Introduced 1914. Reid N.B. design.
Superheated development of J35.
Weight: Loco. 54 tons 14 cwt.
Tender 40 tons 19 cwt.
Pressure: 180 lb. Su.
Cyls.: $19\frac{1}{2}'' \times 26''$.
Driving Wheels: 5' 0".
T.E.: 25,210 lb.
P.V.

64536	64552	64568	64584
64537	64553	64569	64585
64538	64554	64570	64586
64539	64555	64571	64587
64540	64556	64572	64588
64541	64557	64573	64589
64542	64558	64574	64590
64543	64559	64575	64591
64544	64560	64576	64592
64545	64561	64577	64593
64546	64562	64578	64594
64547	64563	64579	64595
64548	64564	64580	64596
64549	64565	64581	64597
64550	64566	64582	64598
64551	64567	64583	64599

64600	64610	64620	64630
64601	64611	64621	64631
64602	64612	64622	64632
64603	64613	64623	64633
64604	64614	64624	64634
64605	64615	64625	64635
64606	64616	64626	64636
64607	64617	64627	64637
64608	64618	64628	64638
64609	64619	64629	64639

Total 104

0-6-0   3P5F   Class J19

Introduced 1912. S. Holden G.E.
design rebuilt with round-topped
firebox from 1934.
*Rebuilt with 19" cyls. and 180 lb.
pressure.
†Rebuilt with 19" cyls. and 160 lb.
pressure.
Weight: Loco. 50 tons 7 cwt.
Tender 38 tons 5 cwt.
Pressure: $\begin{cases} 170 \text{ lb. Su.} \\ 180 \text{ lb. Su.*} \\ 160 \text{ lb. Su.†} \end{cases}$
Cyls.: $\begin{cases} 20'' \times 26''. \\ 19'' \times 26''.*† \end{cases}$
Driving Wheels: 4' 11".
T.E.: $\begin{cases} 27,430 \text{ lb.} \\ 26,215 \text{ lb.*} \\ 23,300 \text{ lb.†} \end{cases}$

64640	64649	64658	64667
64641	64650	64659	64668
64642	64651	64660	64669
64643	64652	64661	64670
64644	64653	64662	64671*
64645	64654	64663	64672†
64646	64655	64664*	64673
64647	64656	64665	64674
64648	64657	64666	

Total 35

0-6-0   5F   Class J20

J20/1 Introduced 1943. Hill G.E.
design with Belpaire firebox (introduced 1920) rebuilt with B12/1-type
boiler with round-topped firebox.
Weight: Loco. 54 tons 15 cwt.
Tender 38 tons 5 cwt.

64675-64963

Pressure: 180 lb. Su.
Cyls.: 20″ × 28″.
Driving Wheels: 4′ 11″.
T.E.: 29,045 lb.
P.V.

64675	64682	64689	64696
64676	64683	64690	64697
64677	64684	64691	64698
64678	64685	64692	64699
64679	64686	64693	
64680	64687	64694	
64681	64688	64695	

Total 25

0-6-0 4P5F Class J39

Introduced 1926. Gresley design.
J39/1 Standard 3,500-gallon tender.
J39/2* Standard 4,200-gallon tender.
J39/3† Various N.E. tenders (3,940-gallon on 64843-5, 4,125-gallon on 64855-9).
Weight: Loco. 57 tons 17 cwt.
Tender { 44 tons 4 cwt.
52 tons 13 cwt.*
and others.
Pressure: 180 lb. Su.
Cyls.: 20″ × 26″.
Driving Wheels: 5′ 2″.
T.E.: 25,665 lb.
P.V.

64700†	64719	64738	64757
64701	64720	64739	64758
64702	64721	64740	64759
64703	64722	64741	64760
64704	64723	64742	64761
64705	64724	64743	64762
64706	64725	64744	64763
64707	64726	64745	64764
64708	64727	64746	64765
64709	64728	64747	64766
64710	64729	64748	64767
64711	64730	64749	64768
64712	64731	64750	64769
64713	64732	64751	64770
64714	64733	64752	64771
64715	64734	64753	64772
64716	64735	64754	64773
64717	64736	64755	64774
64718	64737	64756	64775

64776	64823	64870	64917*
64777	64824	64871	64918*
64778	64825	64872*	64919*
64779	64826	64873*	64920*
64780	64827	64874*	64921*
64781	64828	64875*	64922*
64782	64829	64876*	64923*
64783	64830	64877*	64924*
64784*	64831	64878*	64925*
64785*	64832	64879*	64926†
64786*	64833	64880*	64927*
64787*	64834	64881*	64928*
64788*	64835	64882*	64929*
64789*	64836	64883*	64930*
64790*	64837	64884*	64931*
64791*	64838*	64885*	64932*
64792*	64839*	64886*	64933
64793*	64840*	64887*	64934
64794*	64841*	64888*	64935
64795*	64842*	64889*	64936
64796	64843†	64890*	64937
64797	64844†	64891*	64938
64798	64845†	64892*	64939
64799	64846	64893*	64940
64800	64847	64894*	64941
64801	64848	64895*	64942
64802	64849	64896*	64943
64803	64850	64897*	64944
64804	64851	64898*	64945*
64805	64852	64899*	64946*
64806	64853	64900*	64947*
64807	64854	64901*	64948*
64808	64855†	64902*	64949*
64809	64856†	64903*	64950*
64810	64857†	64904*	64951*
64811	64858†	64905*	64952*
64812	64859†	64906*	64953*
64813	64860	64907*	64954*
64814	64861	64908*	64955*
64815	64862	64909*	64956*
64816	64863	64910*	64957*
64817	64864	64911*	64958*
64818	64865	64912*	64959*
64819	64866	64913*	64960*
64820*	64867	64914*	64961*
64821*	64868	64915*	64962*
64822*	64869	64916*	64963*

64964*	64971†	64978†	64985†
64965*	64972†	64979†	64986†
64966*	64973†	64980†	64987†
64967*	64974†	64981†	64988†
64968*	64975†	64982†	
64969*	64976†	64983†	
64970*	64977†	64984†	

Total

**Class J39/1 155   Class J39/3 28
Class J39/2 106**

0-6-0   2F   Class J21

Introduced 1886. T. W. Worsdell N.E.
design. Majority built as 2-cyl.
compounds and later rebuilt as
simple locos.
*Rebuilt with superheater, Stephenson
valve gear and piston valves.
†Rebuilt with superheater and piston
valves, superheater subsequently
removed.

Weight: Loco. $\begin{cases} 43 \text{ tons } 15 \text{ cwt.}^* \\ 42 \text{ tons } 9 \text{ cwt.}† \end{cases}$
         Tender 36 tons 19 cwt.
Pressure: 160 lb. SS.
Cyls.: 19″ × 24″.
Driving Wheels: 5′ 1¼″.
T.E.: 19,240 lb.

65033†	65064*	65099†	65110†
65039†	65070†	65103*	65117†

Total   8

0-6-0   2F   Class J10

J10/4* Introduced 1896. Pollitt de-
velopment of J10/2 with larger
bearings and larger tender.
J10/6 Introduced 1901. Robinson
locos. with larger bearings and small
tender.
Weight: Loco.   41 tons 6 cwt.
         Tender $\begin{cases} 37 \text{ tons } 6 \text{ cwt.} \\ 43 \text{ tons.}^* \end{cases}$
Pressure: 160 lb.
Cyls.: 18″ × 26″.
Driving Wheels: 5′ 1″.
T.E.: 18,780 lb.

65131	65134*	65140*	65145*
65133*	65138*	65142*	65146*

65157*	65169*	65187	65199
65158*	65177	65192	65208
65166*	65178*	65194	65209
65167*	65184	65198	

Total

Class J10/4 13   Class J10/6 10

0-6-0   2F   Class J36

Introduced 1388. Holmes N.B. design.
Weight: Loco.   41 tons 19 cwt.
         Tender 33 tons 9 cwt.
Pressure: 165 lb.
Cyls.: 18½″ × 26″.
Driving Wheels: 5′ 0″.
T.E.: 19,690 lb.

65210	65211	65214
65216	Byng	
65217	French	
65218		
65221		
65222	Somme	
65224	Mons	
65227		
65228		
65229		
65230		
65232		
65233	Plumer	
65234		
65235	Gough	
65237		
65239		
65241		
65243	Maude	
65246		
65247		
65249		
65251		
65252		
65253	Joffre	
65257		
65258		
65259		
65260		

65261			
65265			
65266			
65267			
65268	Allenby		
65273	65282	65295	65305
65275	65285	65296	65306
65276	65287	65297	65307
65277	65288	65300	65309
65280	65290	65303	65310
65281	65293	65304	
65311	Haig		
65312	65320	65331	65342
65313	65321	65333	65343
65315	65323	65334	65344
65316	65325	65335	65345
65317	65327	65338	65346
65318	65329	65339	
65319	65330	65341	

Total 86

0-6-0   1P2F   Class J15

Introduced 1883. Worsdell G.E. design, modified by J. Holden.
*Fitted with side-window cab for Colne Valley line.
Weight: Loco. 37 tons 2 cwt.
Tender 30 tons 13 cwt.
Pressure: 160 lb.
Cyls:. $17\frac{1}{2}'' \times 24''$.
Driving Wheels: 4′ 11″.
T.E.: 16,940 lb.

65361	65444	65456	65469
65388	65445	65457	65470
65389	65446	65453	65471
65390	65447	65459	65472
65391*	65448	65460	65473
65405*	65449	65461	65474
65420	65450	65462	65475
65424*	65451	65463	65476
65434	65452	65464	65477
65440	65453	65465	65478
65441	65454	65467	65479
65443	65455	65463	

Total 47

0-6-0   2P4F   Class J17

Introduced 1901. J. Holden G.E. design. Many rebuilt from round-top firebox J16, int oduced 1900.
*Fitted with small tender.
Weight: Loco.   45 tons 8 cwt.
Tender $\begin{cases} 38 \text{ tons } 5 \text{ cwt.} \\ 30 \text{ tons } 12 \text{ cwt.*} \end{cases}$
Pressure: 180 lb. Su.
Cyls.: $19'' \times 26''$.
Driving Wheels: 4′ 11″.
T.E.: 24,340 lb.

65502*	65526	65549	65567
65503*	65527	65551	65568
65504*	65528*	65553	65570
65505	65530	65554	65573
65506*	65531	65555	65576
65507*	65532	65556	65577
65511*	65533	65557	65578
65512*	65536	65558	65580
65513*	65538	65559	65581
65514*	65539	65560	65582
65515*	65540	65561	65583
65518*	65541	65562	65584
65519*	65542	65563	65586
65520	65544	65564	65587
65521	65545	65565	65588
65522	65546	65566	65589
65525	65548		

Total 66

0-6-0   3F   Class J25

Introduced 1898. W. Worsdell N.E. design.
*Original design, saturated, with slide valves.
†Rebuilt with superheater and piston valves.
‡Rebuilt with piston valves, superheater removed.
Weight: Loco. $\begin{cases} 39 \text{ tons } 11 \text{ cwt.*} \\ 41 \text{ tons } 14 \text{ cwt.†} \\ 40 \text{ tons } 17 \text{ cwt.‡} \end{cases}$
Tender 36 tons 19 cwt.
Pressure: 160 lb. SS.
Cyls.: $18\frac{1}{2}'' \times 26''$.
Driving Wheels: 4′ 7½″.
T.E.: 21,905 lb.

65645†	65655*	65657*	65663*
65648*	65656*	65662†	65666*

65670*	65693*	65702‡	65717†
65675*	65695*	65706†	65720*
65677‡	65696*	65712*	65726*
65685*	65697*	65713*	65727*
65687*	65698*	65714*	65728*
65691*	65700*		

Total 30

0-6-0 5F Class J26

Introduced 1904. W. Worsdell N.E. design.
Weight: Loco.   46 tons 16 cwt.
　　　　Tender 36 tons 19 cwt.
Pressure: 180 lb.
Cyls.: 18½″ × 26″.
Driving Wheels: 4′ 7¼″.
T.E.: 24,640 lb.

65730	65742	65756	65769
65731	65743	65757	65770
65732	65744	65758	65771
65733	65745	65759	65772
65734	65747	65760	65773
65735	65748	65761	65774
65736	65749	65762	65775
65737	65750	65763	65776
65738	65751	65764	65777
65739	65753	65766	65778
65740	65755	65768	65779
65741			

Total 45

0-6-0 5F Class J27

Introduced 1906. W. Worsdell N.E. design developed from J26.
*Introduced 1921. Raven locos. Super-heated, with piston valves.
†Introduced 1943. Piston valves, super-heater removed.
Weight: Loco. { 47 tons Sat.
　　　　　　{ 49 tons 10 cwt. Su.
　　　　Tender 36 tons 19 cwt.
Pressure: 180 lb. SS.
Cyls.: 18½″ × 26″.
Driving Wheels: 4′ 7¼″.
T.E.: 24,640 lb.

65780	65809	65838	65867†
65781	65810	65839	65868†
65782	65811	65840	65869†
65783	65812	65841	65870†
65784	65813	65842	65871*
65785	65814	65843	65872†
65786	65815	65844	65873†
65787	65816	65845	65874*
65788	65817	65846	65875†
65789	65818	65847	65876†
65790	65819	65848	65877†
65791	65820	65849	65878*
65792	65821	65850	65879†
65793	65822	65851	65880*
65794	65823	65852	65881*
65795	65824	65853	65882†
65796	65825	65854	65883*
65797	65826	65855	65884†
65798	65827	65856	65885†
65799	65828	65857	65886*
65800	65829	65858	65887*
65801	65830	65859	65888†
65802	65831	65860†	65889†
65803	65832	65861†	65890*
65804	65833	65862†	65891†
65805	65834	65863*	65893*
65806	65835	65864†	65894*
65807	65836	65865†	
65808	65837	65866*	

Total 115

0-6-0 6F Class J38

Introduced 1926. Gresley design. Predecessor of J39, with 4′ 8″ wheels, boiler 6″ longer than J39 and smoke-box 6″ shorter.
*Rebuilt with J39 boiler.
Weight: Loco.   58 tons 19 cwt.
　　　　Tender 44 tons 4 cwt.
Pressure: 180 lb. Su.
Cyls.: 20″ × 26″.
Driving Wheels: 4′ 8″.
T.E.: 28,415 lb.
P.V.

65900	65903*	65906*	65909
65901	65904	65907	65910
65902	65905	65908*	65911

149

65912	65918*	65924	65930
65913	65919	65925	65931
65914	65920	65926*	65932
65915	65921	65927*	65933
65916	65922	65928	65934
65917*	65923	65929	

Total 35

0-4-4T   IMT   Class G5

Introduced 1894. W. Worsdell N.E. design.
*Push-and-pull fitted.
Weight: 54 tons 4 cwt.
Pressure: 160 lb.
Cyls.: 18″ × 24″.
Driving Wheels: 5′ 1¼″.
T.E.: 17,265 lb.

67246	67263	67305*	67325
67248	67274	67311*	67329
67253*	67280*	67315	67341
67261*	67281*	67320	67342
67262	67297*	67323*	

Total 19

4-4-2T   IMT   Class C12

Introduced 1898. Ivatt G.N. design.
*Boiler pressure reduced to 170 lb.
†Push-and-pull fitted.
Weight: 62 tons 6 cwt.
Pressure: $\begin{cases} 175 \text{ lb.} \\ 170 \text{ lb.*†} \end{cases}$
Cyls.: 18″ × 26″.
Driving Wheels: 5′ 8″.
T.E.: $\begin{cases} 18,425 \text{ lb.} \\ 17,900 \text{ lb.*†} \end{cases}$

67352	67363*†	67397	67398*

Total 4

4-4-2T   2P1F   Class C13

Introduced 1903. Robinson G.C. design, later rebuilt with superheater.
*Push-and-pull fitted.
Weight: 66 tons 13 cwt.
Pressure: 160 lb. Su.
Cyls.: 18″ × 26″.
Driving Wheels: 5′ 7″.
T.E.: 17,100 lb.

67416*	67418*	67421*	67439
67417*	67420*	67424	

Total 7

4-4-2T   2P1F   Class C14

Introduced 1907. Robinson G.C. design, later superheated, development of C13, with detail differences.
Weight: 71 tons.
Pressure: 160 lb. Su.
Cyls.: 18″ × 26″.
Driving Wheels: 5′ 7″.
T.E.: 17,100 lb.

67445	67447	67448	67450

Total 4

4-4-2T   2P   Class C15

Introduced 1911. Reid N.B. design. Push-and-pull fitted.
Weight: 68 tons 15 cwt.
Pressure: 175 lb.
Cyls.: 18″ × 26″.
Driving Wheels: 5′ 9″.
T.E.: 18,160 lb.

67460	67474

Total 2

4-4-2T   2P   Class C16

Introduced 1915. Reid N.B. design, superheated development of C15.
Weight: 72 tons 10 cwt.
Pressure: 165 lb. Su.
Cyls.: 19″ × 26″.
Driving Wheels: 5′ 9″.
T.E.: 19,080 lb.
P.V.

67482	67487	67491	67497
67484	67488	67492	67500
67485	67489	67494	67501
	67490	67496	67502

Total 16

Classes
2-6-2T   V1 (3MT)   V1 & V3
V3 (4MT)

V1 Introduced 1930. Gresley design.
V3* Introduced 1939. Development of V1 with higher pressure (locos. numbered below 67682 rebuilt from V1).
Weight: $\begin{cases} 84 \text{ tons.} \\ 86 \text{ tons 16 cwt.*} \end{cases}$
Pressure: $\begin{cases} 180 \text{ lb. Su.} \\ 200 \text{ lb. Su.*} \end{cases}$
Cyls.: (3) 16″ × 26″.
Driving Wheels: 5′ 8″.
T.E.: $\begin{cases} 22,465 \text{ lb.} \\ 24,960 \text{ lb.*} \end{cases}$
Walschaerts valve gear and derived motion. P.V.

67600*	67623	67646*	67669*	67713	67735	67757	67779†
67601	67624*	67647	67670*	67714	67736	67758	67780
67602	67625*	67648	67671	67715	67737	67759	67781
67603	67626*	67649	67672*	67716	67738	67760	67782
67604*	67627*	67650	67673	67717	67739	67761*	67783
67605*	67628*	67651*	67674*	67718	67740	67762	67784
67606*	67629	67652*	67675*	67719	67741	67763	67785
67607*	67630	67653*	67676	67720	67742	67764	67786
67608	67631	67654*	67677	67721	67743	67765	67787
67609*	67632*	67655	67678	67722	67744	67766	67788
67610	67633	67656*	67679*	67723	67745	67767	67789
67611*	67634*	67657*	67680	67724	67746	67768	67790
67612*	67635	67658	67681*	67725	67747*	67769	67791
67613	67636*	67659	67682*	67726	67748	67770†	67792
67614	67637	67660*	67683*	67727	67749	67771†	67793
67615*	67638*	67661	67684*	67728	67750	67772†	67794
67616	67639	67662*	67685*	67729	67751	67773	67795
67617*	67640	67663*	67686*	67730	67752	67774	67796
67618	67641	67664	67687*	67731	67753	67775	67797
67619*	67642	67665	67688*	67732	67754	67776†	67798*
67620*	67643*	67666	67689*	67733	67755	67777	67799
67621	67644*	67667	67690*	67734	67756	67778	67800
67622	67645	67668*	67691*				

Total

Class V1 41   **Class V3 51**

Total 100

2-6-4T   4MT   Class L1

Introduced 1945. Thompson design.
*Introduced 1954. Boiler pressure reduced to 200 lb.
†Introduced 1954. Cylinder diameter reduced.
Weight: 89 tons 9 cwt.
Pressure: { 225 lb.
{ 200 lb.*
Cyls.: { (O) 20″ × 26″.
{ (O) 18¾″ × 26″.†
Driving Wheels: 5′ 2″.
T.E.: { 32,080 lb.
{ 28,515 lb.*
{ 28,180 lb.†
Walschaerts valve gear. P.V.

67701	67704	67707	67710
67702	67705	67708	67711
67703	67706	67709	67712

0-6-0ST   4F   Class J94

Introduced 1943. Riddles M.o.S. design.
(Bought from M.o.S., 1946.)
Weight: 48 tons 5 cwt.
Pressure: 170 lb.
Cyls.: 18″ × 26″.
Driving Wheels: 4′ 3″.
T.E.: 23,870 lb.

68006	68020	68034	68048
68007	68021	68035	68049
68008	68022	68036	68050
68009	68023	68037	68051
68010	68024	68038	68052
68011	68025	68039	68053
68012	68026	68040	68054
68013	68027	68041	68055
68014	68028	68042	68056
68015	68029	68043	68057
68016	68030	68044	68058
68017	68031	68045	68059
68018	68032	68046	68060
68019	68033	68047	68061

68062-68316

68062	68067	68072	68077
68063	68068	68073	68078
68064	68069	68074	68079
68065	68070	68075	68080
68066	68071	68076	

Total 75

0-4-0ST   OF   Class Y9

Introduced 1882. Holmes N.B. design.
*Locos. running permanently attached to wooden tender.
Weight: Loco. 27 tons 16 cwt.
   Tender 6 tons.*
Pressure: 130 lb.
Cyls.: (O) 14″ × 20″.
Driving Wheels: 3′ 8″.
T.E.: 9,845 lb.

68095	68102*	68114*	68119*
68097*	68104	68117*	68123
68100*	68108*	68118*	68124
68101	68110		

Total 14

0-4-0T   Unclass.   Class Y1

Sentinel Wagon Works design. Single-speed Geared Sentinel locomotives. The parts of this class differ in details, including size of boiler and fuel capacity.
Y1/1* Introduced 1925.
Y1/2† Introduced 1927.
§Sprocket gear ratio 9:25 (remainder 11:25).
Weight: { 20 tons 17 cwt.*
    19 tons 16 cwt.†
    19 tons 7 cwt.‡
Pressure: 275 lb. Su.
Cyls.: 6¾″ × 9″.
Driving Wheels: 2′ 6″.
T.E.: { 7,260 lb.*†‡
   8,870 lb.§
Poppet valves.
 (See also E.R. Departmental Locos.)

68138† 68150†§

Total
Class Y1/1 3 Class Y1/2 3

0-4-2T   OF   Class Z4

Introduced 1915. Manning-Wardle design for G.N. of S.
Weight: 25 tons 17 cwt.
Pressure: 160 lb.
Cyls.: (O) 13″ × 20″.
Driving Wheels: 3′ 6″.
T.E.: 10,945 lb.

68190 68191   **Total 2**

0-4-2T   OF   Class Z5

Introduced 1915. Manning-Wardle design for G.N. of S.
Weight: 30 tons 18 cwt.
Pressure: 160 lb.
Cyls.: (O) 14″ × 20″.
Driving Wheels: 4′ 0″.
T.E.: 11,105 lb.

68192   **Total 1**

0-6-0T   Unclass.   Class J71

Introduced 1886. T. W. Worsdell N.E. design.
*†Altered cylinder dimensions.
Weight: 37 tons 12 cwt.
Pressure: 140 lb.
Driving Wheels 4′ 7¼″.
Cyls.: { 16″ × 22″.
   16¾″ × 22″.*
   18″ × 22″.†
T.E.: { 12,130 lb.
   13,300 lb.*
   15,355 lb.†

68230*	68254	68269	68295
68233	68260	68272	68305*
68235	68262	68275	68309*
68245	68263	68278	68312†
68246*	68264	68283	68314
68250*	68265	68290	68316*
68251			

Total 25

0-6-0T   OF   Class J88

Introduced 1904. Reid N.B. design with short wheelbase.
Weight: 38 tons 14 cwt.

DEPARTMENTAL LOCOMOTIVES

(Former running no. in brackets)

0-6-0ST 3F Class J52/2

2 (68858)   9 (68840)

0-4-0T Un-class. Class Y3

Introduced 1927.
Sentinel Wagon Works design.
Two-speed Geared Sentinel locos.
Sprocket gear ratio 15:19.
Weight: 20 tons 16 cwt.
Pressure: 275 lb. Su.
Cyls.: 6¾″ × 9″.
Driving Wheels: 2′ 6″.
T.E.: { Low Gear: 15,960 lb.
{ High Gear: 5,960 lb.
Poppet valves.

3 (68181)	38 (68168)
5 (68165)	40 (68173)
7 (68166)	41 (68177)
8 (68183)	42 (68178)
21 (68162)	57 (68160)
	Total 10

0-4-0T Un-class. Class Y1/1

4 (68132)	39 (68131)
6 (68133)	53 (68152)

0-6-0T 2F Class J66

Introduced 1886. J. Holden G.E.
design.
Weight: 40 tons 6 cwt.
Pressure: 160 lb.
Cyls.: 16½″ × 22″.
Driving Wheels: 4′ 0″.
T.E.: 16,970 lb.

31 (68382)	36 (68378)
32 (68370)	**Total 3**

0-4-0T Dock Tank Class Y4

Introduced 1913. Hill G.E. design.
Weight: 38 tons 1 cwt.
Pressure: 180 lb.
Cyls.: (O) 17″ × 20″.
Driving Wheels: 3′ 10″.
T.E.: 19,225 lb.
Walschaerts valve gear.

33 (68129)   **Total 1**

0-4-0 Diesel Mechanical

52 (11104)   **Total 1**

0-4-0T Un-class. Class Y1/2

54 (68153)

0-4-0T Dock Tank Class Y8

Introduced 1890. T. W. Worsdell
N.E. design.
Weight: 15 tons 10 cwt.
Pressure: 140 lb.
Cyls.: 11″ × 15″.
Driving Wheels: 3′ 0″.
T.E.: 6,000 lb.

55 (68091)   **Total 1**

0-4-0 Diesel Mechanical

56

0-6-0 Diesel

Introduced 1958
91   92

NOTE. (For details of Departmental diesel locomotives, see
ABC British Railways Diesels or Diesel Section of
combined volume.)

68320-68563

Pressure: 130 lb.
Cyls.: (O) 15" × 22".
Driving Wheels: 3' 9".
T.E.: 12,155 lb.

68320	68331	68342	68348
68322	68332	68343	68349
68325	68334	68344	68350
68326	68335	68345	68352
68327	68336	68346	68353
68329	68338	68347	68354
68330	68339		

Total 26

0-6-0T 3F Class J73

Introduced 1891. W. Worsdell N.E. design.
Weight: 46 tons 15 cwt.
Pressure: 160 lb.
Cyls.: 19" × 24".
Driving Wheels: 4' 7¼".
T.E.: 21,320 lb.

68355	68360	68363	68364
68359	68361		

Total 6

0-6-0T 2F Class J77

Introduced 1899. W. Worsdell N.E. rebuild of Fletcher 0-4-4T originally built 1874-84.
Some engines of this class have square-cornered and some round-cornered cab roofs.
Weight: 43 tons.
Pressure: 160 lb.
Cyls.: 17" × 22".
Driving Wheels: 4' 1¼".
T.E.: 17,560 lb.

68392	68408	68414	68431
68405	68409	68425	68435
68406	68410		

Total 10

0-6-0T 2F Class J83

Introduced 1900. Holmes N.B. design.
Weight: 45 tons 5 cwt.
Pressure: 150 lb.
Cyls.: 17" × 26".
Driving Wheels: 4' 6".
T.E.: 17,745 lb.

68442	68453	68463	68472
68443	68454	68466	68477
68444	68456	68467	68478
68445	68457	68468	68479
68447	68458	68470	68480
68448	68459	68471	68481
68449	68460		

Total 26

Classes
0-6-0T 2F J67 & J69

J67/1* Introduced 1890. J. Holden G.E. design with 160 lb. pressure.

J67/1† Introduced 1902. Development of J67 with 180 lb. pressure, larger tanks and larger firebox (some rebuilt from J67).

J69/2§ Introduced 1950. J67/1 rebuilt with 180 lb. boiler and larger firebox.

Weight: { 40 tons.*
         { 40 tons 9 cwt.†§
Pressure: { 160 lb.*
          { 180 lb.†§
Cyls.: 16½" × 22".
Driving Wheels: 4' 0".
T.E.: { 16,970 lb.*
      { 19,090 lb.†§

68497†	68510§	68532†	68552†
68498§	68513§	68535†	68553†
68499†	68520§	68538†	68554†
68500†	68522§	68542†	68556†
68501†	68524†	68543†	68557†
68502†	68526†	68545†	68558†
68507†	68528†	68549†	68560†
68508†	68530†	68550†	68563†

68565†	68578†	68602†	68625†
68566†	68579†	68608*	68626†
68569†	68581†	68609†	68629†
68570†	68587†	68612†	68630†
68571†	68591†	68613†	68633†
68573†	68596†	68616*	68635†
68574†	68599†	68619†	68636†
68575†	68600†	68621†	
68577†	68601†	68623†	

Total

Class J67/1 2   Class J69/1 59

Class J69/2 5

0-6-0T   2F   Class J68

Introduced 1912. Hill G.E. development of J69 with side-window cab.
Weight: 42 tons 9 cwt.
Pressure: 180 lb.
Cyls.: $16\frac{1}{2}'' \times 22''$.
Driving Wheels: 4' 0".
T.E.: 19,090 lb.

68638	68644	68650	68660
68639	68645	68652	68661
68640	68646	68655	68663
68641	68647	68655	68664
68642	68648	68656	68665
68643	68649	68658	

Total 23

0-6-0T   2F   Class J72

Introduced 1898. W. Worsdell N.E. design.
*Altered cylinder dimensions.
Weight: 38 tons 12 cwt.
Pressure: 140 lb.

Cyls.: $\begin{cases} 17'' \times 24''. \\ 18'' \times 24''.* \end{cases}$
Driving Wheels: 4' 1¼".
T.E.: $\begin{cases} 16,760 \text{ lb.} \\ 18,790 \text{ lb.*} \end{cases}$

68670	68692	68714	68737
68671	68693	68715	68738
68672	68694	68716	68739
68673	68695	68717	68740
68674	68696	68719	68741
68675	68697	68720	68742
68676	68699	68721	68743
68677	68699	68722	68744
68678	68700	68723	68745
68679	68701	68724	68746
68680	68702	68725	68747
68681	68703	68726	68748
68682	68704	68727	68749
68683	68705	68728	68750
68684	68706	68729	68751
68685*	68707	68730	68752
68686	68708	68731	68753
68687	68709	68732	68754
68688	68710	68733	
68689	68711	68734	
68690	68712	68735	
68691	68713	68736	

(*Class continued with No.* 69001)

0-6-0ST   3F   Class J52

J52/2 Introduced 1897. Ivatt G.N. saddletank with domed boiler.
Weight: 51 tons 14 cwt.
Pressure: 170 lb.
Cyls.: $18'' \times 26''$.
Driving Wheels: 4' 8".
T.E.: 21,735 lb.

(See also E.R. Departmental Locos.)

68824	68837	68862	68869
68831	68846	68866	68875
68834			

Total 11

0-6-0T 4F Class J50

J50/2* Introduced 1922. Gresley G.N. design (68900–19 rebuilt from smaller J51, built 1915–22).

J50/3† Introduced 1926. Post-grouping development with detail differences.

J50/1‡ Introduced 1929. Rebuilt from smaller J51, built 1913–14.

J50/4§ Introduced 1937. Development of J50/3 with larger bunker.

Weight: $\begin{cases} 57 \text{ tons.*} \\ 56 \text{ tons 6 cwt.‡} \\ 58 \text{ tons 3 cwt.†§} \end{cases}$

Pressure: 175 lb.

Cyls.: $18\frac{1}{2}'' \times 26''$.

Driving Wheels: 4' 8".

T.E.: 23,635 lb.

68890‡	68916*	68942†	68967†
68891‡	68917*	68943†	68968†
68892‡	68918*	68944†	68969†
68893‡	68919*	68945†	68970†
68894‡	68920*	68946†	68971†
68895‡	68921*	68947†	68972†
68896‡	68922*	68948†	68973†
68897‡	68923*	68949†	68974†
68898‡	68924*	68950†	68975†
68899‡	68925*	68951†	68976†
68900‡	68926*	68952†	68977†
68901*	68927*	68953†	68978§
68902*	68928*	68954†	68979§
68903*	68929*	68955†	68980§
68904*	68930*	68956†	68981§
68905*	68931*	68957†	68982§
68906*	68932*	68958†	68983§
68907*	68933*	68959†	68984§
68908*	68934*	68960†	68985§
68909*	68935*	68961†	68986§
68910*	68936*	68962†	68987§
68911*	68937*	68963†	68988§
68912*	68938*	68964†	68989§
68913*	68939*	68965†	68990§
68914*	68940†	68966†	68991§
68915*	68941†		

Total

Class J50/1 10	Class J50/3 38
Class J50/2 40	Class J50/4 14

0-6-0T 2F Class J72

(Continued from 68754)

69001	69008	69015	69022
69002	69009	69016	69023
69003	69010	69017	69024
69004	69011	69018	69025
69005	69012	69019	69026
69006	69013	69020	69027
69007	69014	69021	69028

Total 112

0-6-2T 3F Class N10

Introduced 1902. W. Worsdell N.E. design.

Weight: 57 tons 14 cwt.

Pressure: 160 lb.

Cyls.: $18\frac{1}{2}'' \times 26''$.

Driving Wheels: 4' 7¼".

T.E.: 21,905 lb.

69092	69101	69105	69109
69097	69102		

Total 6

0-6-2T 3MT Class N15

N15/2* Introduced 1910. Reid N.B. design developed from N14. Cowlairs Incline banking locos.

N15/1 Introduced 1910. Development of N15/2 with smaller bunker for normal duties.

Weight: $\begin{cases} 62 \text{ tons } 1 \text{ cwt.*} \\ 60 \text{ tons 18 cwt.} \end{cases}$

Pressure: 175 lb.

Cyls.: $18'' \times 26''$.

Driving Wheels: 4' 6".

T.E.: 23,205 lb.

69126*	69129*	69133	69136
69127*	69131*	69134	69137
69128*	69132	69135	69138

69141	69164	69183	69206
69143	69165	69184	69207
69144	69166	69185	69208
69145	69168	69186	69209
69146	69169	69187	69211
69149	69170	69188	69212
69150	69171	69190	69213
69151	69172	69191	69214
69152	69173	69192	69215
69153	69174	69193	69216
69154	69175	69194	69217
69155	69176	69196	69218
69156	69177	69197	69219
69159	69178	69198	69220
69160	69179	69199	69221
69161	69180	69202	69222
69162	69181	69204	69223
69163	69182	69205	69224

Total

Class N15/1 79 Class N15/2 5

0-6-2T 2MT Class N5

N5/2. Introduced 1891. Parker M.S & L. design developed from N4.

*Push-and-pull fitted.

Weight: 62 tons 7 cwt.
Pressure: 160 lb.
Cyls.: 18″ × 26″.
Driving Wheels: 5′ 1″.
T.E.: 18,780 lb.

69257*	69276	69307	69342
69258	69281	69308	69343
69259	69286	69309	69344
69262	69290	69314	69349
69263	69292	69319	69354
69265	69293	69320	69360
69266	69294	69322	69361
69267	69296	69327	69362
69268	69298	69332	69370
69269	69299	69341	
69274			

Total 40

0-6-2T 2MT Class N1

†‡§Introduced 1907. Standard Ivatt G.N. design.

§Rebuilt with superheater and reduced pressure.

‡Fitted with condensing apparatus.

Weight: 65 tons 17 cwt.
Pressure: $\begin{cases} 175 \text{ lb.}†‡ \\ 170 \text{ lb. Su.}§ \end{cases}$
Cyls.: 18″ × 26″.
Driving Wheels: 5′ 8″.
T.E.: $\begin{cases} 18,430 \text{ lb.}†‡ \\ 17,900 \text{ lb.}§ \end{cases}$

69434‡	69450†	69462‡	69477‡
69443†	69452§	69474†	

Total 7

0-6-2T 3P2F Class N2

N2/2* Introduced 1925. Post-grouping development of Gresley G.N. N2/1, introduced 1920, which class is now included in N2/2. Built with condensing apparatus and small chimney.

N2/2† Condensing apparatus removed.

N2/3‡ Introduced 1925. Locos. built non-condensing, originally fitted with large chimney. Some now with small chimney.

N2/4§ Introduced 1928. Development of N2/2, slightly heavier. Built with condensing apparatus and small chimney.

(The small chimneys are to suit the Metropolitan loading gauge, for working to Moorgate. Condensing apparatus has been removed from or added to certain locos. transferred from or to the London area.)

Weight: $\begin{cases} 70 \text{ tons 5 cwt.}*† \\ 70 \text{ tons 8 cwt.}‡ \\ 71 \text{ tons 9 cwt.}§ \end{cases}$

Pressure: 170 lb. Su.
Cyls.: 19″ × 26″.
Driving Wheels: 5′ 8″.
T.E.: 19,945 lb.
P.V.

157

69490*	69521*	69544*	69573§
69491*	69522*	69545*	69574§
69492*	69523*	69546*	69575§
69493*	69524*	69547*	69576§
69495*	69525*	69548*	69577§
69498*	69526*	69549*	69578§
69499*	69528*	69550†	69579§
69504*	69529*	69551†	69580§
69505†	69530*	69552†	69581§
69506†	69531*	69553†	69582§
69507†	69532*	69555*	69583§
69508†	69533*	69556§	69584§
69509†	69534*	69560†	69585§
69510†	69535*	69561†	69586§
69511†	69536*	69563‡	69587§
69512*	69537*	69564‡	69588§
69513*	69538*	69567‡	69589§
69515†	69539*	69568§	69591§
69516†	69540*	69569§	69592§
69517*	69541*	69570§	69593§
69518†	69542*	69571§	69594‡
69520*	69543*	69572§	69596‡

Total

Class N2/2 57   Class N2/4 26
Class N2/3 5

0-6-2T   3MT   Class N7

N7/2[5] Introduced 1926. Post-grouping development of Hill G.E. design (N7) with long-travel valves.

N7/3[1] Introduced 1927. Doncaster-built version of N7/2 but with round-topped firebox.

N7/3[2] Introduced 1943. N7/2 rebuilt with round-topped firebox.

N7/4[3] Introduced 1940. Pre-grouping G.E. design N7, rebuilt with round-topped firebox, retaining short-travel valves.

N7/5[4] Introduced 1943. Post-grouping development of G.E. design N7/1, rebuilt with round-topped firebox, retaining short-travel valves.

Weight: $\begin{cases} 64 \text{ tons.}^{1\,2\,4} \\ 61 \text{ tons } 16 \text{ cwt.}^3 \\ 64 \text{ tons } 17 \text{ cwt.}^5 \end{cases}$

Pressure: 180 lb. Su.
Cyls.: 18″ × 24″.
Driving Wheels: 4′ 10″.
T.E.: 20,515 lb.
Walschaerts valve gear.   P.V.

69600³	69637⁴	69670⁴	69703¹
69602³	69638⁴	69671⁴	69704¹
69603³	69639⁴	69672²	69705¹
69604³	69640⁴	69673²	69706¹
69605³	69641⁴	69674²	69707¹
69610³	69642⁴	69675²	69708¹
69611³	69644⁴	69676²	69709¹
69612³	69645⁴	69677²	69710¹
69613³	69646⁴	69678²	69711ᴸ
69614³	69647⁴	69679²	69712ᴸ
69615³	69648⁴	69680²	69713ᴸ
69616³	69649⁴	69681²	69714ᴸ
69617³	69650⁴	69682²	69715ᴸ
69618³	69651⁴	69683²	69716ᴸ
69619	69652⁴	69684²	69717¹
69620³	69653⁴	69685²	69718¹
69621³	69654⁴	69686²	69719ᴸ
69622⁴	69655⁴	69687²	69720¹
69623⁴	69656⁴	69688²	69721¹
69624⁴	69657⁴	69690²	69722¹
69625⁴	69658⁴	69691²	69723¹
69626⁴	69659⁴	69692²	69724¹
69627⁴	69660⁴	69693²	69725¹
69628⁴	69661⁴	69694²	69726¹
69629⁴	69662⁴	69695⁵	69727¹
69630⁴	69663⁴	69696²	69728¹
69631⁴	69664⁴	69697²	69729¹
69632⁴	69665⁴	69698²	69730⁴
69633⁴	69666⁴	69699²	69731ᴸ
69634⁴	69667⁴	69700²	69732¹
69635⁴	69668⁴	69701²	69733¹
69636⁴	69669⁴	69702¹	

Total

Class N7/2 1 | Class N7/4 17
Class N7/3 60 | Class N7/5 49

4-6-2T 3MT Class A5

A5/1 Introduced 1911. Robinson G.C. design.

A5/2* Introduced 1925. Post-grouping development of A5/1 with reduced boiler mountings and detail differences.

Weight: $\begin{cases} 85 \text{ tons } 18 \text{ cwt.} \\ 90 \text{ tons } 11 \text{ cwt.*} \end{cases}$

Pressure: 180 lb. Su.

Cyls.: $20'' \times 26''$.

Driving Wheels: 5' 7".

T.E.: 23,750 lb.

P.V.

69800	69812	69823	69834*
69801	69813	69824	69835*
69802	69814	69825	69836*
69803	69816	69827	69837*
69805	69817	69828	69838*
69806	69818	69829	69839*
69808	69820	69830*	69840*
69809	69821	69831*	69841*
69810	69822	69832*	69842*
69811			

Total

Class A5/1 25   Class A5/2 12

4-6-2T 3MT Class A8

Introduced 1931. Gresley rebuild of Raven N.E. Class " D " 4-4-4T (introduced 1913).

Weight: 86 tons 18 cwt.

Pressure: 175 lb. Su.

Cyls.: (3) $16\frac{1}{2}'' \times 26''$.

Driving Wheels: 5' 9"

T.E.: 22,940 lb.

P.V.

69850	69860	69873	69885
69851	69861	69874	69886
69852	69863	69875	69887
69853	69864	69877	69888
69854	69866	69879	69889
69855	69867	69880	69891
69856	69869	69882	69892
69857	69870	69883	69893
69858	69871	69884	69894
69859	69872		

Total 39

4-8-0T 5F Class T1

Introduced 1909. W. Worsdell N.E. design.

Weight: 85 tons 8 cwt.

Pressure: 175 lb.

Cyls.: (3) $18'' \times 26''$.

Driving Wheels: $4' 7\frac{1}{4}''$.

T.E.: 34,080 lb.

P.V.

69910	69915	69918	69921
69912	69917	69920	

Total 7

0-8-0T 5F Class Q1

Thompson rebuild of Robinson G.C. Q4 0-8-0, introduced 1902.

Q1/1* Introduced 1942. 1,500 gallon tanks.

Q1/2 Introduced 1943. 2,000 gallon tanks.

Weight: $\begin{cases} 69 \text{ tons } 18 \text{ cwt.*} \\ 73 \text{ tons } 13 \text{ cwt.} \end{cases}$

Pressure: 180 lb.

Cyls.: (O) $19'' \times 26''$.

Driving Wheels: 4' 8".

T.E.: 25,645 lb.

69928*	69931	69933	69935
69929	69932	69934	69936
69930			

Total 9

BRITISH RAILWAYS
EASTERN & NORTH EASTERN REGIONS

CHIEF MECHANICAL ENGINEER
A. H. Peppercorn ... 1948–1949
(post abolished)

LOCOMOTIVE SUPERINTENDENTS AND CHIEF MECHANICAL ENGINEERS OF THE L.N.E.R.

Sir Nigel Gresley 1923–1941	E. Thompson 1941–1946
A. H. Peppercorn ... 1946–1947	

GREAT NORTHERN RAILWAY

A. Sturrock	...	...	1850–1866
P. Stirling	...	...	1866–1895
H. A. Ivatt	...	...	1896–1911
H. N. Gresley	...	...	1911–1922

NORTH EASTERN RAILWAY

E. Fletcher	...	...	1854–1883
A. McDonnell*	...	...	1883–1884
T. W. Worsdell	...	...	1885–1890
W. Worsdell	...	...	1890–1910
Sir Vincent Raven		...	1910–1922

GREAT EASTERN RAILWAY

R. Sinclair	...	...	1862–1866
S. W. Johnson	...	...	1866–1873
W. Adams	...	...	1873–1878
M. Bromley	...	...	1878–1881
T. W. Worsdell	...	...	1881–1885
J. Holden	...	...	1885–1907
S. D. Holden	...	...	1908–1912
A. J. Hill	...	...	1912–1922

LANCASHIRE, DERBYSHIRE AND EAST COAST RAILWAY

R. A. Thom	...	...	1902–1907

MANCHESTER, SHEFFIELD AND LINCOLNSHIRE RAILWAY

Richard Peacock	...	...	–1854
W. G. Craig	...	...	1854–1859

Charles Sacré	...	...	1859–1886
T. Parker	...	...	1886–1893
H. Pollitt	...	...	1893–1897

GREAT CENTRAL RAILWAY

H. Pollitt	...	...	1897–1900
J. G. Robinson	...	...	1900–1922

HULL AND BARNSLEY RAILWAY

M. Stirling	...	...	1885–1922

MIDLAND AND GREAT NORTHERN JOINT RAILWAY

W. Marriott	...	...	1884–1924

NORTH BRITISH RAILWAY

T. Wheatley†	...	...	1867–1874
D. Drummond	...	...	1875–1882
M. Holmes	...	...	1882–1903
W. P. Reid	...	...	1903–1919
W. Chalmers	...	...	1919–1922

GREAT NORTH OF SCOTLAND RAILWAY

D. K. Clark	...	...	1853–1855
J. F. Ruthven	...	...	1855–1857
W. Cowan	...	...	1857–1883
J. Manson	...	...	1883–1890
J. Johnson	...	...	1890–1894
W. Pickersgill	...	...	1894–1914
T. E. Heywood	...	...	1914–1922

Between McDonnell and T. W. Worsdell there was an interval during which the office was covered by a Locomotive Committee.

† Previous to whom the records are indeterminate.

Class V2 2-6-2 No. 60809 *The Snapper, The East Yorkshire Regiment, The Duke of York's Own* [B. K. B. Green

Class B1 4-6-0 No. 61095 (with self-weighing tender) [P. H. Wells

Class B16/1 4-6-0 No. 61441 [B. K. B. Green

Class A1 4-6-2 No. 60156 *Great Central* [G. Wheeler

Class A3 4-6-2 No. 60050 *Persimmon* [A. E. Brown

Class A4 4-6-2 No. 60007 *Sir Nigel Gresley* (with modified double chimney) [G. Wheeler

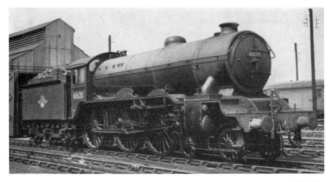

Class B17/6 4-6-0 No. 61620 *Clumber*   [K. R. Pirt

Class B2 4-6-0 No. 61639 *Norwich City*   [K. R. Pirt

Class B12/3 4-6-0 No. 61573   [P. H. Wells

Class K1 2-6-0 No. 62016   [R. K. Evans

Class K2/2 2-6-0 No. 61771   [R. C. Riley

Class K4 2-6-0 No. 61998 *MacLeod of MacLeod*   [B. K. B. Green

Class K3/2 2-6-0 No. 61835 [*K. R. Pirt*

Class D49/1 4-4-0 No. 62719 *Peebles-shire* (fitted with G.C. tender) [*I. S. Swanson*

Class D30/2 4-4-0 No. 62432 *Quentin Durward* [*W. S. Sellar*

Class D16/3 4-4-0 No. 62530 [K. R. Pirt

Class D11/1 4-4-0 No. 62662 *Prince of Wales* [T. Booth

Class D34 4-4-0 No. 62471 *Glen Falloch* [W. S. Sellar

Class O1 2-8-0 No. 63650   [R. C. Riley

Class Q6 0-8-0 No. 63392   [B. K. B. Green

Class Q7 0-8-0 No. 63464   [B. K. B. Green

Class J11/3 0-6-0 No. 64394   [*P. Ransome-Wallis*

Class J38 0-6-0 No. 65905   [*R. E. Vincent*

Class J39/1 0-6-0 No. 64783   [*R. E. Vincent*

Class J25 0-6-0 No. 65693   [K. R. Pirt

Class J26 0-6-0 No. 65762   [P. H. Groom

Class J15 0-6-0 No. 65420   [K. R. Pirt

Class J36 0-6-0 No. 65243 *Maude*

[*David A. Anderson*

Class J35/5 0-6-0 No. 64470

[*P. H. Groom*

Class J37 0-6-0 No. 64628

[*L. Marshall*

Above: Class J94
0-6-0ST No. 68023
[P. H. Groom

Left: Class Z4
0-4-2T No. 68190
[Brian E. Morrison

Below: Class Z5
0-4-2T No. 68152
[R. E. Vincent

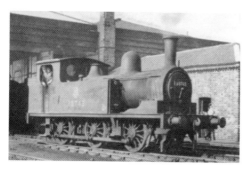

Above: Class G5
0-4-4T No. 67342
[*B. K. B. Green*

Left: Class J72
0-6-0T No. 68743
[*Brian E. Morrison*

Below: Class J77
0-6-0T No. 68408
[*C. Lawson Kerr*

Class N2/2 0-6-2T No. 69510   [W. S. Sellar

Class N2/4 0-6-2T No. 69589   [B. K. B. Green

Class N15/1 0-6-2T No. 69169   [D. Marriott

Above: Class N7/3
0-6-2T No. 69709
[R. A. Panting

Right: Class N7/5
0-6-2T No. 69638
[T. K. Widd

Below: Class N5/2
0-6-2T No. 69290
[Brian E. Morrison

Class A8 4-6-2T No. 69371   [P. H. Groom

Class V1 2-6-2T No. 67610   [J. R. Paterson

Class L1 2-6-4T No. 67768   [K. R. Pirt

Class A5/1 2-6-4T No. 69808 [R. C. Riley

Class Q1 0-8-0T No. 69932 [R. K. Evans

Class T1 4-8-0T No. 69910 [W. A. Richards

BRITISH RAILWAYS STANDARD LOCOMOTIVES

Chief Officer (Mechanical Engineering) :
R. C. BOND

4-6-2　　　　　**7P6F**

Introduced 1951. Designed at Derby.
Weight: Loco. 94 tons 0 cwt.
Pressure: 250 lb. Su.
Cyls.: (O) 20″ × 28″.
Driving Wheels: 6′ 2″. T.E.: 32,150 lb.
Walschaerts valve gear. P.V.

70000	Britannia
70001	Lord Hurcomb
70002	Geoffrey Chaucer
70003	John Bunyan
70004	William Shakespeare
70005	John Milton
70006	Robert Burns
70007	Coeur-de-Lion
70008	Black Prince
70009	Alfred the Great
70010	Owen Glendower
70011	Hotspur
70012	John of Gaunt
70013	Oliver Cromwell
70014	Iron Duke
70015	Apollo
70016	Ariel
70017	Arrow
70018	Flying Dutchman
70019	Lightning
70020	Mercury
70021	Morning Star
70022	Tornado
70023	Venus
70024	Vulcan
70025	Western Star
70026	Polar Star
70027	Rising Star
70028	Royal Star
70029	Shooting Star
70030	William Wordsworth
70031	Byron
70032	Tennyson
70033	Charles Dickens
70034	Thomas Hardy
70035	Rudyard Kipling
70036	Boadicea
70037	Hereward the Wake
70038	Robin Hood
70039	Sir Christopher Wren
70040	Clive of India
70041	Sir John Moore
70042	Lord Roberts
70043	Lord Kitchener
70044	Earl Haig
70045	Lord Rowallan
70046	
70047	
70048	The Territorial Army 1908-1958
70049	
70050	Firth of Clyde
70051	Firth of Forth
70052	Firth of Tay
70053	Moray Firth
70054	Dornoch Firth

Total 55

4-6-2　　　　　**8P**

Introduced 1954. Designed at Derby.
Weight: Loco. 101 tons 5 cwt.
Pressure: 250 lb. Su.
Cyls.: (3) 18″ × 28″.
Driving Wheels: 6′ 2″. T.E.: 39,080 lb
Caprotti valve gear.

71000　Duke of Gloucester

Total 1

4-6-2　　　　　**6P5F**

Introduced 1952. Designed at Derby.
Weight: Loco. 86 tons 19 cwt.
Pressure: 225 lb. Su.
Cyls.: (O) 19½″ × 28″.
Driving Wheels: 6′ 2″. T.E.: 27,520 lb.
Walschaerts valve gear. P.V.

72000　Clan Buchanan
72001　Clan Cameron
72002　Clan Campbell

72003	Clan Fraser	
72004	Clan Macdonald	
72005	Clan Macgregor	
72006	Clan Mackenzie	
72007	Clan Mackintosh	
72008	Clan Macleod	
72009	Clan Stewart	**Total 10**

4-6-0   5

Introduced 1951. Designed at Doncaster.
*Introduced 1956. Fitted with Caprotti valve gear.
Weight: Loco. 76 tons 4 cwt.
Pressure: 225 lb. Su.
Cyls.: (O) 19″ × 28″.
Driving Wheels: 6′ 2″. T.E.: 26,120 lb.
Walschaerts valve gear. P.V.

73000	73028	73056	73084
73001	73029	73057	73085
73002	73030	73058	73086
73003	73031	73059	73087
73004	73032	73060	73088
73005	73033	73061	73089
73006	73034	73062	73090
73007	73035	73063	73091
73008	73036	73064	73092
73009	73037	73065	73093
73010	73038	73066	73094
73011	73039	73067	73095
73012	73040	73068	73096
73013	73041	73069	73097
73014	73042	73070	73098
73015	73043	73071	73099
73016	73044	73072	73100
73017	73045	73073	73101
73018	73046	73074	73102
73019	73047	73075	73103
73020	73048	73076	73104
73021	73049	73077	73105
73022	73050	73078	73106
73023	73051	73079	73107
73024	73052	73080	73108
73025	73053	73081	73109
73026	73054	73082	73110
73027	73055	73083	73111

73112	73127*	73142*	73157
73113	73128*	73143*	73158
73114	73129*	73144*	73159
73115	73130*	73145*	73160
73116	73131*	73146*	73161
73117	73132*	73147*	73162
73118	73133*	73148*	73163
73119	73134*	73149*	73164
73120	73135*	73150*	73165
73121	73136*	73151*	73166
73122	73137*	73152*	73167
73123	73138*	73153*	73168
73124	73139*	73154*	73169
73125*	73140*	73155	73170
73126*	73141*	73156	73171

Total 172

4-6-0   4

Introduced 1951. Designed at Brighton.
*Introduced 1957. Fitted with double chimney.
Weight: Loco. 69 tons 0 cwt.
Pressure: 225 lb. Su.
Cyls.: (O) 18″ × 28″.
Driving Wheels: 5′ 8″. T.E.: 25,100 lb.
Walschaerts valve gear. P.V.

75000	75020	75040	75060
75001	75021	75041	75061
75002	75022	75042	75062
75003	75023	75043	75063
75004	75024	75044	75064
75005	75025	75045	75065
75006	75026	75046	75066
75007	75027	75047	75067
75008	75028	75048	75068
75009	75029*	75049	75069
75010	75030	75050	75070
75011	75031	75051	75071
75012	75032	75052	75072
75013	75033	75053	75073
75014	75034	75054	75074
75015	75035	75055	75075
75016	75036	75056	75076
75017	75037	75057	75077
75018	75038	75058	75078
75019	75039	75059	75079

Total 80

2-6-0   4

Introduced 1953. Designed at Doncaster.
Weight: Loco. 59 tons 2 cwt.
Pressure: 225 lb. Su.
Cyls.: (O) 17½″ × 26″.
Driving Wheels: 5′ 3″. T.E.: 24,170 lb.
Walschaerts valve gear. P.V.

76000	76029	76058	76087
76001	76030	76059	76088
76002	76031	76060	76089
76003	76032	76061	76090
76004	76033	76062	76091
76005	76034	76063	76092
76006	76035	76064	76093
76007	76036	76065	76094
76008	76037	76066	76095
76009	76038	76067	76096
76010	76039	76068	76097
76011	76040	76069	76098
76012	76041	76070	76099
76013	76042	76071	76100
76014	76043	76072	76101
76015	76044	76073	76102
76016	76045	76074	76103
76017	76046	76075	76104
76018	76047	76076	76105
76019	76048	76077	76106
76020	76049	76078	76107
76021	76050	76079	76108
76022	76051	76080	76109
76023	76052	76081	76110
76024	76053	76082	76111
76025	76054	76083	76112
76026	76055	76084	76113
76027	76056	76085	76114
76028	76057	76086	

Total 115

2-6-0   3

Introduced 1954. Designed at Swindon.
Weight: Loco. 57 tons 9 cwt.
Pressure: 200 lb. Su.
Cyls.: (O) 17½″ × 26″.
Driving Wheels: 5′ 3″. T.E.: 21,490 lb.
Walschaerts valve gear. P.V.

77000	77005	77010	77015
77001	77006	77011	77016
77002	77007	77012	77017
77003	77008	77013	77018
77004	77009	77014	77019

Total 20

2-6-0   2

Introduced 1953. Designed at Derby.
Weight: Loco. 49 tons 5 cwt.
Pressure: 200 lb. Su.
Cyls.: (O) 16½″ × 24″.
Driving Wheels: 5′ 0″. T.E.: 18,515 lb.
Walschaerts valve gear. P.V.

78000	78017	78034	78051
78001	78018	78035	78052
78002	78019	78036	78053
78003	78020	78037	78054
78004	78021	78038	78055
78005	78022	78039	78056
78006	78023	78040	78057
78007	78024	78041	78058
78008	78025	78042	78059
78009	78026	78043	78060
78010	78027	78044	78061
78011	78028	78045	78062
78012	78029	78046	78063
78013	78030	78047	78064
78014	78031	78048	
78015	78032	78049	
78016	78033	78050	

Total 65

2-6-4T   4

Introduced 1951. Designed at Brighton.
Weight: 88 tons 10 cwt.
Pressure: 225 lb. Su.
Cyls.: (O) 18″ × 28″.
Driving Wheels: 5′ 8″. T.E.: 25,100 lb.
Walschaerts valve gear. P.V.

80000	80005	80010	80015
80001	80006	80011	80016
80002	80007	80012	80017
80003	80008	80013	80018
80004	80009	80014	80019

80020	80054	80088	80122
80021	80055	80089	80123
80022	80056	80090	80124
80023	80057	80091	80125
80024	80058	80092	80126
80025	80059	80093	80127
80026	80060	80094	80128
80027	80061	80095	80129
80028	80062	80096	80130
80029	80063	80097	80131
80030	80064	80098	80132
80031	80065	80099	80133
80032	80066	80100	80134
80033	80067	80101	80135
80034	80068	80102	80136
80035	80069	80103	80137
80036	80070	80104	80138
80037	80071	80105	80139
80038	80072	80106	80140
80039	80073	80107	80141
80040	80074	80108	80142
80041	80075	80109	80143
80042	80076	80110	80144
80043	80077	80111	80145
80044	80078	80112	80146
80045	80079	80113	80147
80046	80080	80114	80148
80047	80081	80115	80149
80048	80082	80116	80150
80049	80083	80117	80151
80050	80084	80118	80152
80051	80085	80119	80153
80052	80086	80120	80154
80053	80087	80121	

Total 155

2-6-2T 3

Introduced 1952. Designed at Swindon.
Weight: 73 tons 10 cwt.
Pressure: 200 lb. Su.
Cyls.: (O) 17½″ × 26″.
Driving Wheels: 5′ 3″. T.E.: 21,490 lb.
Walschaerts valve gear. P.V.

82000	82002	82004	82006
82001	82003	82005	82007

82008	82018	82028	82038
82009	82019	82029	82039
82010	82020	82030	82040
82011	82021	82031	82041
82012	82022	82032	82042
82013	82023	82033	82043
82014	82024	82034	82044
82015	82025	82035	
82016	82026	82036	
82017	82027	82037	

Total 45

2-6-2T 2

Introduced 1953. Designed at Derby.
Weight: 63 tons 5 cwt.
Pressure: 200 lb. Su.
Cyls.: (O) 16½″ × 24″.
Driving Wheels: 5′ 0″. T.E.: 18,515 lb.
Walschaerts valve gear. P.V.

84000	84008	84016	84024
84001	84009	84017	84025
84002	84010	84018	84026
84003	84011	84019	84027
84004	84012	84020	84028
84005	84013	84021	84029
84006	84014	84022	
84007	84015	84023	

Total 30

2-8-0 8F WD

Ministry of Supply " Austerity " 2-8-0
locomotives purchased by British
Railways, 1948.
Introduced 1943. Riddles M.o.S. design.
Weight: Loco. 70 tons 5 cwt.
       Tender 55 tons 10 cwt.
Pressure: 225 lb. Su.
Cyls.: (O) 19″ × 28″.
Driving Wheels: 4′ 8½″. T.E.: 34,215 lb.
Walschaerts valve gear. P.V.

90000	90009	90018	90027
90001	90010	90019	90028
90002	90011	90020	90029
90003	90012	90021	90030
90004	90013	90022	90031
90005	90014	90023	90032
90006	90015	90024	90033
90007	90016	90025	90034
90008	90017	90026	90035

90036	90083	90130	90177	90224	90271	90318	90365
90037	90084	90131	90178	90225	90272	90319	90366
90038	90085	90132	90179	90226	90273	90320	90367
90039	90086	90133	90180	90227	90274	90321	90368
90040	90087	90134	90181	90228	90275	90322	90369
90041	90088	90135	90182	90229	90276	90323	90370
90042	90089	90136	90183	90230	90277	90324	90371
90043	90090	90137	90184	90231	90278	90325	90372
90044	90091	90138	90185	90232	90279	90326	90373
90045	90092	90139	90186	90233	90280	90327	90374
90046	90093	90140	90187	90234	90281	90328	90375
90047	90094	90141	90188	90235	90282	90329	90376
90048	90095	90142	90189	90236	90283	90330	90377
90049	90096	90143	90190	90237	90284	90331	90378
90050	90097	90144	90191	90238	90285	90332	90379
90051	90098	90145	90192	90239	90286	90333	90380
90052	90099	90146	90193	90240	90287	90334	90381
90053	90100	90147	90194	90241	90288	90335	90382
90054	90101	90148	90195	90242	90289	90336	90383
90055	90102	90149	90196	90243	90290	90337	90384
90056	90103	90150	90197	90244	90291	90338	90385
90057	90104	90151	90198	90245	90292	90339	90386
90058	90105	90152	90199	90246	90293	90340	90387
90059	90106	90153	90200	90247	90294	90341	90388
90060	90107	90154	90201	90248	90295	90342	90389
90061	90108	90155	90202	90249	90296	90343	90390
90062	90109	90156	90203	90250	90297	90344	90391
90063	90110	90157	90204	90251	90298	90345	90392
90064	90111	90158	90205	90252	90299	90346	90393
90065	90112	90159	90206	90253	90300	90347	90394
90066	90113	90160	90207	90254	90301	90348	90395
90067	90114	90161	90208	90255	90302	90349	90396
90068	90115	90162	90209	90256	90303	90350	90397
90069	90116	90163	90210	90257	90304	90351	90398
90070	90117	90164	90211	90258	90305	90352	90399
90071	90118	90165	90212	90259	90306	90353	90400
90072	90119	90166	90213	90260	90307	90354	90401
90073	90120	90167	90214	90261	90308	90355	90402
90074	90121	90168	90215	90262	90309	90356	90403
90075	90122	90169	90216	90263	90310	90357	90404
90076	90123	90170	90217	90264	90311	90358	90405
90077	90124	90171	90218	90265	90312	90359	90406
90078	90125	90172	90219	90266	90313	90360	90407
90079	90126	90173	90220	90267	90314	90361	90408
90080	90127	90174	90221	90268	90315	90362	90409
90081	90128	90175	90222	90269	90316	90363	90410
90082	90129	90176	90223	90270	90317	90364	90411

90412	90459	90506	90553	90600	90634	90668	90702
90413	90460	90507	90554	90601	90635	90669	90703
90414	90461	90508	90555	90602	90636	90670	90704
90415	90462	90509	90556	90603	90637	90671	90705
90416	90463	90510	90557	90604	90638	90672	90706
90417	90464	90511	90558	90605	90639	90673	90707
90418	90465	90512	90559	90606	90640	90674	90708
90419	90466	90513	90560	90607	90641	90675	90709
90420	90467	90514	90561	90608	90642	90676	90710
90421	90468	90515	90562	90609	90643	90677	90711
90422	90469	90516	90563	90610	90644	90678	90712
90423	90470	90517	90564	90611	90645	90679	90713
90424	90471	90518	90565	90612	90646	90680	90714
90425	90472	90519	90566	90613	90647	90681	90715
90426	90473	90520	90567	90614	90648	90682	90716
90427	90474	90521	90568	90615	90649	90683	90717
90428	90475	90522	90569	90616	90650	90684	90718
90429	90476	90523	90570	90617	90651	90685	90719
90430	90477	90524	90571	90618	90652	90686	90720
90431	90478	90525	90572	90619	90653	90687	90721
90432	90479	90526	90573	90620	90654	90688	90722
90433	90480	90527	90574	90621	90655	90689	90723
90434	90481	90528	90575	90622	90656	90690	90724
90435	90482	90529	90576	90623	90657	90691	90725
90436	90483	90530	90577	90624	90658	90692	90726
90437	90484	90531	90578	90625	90659	90693	90727
90438	90485	90532	90579	90626	90660	90694	90728
90439	90486	90533	90580	90627	90661	90695	90729
90440	90487	90534	90581	90628	90662	90696	90730
90441	90488	90535	90582	90629	90663	90697	90731
90442	90489	90536	90583	90630	90664	90698	90732
90443	90490	90537	90584	90631	90665	90699	Vulcan
90444	90491	90538	90585	90632	90666	90700	
90445	90492	90539	90586	90633	90667	90701	
90446	90493	90540	90587				
90447	90494	90541	90588				
90448	90495	90542	90589			**Total 733**	
90449	90496	90543	90590				
90450	90497	90544	90591				
90451	90498	90545	90592	**2-10-0**			**WD**
90452	90499	90546	90593				
90453	90500	90547	90594				
90454	90501	90548	90595				
90455	90502	90549	90596				
90456	90503	90550	90597				
90457	90504	90551	90598				
90458	90505	90552	90599				

2-10-0 **WD**

Ministry of Supply " Austerity " 2-10-0
    locomotives purchased by British
    Railways, 1948.
Introduced 1943. Riddles M.o.S. design.
Weight: Loco. 78 tons 6 cwt.
            Tender 55 tons 10 cwt.
Pressure: 225 lb. Su.
Cyls.: (O) 19" × 28".
Driving Wheels: 4' 8½". T.E.: 34,215 lb.
Walschaerts valve gear. P.V.

90750	90757	90764	90771
90751	90758	90765	90772
90752	90759	90766	90773
90753	90760	90767	90774
90754	90761	90768	
90755	90762	90769	
90756	90763	90770	

Total 25

2-10-0 9F

Introduced 1954. Designed at Brighton.
*Introduced 1955. Fitted with Crosti boiler.
†Introduced 1957. Fitted with double chimney.
‡Introduced 1958. Fitted with Mechanical Stoker.
Weight: Loco. ⎰ 86 tons 14 cwt.
⎱ 90 tons 4 cwt.*
Pressure: 250 lb. Su.
Cyls.: (O) 20″ × 28″.
Driving Wheels: 5′ 0″. T.E.: 39,670 lb.
Walschaerts valve gear. P.V.

92000	92025*	92050	92075
92001	92026*	92051	92076
92002	92027*	92052	92077
92003	92028*	92053	92078
92004	92029*	92054	92079
92005	92030	92055	92080
92006	92031	92056	92081
92007	92032	92057	92082
92008	92033	92058	92083
92009	92034	92059	92084
92010	92035	92060	92085
92011	92036	92061	92086
92012	92037	92062	92087
92013	92038	92063	92088
92014	92039	92064	92089
92015	92040	92065	92090
92016	92041	92066	92091
92017	92042	92067	92092
92018	92043	92068	92093
92019	92044	92069	92094
92020*	92045	92070	92095
92021*	92046	92071	92096
92022*	92047	92072	92097
92023*	92048	92073	92098
92024*	92049	92074	92099

92100	92138	92176	92214
92101	92139	92177	92215
92102	92140	92178†	92216
92103	92141	92179	92217
92104	92142	92180	92218
92105	92143	92181	92219
92106	92144	92182	92220
92107	92145	92183	92221
92108	92146	92184†	92222
92109	92147	92185†	92223
92110	92148	92186	92224
92111	92149	92187†	92225
92112	92150	92188	92226
92113	92151	92189	92227
92114	92152	92190	92228
92115	92153	92191	92229
92116	92154	92192	92230
92117	92155	92193	92231
92118	92156	92194	92232
92119	92157	92195	92233
92120	92158	92196	92234
92121	92159	92197	92235
92122	92160	92198	92236
92123	92161	92199	92237
92124	92162	92200	92238
92125	92163	92201	92239
92126	92164	92202	92240
92127	92165‡	92203	92241
92128	92166‡	92204	92242
92129	92167‡	92205	92243
92130	92168	92206	92244
92131	92169	92207	92245
92132	92170	92208	92246
92133	92171	92209	92247
92134	92172	92210	92248
92135	92173	92211	92249
92136	92174	92212	92250
92137	92175	92213	

Engines of this class are still being delivered.

183

BRITISH RAILWAYS STANDARD TENDERS

N.B.—These pairings are not permanent and are liable to alteration with changed operating conditions.

Type	Capacity		Weight in full W.O.		Locos. to which Allocated
	Water galls.	Coal tons	tons	cwt.	
BRI ...	4,250	7	49	3	70000–24/30–44 72000–9 73000–49
BRIA ...	5,000	7	52	10	70025–29
BRIB ...	4,725	7	50	5	92020–29/60–6/97–9 73080–89 73100–9/20–34/45–71 75065–79 76053–69
BRIC ...	4,725	9	53	5	92015–19/45–59/77–86 92100–39/50–67 73065–79/90–9 73135–44
BRID ...	4,725	9	54	10	70045–54
BRIE ...	4,725	10	55	10	71000
BRIF ...	5,625	7	55	5	92010–14/30–44/67–76 92087–96 92140–49/68–92202 73110–19
BRIG ...	5,000	7	52	10	92000–9 73050–52
BRIH ...	4,250	7	49	3	73053–64
BR2 ...	3,500	6	42	3	75000–49 76000–44
BR2A ...	3,500	6	42	3	75050–64/80–9 76045–52/70–76114 77000–24
BR3 ...	3,000	4	36	17	78000–64

Class 6P5F 4-6-2 No. 72001 *Clan Cameron*   [W. S. Sellar

Class 7P6F 4-6-2 No. 70048 *The Territorial Army 1908–1958*   [British Railways

Class 8P 4-6-2 No. 71000 *Duke of Gloucester*   T. B. Paisley

Class 4 4-6-0 No. 75004   [B. K. B Green

Class 5 (Riddles) 4-6-0 No. 73019   [R. J. Buckley

Class 5 (Riddles) 4-6-0 No. 73128 (with Caprotti valve gear)   [B. K. B. Green

BRITISH RAILWAYS DIESEL
LOCOMOTIVE CLASSES

1Co-Co1   "4"

To be introduced:
Locomotive manufacturer: B.R. Derby/
   Sulzer.
Total b.h.p.: 2,300.
Engine(s):
Transmission: **Electric**
Weight:
Driving Wheels:
Maximum Tractive effort:

D1	D4	D7	D10
D2	D5	D8	
D3	D6	D9	

1Co-Co1   "4"

Introduced: 1958.
Locomotive manufacturer: English Elec-
   tric.
Total b.h.p.: 2,000.
Engine: English Electric 16SVT Mk. II of
   2,000 b.h.p. at 850 r.p.m.
Transmission: **Electric.** Six English
   Electric nose-suspended traction
   motors.
Weight: 133 tons
Driving Wheels: 3′ 9″.
Maximum tractive effort: 52,000 lb.

D200	D203	D206	D208
D201	D204	D207	D209
D202	D205		

A1A-A1A   "4"

"WARSHIP" CLASS

Introduced: 1958.
Locomotive manufacturer: North British
   Locomotive Co.
Total b.h.p.: 2,000.
Engines: Two N.B.L./M.A.N. type L12V
   18/21S 12-cyl. of 1,000 b.h.p.
Transmission: **Hydraulic.** Two Hardy
   Spicer cardan shafts to Voith-North
   British type L306r hydraulic trans-
   missions each containing three torque
   converters.
Weight: 117 tons 8 cwt.
Driving Wheels: 3′ 7″.
Maximum tractive effort: 50,000 lb.

D600	Active
D601	Ark Royal
D602	Bulldog
D603	Conquest
D604	Cossack

B-B   "4"

"WARSHIP" CLASS

Introduced: 1958.
Locomotive manufacturer: Swindon
   Works, B.R.
Total b.h.p.: 2,200 (nominal).
Engines: Two Maybach MD 650 V-type
   of 1,152 b.h.p. at 1,530 r.p.m.
   *(1,056 b.h.p. at 1,400 r.p.m.)
Transmission: **Hydraulic.** Two Mekydro
   type K104 hydraulic transmissions
   containing permanently filled single
   torque converter and four-speed
   automatic gearbox.
Weight: 78 tons.
Driving Wheels: 3′ 3½″.
Maximum tractive effort: 52,400 lb.

D800* Sir Brian Robertson			
D801*	D809	D817	D825
D802*	D810	D818	D826
D803	D811	D819	D827
D804	D312	D820	D828
D805	D813	D821	D829
D806	D814	D822	D830
D807	D815	D823	D831
D808	D816	D824	

0-6-0   Shunter

Introduced: 1957.
Locomotive manufacturer: B.R.
Total b.h.p.: 204.
Engine: Gardner type 8L3 of 204 b.h.p.
   at 1,200 r.p.m.
Transmission: **Mechanical.** Vulcan-
   Sinclair type 23 fluid coupling.
   Wilson-Drewry C.A.5 type five-speed
   epicyclic gearbox. Type RF II spiral
   bevel reverse and final drive unit.
Weight: 30 tons 16 cwt.
Driving Wheels: 3′ 7″.
Maximum tractive effort: 15,650 lb.
Classified **DJI5** by the E. & N.E.R.

   (Original numbers in brackets)

D2000 (11187)	D2012 (11199)
D2001 (11188)	D2013 (11200)
D2002 (11189)	D2014 (11201)
D2003 (11190)	D2015 (11202)
D2004 (11191)	D2016 (11203)
D2005 (11192)	D2017 (11204)
D2006 (11193)	D2018 (11205)
D2007 (11194)	D2019 (11206)
D2008 (11195)	D2020 (11207)
D2009 (11196)	D2021 (11208)
D2010 (11197)	D2022 (11209)
D2011 (11198)	

D2023	D2041	D2059	D2077
D2024	D2042	D2060	D2078
D2025	D2043	D2061	D2079
D2026	D2044	D2062	D2080
D2027	D2045	D2063	D2081
D2028	D2046	D2064	D2082
D2029	D2047	D2065	D2083
D2030	D2048	D2066	D2084
D2031	D2049	D2067	D2085
D2032	D2050	D2068	D2086
D2033	D2051	D2069	D2087
D2034	D2052	D2070	D2088
D2035	D2053	D2071	
D2036	D2054	D2072	
D2037	D2055	D2073	
D2038	D2056	D2074	
D2039	D2057	D2075	
D2040	D2058	D2076	

0-6-0   Shunter

Introduced: 1952.
Locomotive manufacturer: Drewry.
Total b.h.p.: 204.
Engine: Gardner type 8L3 of 204 b.h.p.
at 1,200 r.p.m.
Transmission: **Mechanical.** Vulcan-
Sinclair type 23 fluid coupling.
Wilson-Drewry C.A. 5 type five-speed
epicyclic gearbox. Type RF 11 spiral
bevel reverse and final drive unit.
Weight: 29 tons 15 cwt.
Driving Wheels: 3' 3".
Maximum tractive effort: 16,850 lb.
Classified **DJ12/1** by the E. & N.E.R.

(Original numbers in brackets)

D2200 (11100)	D2208 (11109)
D2201 (11101)	D2209 (11110)
D2202 (11102)	D2210 (11111)
D2203 (11103)	D2211 (11112)
D2204 (11105)	D2212 (11113)
D2205 (11106)	D2213 (11114)
D2206 (11107)	D2214 (11115)
D2207 (11108)	

0-6-0   Shunter

Introduced: 1955.
Locomotive manufacturer: Drewry.
Total b.h.p.: 204.
Engine: Gardner type 8L3 of 204 b.h.p.
at 1,200 r.p.m.
Transmission: **Mechanical.** Vulcan-
Sinclair type 23 fluid coupling.
Wilson-Drewry C.A. 5 type five-speed
epicyclic gearbox. Type RF 11 spiral
bevel reverse and final drive unit.
Weight: 29 tons 15 cwt.
Driving Wheels: 3' 6".
Maximum tractive effort: 15,650 lb.
Classified **DJ12/2** by the E. & N.E.R.

(Original numbers in brackets)

D2215 (11121)	D2229 (11135)
D2216 (11122)	D2230 (11149)
D2217 (11123)	D2231 (11150)
D2218 (11124)	D2232 (11151)
D2219 (11125)	D2233 (11152)
D2220 (11126)	D2234 (11153)
D2221 (11127)	D2235 (11154)
D2222 (11128)	D2236 (11155)
D2223 (11129)	D2237 (11156)
D2224 (11130)	D2238 (11157)
D2225 (11131)	D2239 (11158)
D2226 (11132)	D2240 (11159)
D2227 (11133)	D2241 (11160)
D2228 (11134)	

0-6-0   Shunter

**D2242-D2273, FOR PARTICULARS
SEE D2200-D2214.**

(Original numbers in brackets)

D2242 (11212)	D2244 (11214)
D2243 (11213)	D2245 (11215)

D2246 (11216)	D2253 (11223)
D2247 (11217)	D2254 (11224)
D2248 (11218)	D2255 (11225)
D2249 (11219)	D2256 (11226)
D2250 (11220)	D2257 (11227)
D2251 (11221)	D2258 (11228)
D2252 (11222)	D2259 (11229)

D2260	D2264	D2268	D2272
D2261	D2265	D2269	D2273
D2262	D2266	D2270	
D2263	D2267	D2271	

0-6-0 Shunter

Introduced: 1956.
Locomotive manufacturer: Barclay.
Total b.h.p.: 204.
Engine: Gardner type 8L3 of 204 b.h.p. at 1,200 r.p.m.
Transmission: **Mechanical.** Vulcan-Sinclair type 23 fluid coupling. Wilson C.A.4 type four-speed epicyclic gearbox. Wiseman type 15 RLGB reverse and final drive unit.
Weight: 32 tons 0 cwt.
Driving Wheels: 3′ 6″.
Maximum tractive effort: 15,340 lb.
Classified **DJ14** by the E. & N.E.R.

(Original numbers in brackets)

D2400 (11177)	D2405 (11182)
D2401 (11178)	D2406 (11183)
D2402 (11179)	D2407 (11184)
D2403 (11180)	D2408 (11185)
D2404 (11181)	D2409 (11186)

0-4-0 Shunter

Introduced: 1958.
Locomotive manufacturer: Barclay.
Total b.h.p.: 204.
Engine: Gardner type 8L3 of 204 b.h.p. at 1,200 r.p.m.
Transmission: **Mechanical.** Vulcan-Sinclair type 23 fluid coupling. Wilson-Drewry C.A. 5 type five-speed epicyclic gearbox. Wiseman type 15. R.L.G.B. reverse and final drive unit.
Weight: 35 tons.
Driving Wheels: 3′ 7″.
Maximum tractive effort: 20,000 lb.

D2410	D2414	D2418	D2422
D2411	D2415	D2419	D2423
D2412	D2416	D2420	D2424
D2413	D2417	D2421	

0-6-0 Shunter

Introduced: 1956.
Locomotive manufacturer: Hudswell-Clarke.
Total b.h.p.: 204.
Engine: Gardner type 8L3 of 204 b.h.p. at 1,200 r.p.m.
Transmission: **Mechanical.** S.C.R.5 type, size 23 scoop control fluid coupling. Three-speed " SSS Power-flow " double synchro-type gearbox and final drive.
Weight: 36 tons 7 cwt.
Driving Wheels: 3′ 6″.
Maximum tractive effort: 16,100 lb.

(Original numbers in brackets)

D2500 (11116)	D2505 (11144)
D2501 (11117)	D2506 (11145)
D2502 (11118)	D2507 (11146)
D2503 (11119)	D2508 (11147)
D2504 (11120)	D2509 (11148)

0-6-0 Shunter

Introduced: 1955.
Locomotive manufacturer: Hunslet.
Total b.h.p.: 204.
Engine: Gardner type 8L3 of 204 b.h.p. at 1,200 r.p.m.
Transmission: **Mechanical.** Hunslet patent friction clutch. Hunslet four-speed gearbox incorporating reverse and final drive gears.
Weight: 30 tons 0 cwt.
Driving Wheels: 3′ 4″.
Maximum tractive effort: 14,500 lb.
Classified **DJ13** by the E. & N.E.R.

(Original numbers in brackets)

D2550 (11136)	D2562 (11165)
D2551 (11137)	D2563 (11166)
D2552 (11138)	D2564 (11167)
D2553 (11139)	D2565 (11168)
D2554 (11140)	D2566 (11169)
D2555 (11141)	D2567 (11170)
D2556 (11142)	D2568 (11171)
D2557 (11143)	D2569 (11172)
D2558 (11161)	D2570 (11173)
D2559 (11162)	D2571 (11174)
D2560 (11163)	D2572 (11175)
D2561 (11164)	D2573 (11176)

D2574	D2577	D2580	D2583
D2575	D2578	D2581	D2584
D2576	D2579	D2582	D2585

D2720	D2727	D2734	D2741
D2721	D2728	D2735	D2742
D2722	D2729	D2736	D2743
D2723	D2730	D2737	D2744
D2724	D2731	D2738	
D2725	D2732	D2739	
D2726	D2733	D2740	

0-4-0   Shunter

Introduced: 1953.
Locomotive manufacturer: North British.
Total b.h.p.: 200.
Engine: Paxman type 6RPH of 200 b.h.p. at 1,000 r.p.m.
Transmission: **Hydraulic.** Voith-North British hydraulic torque converter type L33YU. North British bevel gears and reversing dog clutch coupled through reduction gearing to jackshaft.
Weight: 32 tons.
Driving Wheels: 3′ 6″.
Maximum tractive effort: 21,500 lb.
Classified **DY11** by the E. & N.E.R.

(Original numbers in brackets)

D2700 (11700)	D2704 (11704)
D2701 (11701)	D2705 (11705)
D2702 (11702)	D2706 (11706)
D2703 (11703)	D2707 (11707)

0-4-0   Shunter

Introduced: 1957.
Locomotive manufacturer: North British.
Total b.h.p.: 225.
Engine: North British type M.A.N. W6V 17.5/22A of 225 b.h.p. at 1,100 r.p.m. (12 hr. rating).
Transmission: **Hydraulic.** Voith-North British hydraulic torque converter type LCCYU. North British bevel gears and reversing dog clutch coupled through reduction gearing to jackshaft.
Weight: 30 tons.
Driving Wheels: 3′ 6″.
Maximum tractive effort: 20,080 lb.
Classified **DY11** by the E. & N.E.R.

(Original numbers in brackets)

D2708 (11708)	D2714 (11714)
D2709 (11709)	D2715 (11715)
D2710 (11710)	D2716 (11716)
D2711 (11711)	D2717 (11717)
D2712 (11712)	D2718 (11718)
D2713 (11713)	D2719 (11719)

0-4-0   Shunter

Introduced: 1958.
Locomotive manufacturer: North British Locomotive Co.
Total b.h.p.: 330.
Engine: North British/M.A.N. type W6V 17.5/22 AS, super-charged.
Transmission: **Hydraulic.** Voith-North British hydraulic torque converter type L24V. North British spiral bevel gears, reversing and reduction gears to jackshaft.
Weight: 36 tons.
Driving Wheels: 3′ 9″.
Maximum tractive effort: 24,100 lb.

D2900	D2903	D2906	D2909
D2901	D2904	D2907	D2910
D2902	D2905	D2908	

0-4-0   Shunter

Introduced: 1955.
Locomotive manufacturer: Hunslet.
Total b.h.p.: 153.
Engine: Gardner type 6L3 of 153 b.h.p. at 1,200 r.p.m.
Transmission: **Mechanical.** Hunslet patent friction clutch. Hunslet four-speed gearbox incorporating reverse and final drive gears.
Weight: 22 tons 9 cwt.
Driving Wheels: 3′ 4″.
Maximum tractive effort: 10,800 lb.
Classified **DY1** by E. & N.E.R.

(Original numbers in brackets)

D2950 (11500)	D2952 (11502)
D2951 (11501)	

0-4-0   Shunter

Introduced: 1956.
Locomotive manufacturer: Barclay.
Total b.h.p.: 153.
Engine: Gardner type 6L3 of 153 b.h.p. at 1,200 r.p.m.
Transmission: **Mechanical.** Vulcan-Sinclair rigid type hydraulic coupling. Wilson S.E.4 type four-speed epicyclic gearbox. Wiseman type 15 RLGB reverse and final drive unit.
Weight: 25 tons.
Driving Wheels: 3' 2".
Maximum tractive effort: 12,750 lb.
Classified **DY2** by E. & N.E.R.

(Original numbers in brackets)

D2953 (11503)	D2955 (11505)
D2954 (11504)	D2956 (11506)

0-4-0   Shunter

Introduced: 1956.
Locomotive manufacturer: Ruston & Hornsby.
Total b.h.p.: 165.
Engine: Ruston type 6VPHL of 165 b.h.p. at 1,250 r.p.m. (1 hr. rating).
Transmission: **Mechanical.** Oil pressure-operated S.L.M. type friction clutches incorporated in Ruston constant mesh type gearbox. Reverse gear and final drive unit incorporating bevel gears and dog clutches and reduction gear to final drive.
Weight: 28 tons.
Driving Wheels: 3' 4".
Maximum tractive effort: 14,350 lb.
Classified **DY5** by the E. & N.E.R.

(Original numbers in brackets)

D2957 (11507)	D2958 (11508)

0-6-0   Shunter

Engines D3000-D3336 were originally numbered 13000-13336 and are being renumbered as they are overhauled.

Introduced: 1953.
Locomotive manufacturer: British Railways.
Total b.h.p.: 400.
Engine: English Electric 6 cyl. type 6KT of 400 b.h.p. at 680 r.p.m.
Transmission: **Electric.** Two English Electric nose-suspended traction motors. Double reduction gear drive.
Weight: 49 tons 0 cwt.
Driving Wheels: 4' 6".
Maximum tractive effort: 35,000 lb.
Classified **DEJ4** by the E. & N.E.R.

Note: Nos. D3000–91 and 3102–3116 fitted with vacuum brake equipment.

D3000	D3030	D3060	D3090
D3001	D3031	D3061	D3091
D3002	D3032	D3062	D3092
D3003	D3033	D3063	D3093
D3004	D3034	D3064	D3094
D3005	D3035	D3065	D3095
D3006	D3036	D3066	D3096
D3007	D3037	D3067	D3097
D3008	D3038	D3068	D3098
D3009	D3039	D3069	D3099
D3010	D3040	D3070	D3100
D3011	D3041	D3071	D3101
D3012	D3042	D3072	D3102
D3013	D3043	D3073	D3103
D3014	D3044	D3074	D3104
D3015	D3045	D3075	D3105
D3016	D3046	D3076	D3106
D3017	D3047	D3077	D3107
D3018	D3048	D3078	D3108
D3019	D3049	D3079	D3109
D3020	D3050	D3080	D3110
D3021	D3051	D3081	D3111
D3022	D3052	D3082	D3112
D3023	D3053	D3083	D3113
D3024	D3054	D3084	D3114
D3025	D3055	D3085	D3115
D3026	D3056	D3086	D3116
D3027	D3057	D3087	
D3028	D3058	D3098	
D3029	D3059	D3089	

0-6-0   Shunter

Introduced: 1955.
Locomotive manufacturer: British Railways.
Total b.h.p.: 350.
Engine: Crossley 6 cyl. type ESNT 6 of 350 b.h.p. at 825 r.p.m. (continuous rating).
Transmission: **Electric.** Two Crompton Parkinson nose-suspended traction motors. Double reduction gear drive.
Weight: 47 tons 10 cwt.
Driving Wheels: 4′ 6″.
Maximum tractive effort: 35,000 lb.

D3117	D3120	D3123	D3126
D3118	D3121	D3124	
D3119	D3122	D3125	

0-6-0   Shunter

Introduced: 1953.
Locomotive manufacturer: British Railways.
Total b.h.p.: 400.
Engine: English Electric 6 cyl. type 6KT of 400 b.h.p. at 680 r.p.m.
Transmission: **Electric.** Two English Electric nose-suspended traction motors. Double reduction gear drive.
Weight: 48 tons 0 cwt.
Driving Wheels: 4′ 6″.
Maximum tractive effort: 35,000 lb.
Fitted with vacuum brake equipment.
Classified **DEJ4** by the E. & N.E.R.

D3127	D3130	D3133	D3136
D3128	D3131	D3134	
D3129	D3132	D3135	

0-6-0   Shunter

Introduced: 1955.
Locomotive manufacturer: British Railways.
Total b.h.p.: 370.
Engine: Blackstone 6 cyl. type ER6T of 370 b.h.p. at 750 r.p.m.
Transmission: **Electric.** Two G.E.C. nose-suspended traction motors, Double reduction gear drive.
Weight: 47 tons 10 cwt.
Driving Wheels: 4′ 6″.
Maximum tractive effort: 35,000 lb.
Fitted with vacuum brake equipment.

D3137	D3141	D3145	D3149
D3138	D3142	D3146	D3150
D3139	D3143	D3147	D3151
D3140	D3144	D3148	

0-6-0   Shunter

Introduced: 1955.
Locomotive manufacturer: British Railways.
Total b.h.p.: 370.
Engine: Blackstone 6 cyl. type ER6T of 370 b.h.p. at 750 r.p.m.
Transmission: Two B.T.H. nose-suspended traction motors. Double reduction gear drive.
Weight: 47 tons 0 cwt.
Driving Wheels: 4′ 6″.
Maximum tractive effort: 35,000 lb.
Classified **DEJ6** by the E. & N.E.R.

D3152	D3156	D3160	D3164
D3153	D3157	D3161	D3165
D3154	D3158	D3162	D3166
D3155	D3159	D3163	

D3167-D3438. FOR PARTICULARS SEE Nos. D3127-D3136.

D3167	D3189	D3211	D3233
D3168	D3190	D3212	D3234
D3169	D3191	D3213	D3235
D3170	D3192	D3214	D3236
D3171	D3193	D3215	D3237
D3172	D3194	D3216	D3238
D3173	D3195	D3217	D3239
D3174	D3196	D3218	D3240
D3175	D3197	D3219	D3241
D3176	D3198	D3220	D3242
D3177	D3199	D3221	D3243
D3178	D3200	D3222	D3244
D3179	D3201	D3223	D3245
D3180	D3202	D3224	D3246
D3181	D3203	D3225	D3247
D3182	D3204	D3226	D3243
D3183	D3205	D3227	D3249
D3184	D3206	D3228	D3250
D3185	D3207	D3229	D3251
D3186	D3208	D3230	D3252
D3187	D3209	D3231	D3253
D3188	D3210	D3232	D3254

D3255	D3301	D3347	D3393
D3256	D3302	D3348	D3394
D3257	D3303	D3349	D3395
D3258	D3304	D3350	D3396
D3259	D3305	D3351	D3397
D3260	D3306	D3352	D3398
D3261	D3307	D3353	D3399
D3262	D3308	D3354	D3400
D3263	D3309	D3355	D3401
D3264	D3310	D3356	D3402
D3265	D3311	D3357	D3403
D3266	D3312	D3358	D3404
D3267	D3313	D3359	D3405
D3268	D3314	D3360	D3406
D3269	D3315	D3361	D3407
D3270	D3316	D3362	D3408
D3271	D3317	D3363	D3409
D3272	D3318	D3364	D3410
D3273	D3319	D3365	D3411
D3274	D3320	D3366	D3412
D3275	D3321	D3367	D3413
D3276	D3322	D3368	D3414
D3277	D3323	D3369	D3415
D3278	D3324	D3370	D3416
D3279	D3325	D3371	D3417
D3280	D3326	D3372	D3418
D3281	D3327	D3373	D3419
D3282	D3328	D3374	D3420
D3283	D3329	D3375	D3421
D3284	D3330	D3376	D3422
D3285	D3331	D3377	D3423
D3286	D3332	D3378	D3424
D3287	D3333	D3379	D3425
D3288	D3334	D3380	D3426
D3289	D3335	D3381	D3427
D3290	D3336	D3382	D3428
D3291	D3337	D3383	D3429
D3292	D3338	D3384	D3430
D3293	D3339	D3385	D3431
D3294	D3340	D3386	D3432
D3295	D3341	D3387	D3433
D3296	D3342	D3388	D3434
D3297	D3343	D3389	D3435
D3298	D3344	D3390	D3436
D3299	D3345	D3391	D3437
D3300	D3346	D3392	D3438

D3439-D3453. FOR PARTICULARS SEE D3137-3151.

D3439	D3443	D3447	D3451
D3440	D3444	D3448	D3452
D3441	D3445	D3449	D3453
D3442	D3446	D3450	

D3454-D3472. FOR PARTICULARS SEE D3127-D3136.

D3454	D3459	D3464	D3469
D3455	D3460	D3465	D3470
D3456	D3461	D3466	D3471
D3457	D3462	D3467	D3472
D3458	D3463	D3468	

D3473-D3502. FOR PARTICULARS SEE D3137-D3151.

D3473	D3431	D3489	D3497
D3474	D3432	D3490	D3498
D3475	D3483	D3491	D3499
D3476	D3484	D3492	D3500
D3477	D3485	D3493	D3501
D3478	D3486	D3494	D3502
D3479	D3487	D3495	
D3480	D3483	D3496	

D3503-D3611. FOR PARTICULARS SEE D3127-D3136.

D3503	D3523	D3543	D3563
D3504	D3524	D3544	D3564
D3505	D3525	D3545	D3565
D3506	D3526	D3546	D3566
D3507	D3527	D3547	D3567
D3503	D3528	D3548	D3568
D3509	D3529	D3549	D3569
D3510	D3530	D3550	D3570
D3511	D3531	D3551	D3571
D3512	D3532	D3552	D3572
D3513	D3533	D3553	D3573
D3514	D3534	D3554	D3574
D3515	D3535	D3555	D3575
D3516	D3536	D3556	D3576
D3517	D3537	D3557	D3577
D3518	D3538	D3558	D3578
D3519	D3539	D3559	D3579
D3520	D3540	D3560	D3580
D3521	D3541	D3561	D3581
D3522	D3542	D3562	D3582

D3583	D3591	D3599	D3607
D3584	D3592	D3600	D3608
D3585	D3593	D3601	D3609
D3586	D3594	D3602	D3610
D3587	D3595	D3603	D3611
D3588	D3596	D3604	
D3589	D3597	D3605	
D3590	D3598	D3606	

D3612-D3651. FOR PARTICULARS SEE D3137-D3151.

D3612	D3622	D3632	D3642
D3613	D3623	D3633	D3643
D3614	D3624	D3634	D3644
D3615	D3625	D3635	D3645
D3616	D3626	D3636	D3646
D3617	D3627	D3637	D3647
D3618	D3628	D3638	D3648
D3619	D3629	D3639	D3649
D3620	D3630	D3640	D3650
D3621	D3631	D3641	D3651

D3652-D3686. FOR PARTICULARS SEE D3127-D3136.

D3652	D3661	D3670	D3679
D3653	D3662	D3671	D3680
D3654	D3663	D3672	D3681
D3655	D3664	D3673	D3682
D3656	D3665	D3674	D3683
D3657	D3666	D3675	D3684
D3658	D3667	D3676	D3685
D3659	D3668	D3677	D3686
D3660	D3669	D3678	

Bo-Bo   "2"

Introduced: 1958.
Locomotive manufacturer: B.R. Derby/ B.T.H.
Total b.h.p.: 1,160.
Engine: Sulzer 6-cyl. type 6LDA28 of 1,160 b.h.p. at 750 r.p.m.
Transmission: **Electric.** Four B.T.H. axle-hung, nose-suspended traction motors of 213 h.p. (continuous rating).
Weight: 75 tons.
Driving Wheels: 3′ 9″.
Maximum tractive effort: 40,000 lb.

D5000	D5005	D5010	D5015
D5001	D5006	D5011	D5016
D5002	D5007	D5012	D5017
D5003	D5008	D5013	D5018
D5004	D5009	D5014	D5019

Bo-Bo   "2"

Introduced: 1958.
Locomotive manufacturer: Birmingham R.C. & W. Co.
Total b.h.p.: 1,160.
Engine: Vickers Armstrong/Sulzer 6-cyl. type of 1,160 b.h.p. at 750 r.p.m.
Transmission: **Electric.** Four Crompton Parkinson axle-hung, nose-suspended traction motors.
Weight: 77 tons 10 cwt.
Driving Wheels: 3′ 7″.
Maximum tractive effort: 42,000 lb.

D5300	D5305	D5310	D5315
D5301	D5306	D5311	D5316
D5302	D5307	D5312	D5317
D5303	D5308	D5313	D5318
D5304	D5309	D5314	D5319

AIA-AIA   "2"

Introduced: 1957.
Locomotive manufacturer: Brush Traction Ltd.
Total b.h.p.: 1,250.
Engine: Mirrlees, Bickerton & Day 12-cyl. JVS12T of 1,250 b.h.p. at 850 r.p.m.
Transmission: **Electric.** Four Brush 250 h.p. traction motors, single reduction gear drive.
Weight: 104 tons.
Driving Wheels: 3′ 7″.
Maximum tractive effort: 42,000 lb.

D5500	D5505	D5510	D5515
D5501	D5506	D5511	D5516
D5502	D5507	D5512	D5517
D5503	D5508	D5513	D5518
D5504	D5509	D5514	D5519

Co-Bo   " 2 "

Introduced: 1958.
Locomotive manufacturer: Metropolitan
   Vickers.
Total b.h.p.: 1,200.
Engine(s):
Transmission: **Electric.**
Weight:
Driving Wheels:
Maximum tractive effort:

D5700	D5705	D5710	D5715
D5701	D5706	D5711	D5716
D5702	D5707	D5712	D5717
D5703	D5708	D5713	D5718
D5704	D5709	D5714	D5719

Bo-Bo   " 2 "

To be introduced:
Locomotive manufacturer: English Elec-
   tric.
Total b.h.p.: 1,100.
Engine: English Electric 9-cyl. " Deltic "
   type of 1,100 b.h.p.
Transmission: **Electric.** Four English
   Electric nose-suspended traction
   motors.
Weight: 72 tons.
Driving Wheels:
Maximum tractive effort:

D5900	D5903	D5906	D5909
D5901	D5904	D5907	
D5902	D5905	D5908	

Bo-Bo   " 2 "

To be introduced:
Locomotive manufacturer: North British
   Locomotive Co.
Total b.h.p.: 1,000.
Engine: M.A.N. 1,000 b.h.p.
Transmission: **Electric.** Four G.E.C.
   nose-suspended traction motors.
Weight: 72 tons.
Driving Wheels: 3′ 7″.
Maximum tractive effort: 45,000 lb.

D6100	D6103	D6106	D6109
D6101	D6104	D6107	
D6102	D6105	D6108	

B-B   " 2 "

To be introduced:
Locomotive manufacturer: North British
   Locomotive Co.
Total b.h.p.: 1,000.
Engine(s):
Transmission: **Hydraulic.**
Weight:
Driving Wheels:
Maximum tractive effort:

| D6300 | D6302 | D6304 | D6305 |
| D6301 | D6303 | | |

Bo-Bo   " 3 "

To be introduced:
Locomotive manufacturer: Birmingham
   R.C. & W. Co.
Total b.h.p.: 1,550.
Engine(s):
Transmission: **Electric.**
Weight:
Driving Wheels:
Maximum tractive effort:

D6500	D6512	D6524	D6536
D6501	D6513	D6525	D6537
D6502	D6514	D6526	D6538
D6503	D6515	D6527	D6539
D6504	D6516	D6528	D6540
D6505	D6517	D6529	D6541
D6506	D6518	D6530	D6542
D6507	D6519	D6531	D6543
D6508	D6520	D6532	D6544
D6509	D6521	D6533	
D6510	D6522	D6534	
D6511	D6523	D6535	

Bo-Bo   " 1 "

Introduced: 1957.
Locomotive manufacturer: English Elec-
   tric Co./Vulcan Foundry Ltd.
Total b.h.p.: 1,000.
Engine: English Electric 8 SVT Mk. II of
   1,000 b.h.p. at 850 r.p.m. (con-
   tinuous).
Transmission: **Electric.** Four axle-
   hung, nose-suspended d.c. traction
   motors.
Weight: 72 tons.
Driving Wheels: 3′ 7″.
Maximum tractive effort: 42,000 lb.

| D8000 | D8001 | D8002 | D8003 |

D8004	D8008	D8012	D8016
D8005	D8009	D8013	D8017
D8006	D8010	D8014	D8018
D8007	D8011	D8015	D8019

Bo-Bo   " I "

Introduced: 1957.
Locomotive manufacturer: British Thomson-Houston Co./Clayton.
Total b.h.p.: 800.
Engine: Paxman 16-cyl. YHXL " V "-type pressure charged by two Napier exhaust gas-driven turbo chargers. 800 b.h.p. at 1,250 r.p.m.
Transmission: **Electric.** Four B.T.H. nose-suspended traction motors with single reduction gear drive.
Weight: 68 tons.
Driving Wheels: 3′ 3½″.
Maximum tractive effort: 37,500 lb.

D8200	D9203	D3206	D3208
D8201	D8204	D8207	D3209
D8202	D8205		

Bo-Bo   " I "

Introduced: 1958.
Locomotive manufacturer: North British Locomotive Co.
Total b.h.p.: 800.
Engine: Paxman 16-cyl. type 16YHXL of 800 b.h.p. at 1,250 r.p.m.
Transmission: **Electric.** Four G.E.C. axle-hung nose-suspended traction motors.
Weight: 68 tons.
Driving Wheels: 3′ 7″.
Maximum tractive effort: 42,000 lb.

D8400	D8403	D8406	D8408
D8401	D8404	D8407	D8409
D8402	D8405		

Co-Co   5P/5F

Introduced: 1947.
Locomotive manufacturer: Derby Works, B.R.
Total b.h.p.: 1,600 at 750 r.p.m. (continuous rating).
Engine: English Electric Co. 16-cyl. 1,600 b.h.p.
Transmission: **Electric.** Six nose-suspended motors, single reduction gear drive.
Weight: 127 tons 13 cwt.
Driving Wheels: 3′ 6″.
Maximum tractive effort: 41,400 lb.

10000	10001	**Total 2**

2-D-2   6P/5F

Introduced: 1951.
Locomotive manufacturer: Derby Works, B.R.
Total b.h.p.: 2,000 (continuous rating).
Engines: Four Davey Paxman 12-cyl. 500 b.h.p.
Transmission: **Mechanical.** Fell patent differential drive and fluid couplings.
Weight: 120 tons.
Driving Wheels: 4′ 3″.
Maximum tractive effort: 25,000 lb.

10100	**Total 1**

1Co-Co1   { 10201/2 5P/5F }
                { 10203 6P/6F }

Introduced: { 1951
                { 1954*
Locomotive manufacturer: Ashford Works, B.R.
Total b.h.p.: { 1,600
                 { 1,750*
Engine: English Electric Co. 16-cyl. 1,600 b.h.p. (1,750 b.h.p.)*
Transmission: **Electric.** Six nose-suspended, axle-hung d.c. motors of 260 b.h.p. (1-hour rating).
Weight: { 135 tons.
           { 132 tons.*
Driving Wheels: 3′ 7″.
Maximum tractive effort: { 48,000 lb.
                            { 50,000 lb.*

10201	10202	*10203
		Total 3

Bo-Bo   3P/3F

Introduced: 1950.
Locomotive manufacturer: North British Locomotive Co.
Total b.h.p.: 827.
Engine: Davey Paxman type RPHXL. 16-cyl., 827 b.h.p. at 1,250 r.p.m.
Transmission: **Electric.** Four British Thomson - Houston Co. nose-suspended motors, single reduction gear drive.
Weight: 69 tons 16 cwt.
Driving Wheels: 3′ 6″.
Maximum tractive effort: 34,500 lb.

10800	**Total 1**

0-6-0   Shunter

Introduced: 1950.
Locomotive manufacturer: Ashford Works, B.R.
Total b.h.p.: 500.
Engine: Davey Paxman type 12RPH " V " 12-cyl. 500 b.h.p. at 1,250 r.p.m.
Transmission: **Mechanical** with S.S.S. Powerflow three-speed gearbox and Vulcan-Sinclair scoop-control fluid coupling.
Weight: 49 tons 9 cwt.
Driving Wheels: 4' 6".
Maximum tractive effort: 33,500 lb. (in low gear).

11001   **Total 1**

0-6-0   Shunter

Introduced: 1936.
Locomotive manufacturer: English Electric for L.M.S.
Total b.h.p.: 350.
Engine: English Electric 6-cyl. 350 b.h.p.
Transmission: **Electric.** Two nose-suspended motors, single reduction gear drive.
Weight: 51 tons.
Driving Wheels: 4' 0½".
Maximum tractive effort: 30,000 lb.

12000   12001   **Total 2**

0-6-0   Shunter

Introduced: 1939.
Locomotive manufacturer: Derby Works, B.R.
Total b.h.p.: 350.
Engine: English Electric, 6-cyl. 350 b.h.p.
Transmission: **Electric.** Single motor; jackshaft drive.
Weight: 54 tons 16 cwt.
Driving Wheels: 4' 3".
Maximum tractive effort: 33,000 lb.

12003   12004   12005   12006

12007	12014	12021	12028
12008	12015	12022	12029
12009	12016	12023	12030
12010	12017	12024	12031
12011	12018	12025	12032
12012	12019	12026	
12013	12020	12027	

Total 30

0-6-0   Shunter

Introduced: 1945.
Locomotive manufacturer: Derby Works, B.R.
Total b.h.p.: 350.
Engine: English Electric, 6-cyl. 350 h.p.
Transmission: **Electric.** Two 135 h.p. nose-suspended motors, double reduction gear drive.
Weight: 47 tons 5 cwt.
Driving Wheels: 4' 0½".
Maximum tractive effort: 35,000 lb.
Classified **DEJ3** by the E. & N.E.R.

12033	12057	12081	12105
12034	12058	12082	12106
12035	12059	12083	12107
12036	12060	12084	12108
12037	12061	12085	12109
12038	12062	12086	12110
12039	12063	12087	12111
12040	12064	12088	12112
12041	12065	12089	12113
12042	12066	12090	12114
12043	12067	12091	12115
12044	12068	12092	12116
12045	12069	12093	12117
12046	12070	12094	12118
12047	12071	12095	12119
12048	12072	12096	12120
12049	12073	12097	12121
12050	12074	12098	12122
12051	12075	12099	12123
12052	12076	12100	12124
12053	12077	12101	12125
12054	12078	12102	12126
12055	12079	12103	12127
12056	12080	12104	12128

12129	12132	12135	12138
12130	12133	12136	
12131	12134	12137	

Total 106

0-6-0   Shunter

Introduced: 1944.
Locomotive manufacturer: Doncaster Works, B.R.
Total b.h.p.: 350.
Engine: English Electric, 6-cyl. 350 b.h.p.
Transmission: **Electric.** Two 135 h.p. nose-suspended motors, double reduction gear drive.
Weight: 50 tons.
Driving Wheels: 4' 0".
Maximum tractive effort: 32,000 lb.
Classified **DEJ1** by the E. & N.E.R.

15000	15001	15002	15003

Total 4

0-6-0   Shunter

Introduced: 1949.
Locomotive manufacturer: Doncaster Works, B.R.
Total b.h.p.: 360.
Engine: Petter SS4 4-cyl. 360 b.h.p.
Transmission: **Electric.** Two 135 h.p. nose-suspended traction motors, double reduction gear drive.
Weight: 51 tons.
Driving Wheels: 4' 0".
Maximum tractive effort: 32,000 lb.
Classified **DEJ2** by the E. & N.E.R.

15004   **Total 1**

0-6-0   Shunter

Introduced: 1936.
Locomotive manufacturer: English Electric for G.W.R.
Total b.h.p.: 350.
Engine: English Electric, 6-cyl. 350 b.h.p.
Transmission: **Electric.** Two nose-suspended motors, single reduction gear drive.
Weight: 51 tons 10 cwt.
Driving Wheels: 4' 1".
Maximum tractive effort: 30,000 lb.

15100   **Total 1**

0-6-0   Shunter

Introduced: 1948.
Locomotive manufacturer: Swindon Works, B.R.
Total b.h.p.: 350.
Engine: English Electric, 6-cyl. 350 b.h.p.
Transmission: **Electric.** Two 135 h.p. nose-suspended motors, double reduction gear drive.
Weight: 50 tons.
Driving Wheels: 4' 0½".
Maximum tractive effort: 33,500 lb.

15101	15103	15105
15102	15104	15106

Total 6

0-6-0   Shunter

Introduced: 1937.
Locomotive manufacturer: Ashford Works, B.R.
Total b.h.p.: 350.
Engine: English Electric, 6-cyl. 350 b.h.p.
Transmission: **Electric.** Two nose-suspended motors, single reduction gear drive.
Weight: 55 tons 5 cwt.
Driving Wheels: 4' 6".
Maximum tractive effort: 30,000 lb.

15201	15202	15203

Total 3

0-6-0   Shunter

Introduced: 1949.
Locomotive manufacturer: Ashford Works, B.R.
Total b.h.p.: 350.
Engine: English Electric, 6-cyl. 350 b.h.p.
Transmission: **Electric.** Two 135 h.p. nose-suspended motors, double reduction gear drive.
Weight: 45 tons.
Driving Wheels: 4' 6".
Maximum tractive effort: 24,000 lb.

15211	15218	15225	15232
15212	15219	15226	15233
15213	15220	15227	15234
15214	15221	15228	15235
15215	15222	15229	15236
15216	15223	15230	
15217	15224	15231	

Total 26

Co-Co   " Deltic "

NOTE: British Railways are providing facilities for road tests of this locomotive, which remains the property of the manufacturer, and is not included in B.R. stock.

Introduced: 1955.
Locomotive manufacturer: English Electric.
Total b.h.p.: 3,300.
Engines: Napier " Deltic."
Transmission: **Electric.**
Weight: 106 tons.
Driving Wheels:
Maximum tractive effort: 60,000 lb.

SERVICE LOCOMOTIVES

Western Region

0-4-0

Introduced: 1957.
Locomotive manufacturer: Ruston & Hornsby.
Total b.h.p.: 88.
Engine: Ruston & Hornsby 4-cyl. type of 83 b.h.p.
Transmission: **Mechanical.** Chain driven from gearbox.
Weight: 17 tons.
Wheel Diameter: 3′ 0″.
Maximum tractive effort: 9,500 lb.
20

0-6-0

Introduced: 1953.
Locomotive Manufacturer: Ruston & Hornsby.
Total b.h.p.: 165.
Engine: Ruston & Hornsby 6-cyl. type of 165 b.h.p.
Transmission: **Electric.** One B.T.H. nose-suspended traction motor.
Weight: 30 tons.
Driving Wheels: 3′ 2½″.
Maximum tractive effort: 17,000 lb.
PWM650

Southern Region

0-4-0

Introduced: 1947.
Locomotive manufacturer: John Fowler & Co.
Total b.h.p.: 150.

Engine: Fowler.
Transmission: **Mechanical.** Four-speed gearbox.
Weight: 29 tons.
Driving Wheels: 3′ 3″.
Maximum tractive effort: 15,000 lb.
DS600

0-6-0

Introduced: 1947.
Locomotive manufacturer: Drewry.
Total b.h.p.: 204.
Engine: Gardner 8L3 of 204 b.h.p.
Transmission: **Mechanical.** Five-speed gearbox.
Weight: 24 tons 15 cwt.
Driving Wheels: 3′ 3″.
Maximum tractive effort: 16,850 lb.
DS1173

London Midland Region

0-4-0

Introduced: 1936.
Locomotive manufacturer: John Fowler & Co.
Total b.h.p.: 88.
Engine: Ruston & Hornsby 6-cyl. type VQ of 88 b.h.p.
Transmission: **Mechanical.** Four-speed constant mesh gearbox with multiple disc dry clutch manually operated.
Weight: 25 tons.
Driving Wheels: 3′ 0″.
Maximum tractive effort: 8,940 lb.
ED1

0-4-0

Introduced: 1936.
Locomotive manufacturer: John Fowler & Co.
Total b.h.p.: 150.
Engine: Fowler type 4C vertical of 150 b.h.p. at 1,000 r.p.m. (1 hr. rating).
Transmission: **Mechanical.** Four-speed gearbox.
Weight: 29 tons.
Driving Wheels: 3′ 3″.
Maximum tractive effort: 15,000 lb.

| ED2 | ED4 | ED5 | ED6 |
| ED3 | | | |

0-4-0

Introduced: 1955.
Locomotive manufacturer: John Fowler & Co.
Total b.h.p.: 150.
Engine: Fowler 4-cyl. type C of 150 b.h.p.
Transmission: **Mechanical.** Three-lobe synchromesh gearbox with multiple disc dry clutch manually operated.
Weight: 29 tons.
Driving Wheels: 3′ 3″.
Maximum tractive effort: 15,000 lb.

ED7

0-4-0

Introduced: 1958.
Locomotive manufacturer: Ruston & Hornsby.
Total b.h.p.:
Engine: Ruston type 4YCL.
Transmission: **Mechanical.** Chain drive.
Weight: 8 tons 4 cwt.
Driving Wheels: 2′ 6″.
Maximum tractive effort: 4,200 lb.
Gauge: 3′ 0″.

ED10

Eastern Region

0-4-0

Introduced: 1950.
Locomotive manufacturer: Hibberd & Co.
Total b.h.p.: 52.
Engine: English National 4-cyl. Gas type. DA4 of 52 b.h.p. at 1,250 r.p.m.
Transmission: **Mechanical.** Spur-type three-speed gearbox with roller chains.
Weight: 11 tons.
Driving Wheels:
Maximum tractive effort:

52 (11104)

0-4-0

Introduced: 1955.
Locomotive manufacturer: Ruston & Hornsby.
Total b.h.p.: 88.
Engine: Ruston & Hornsby Mark 4V vertical 4-cyl. of 88 b.h.p.
Transmission: **Mechanical.**
Weight: 17 tons.
Driving Wheels: 3′ 0″.
Maximum tractive effort: 9,500 lb.

56

North Eastern Region
0-6-0

Introduced: 1958.
Locomotive manufacturer: Swindon Works, B.R.
Total b.h.p.: 200.
Engine: Gardner type 8L3 of 204 b.h.p. at 1,200 r.p.m.
Transmission: **Mechanical.** Wilson-Drewry Director air-operated epicyclic gearbox. R.F.11 Spiral Bevel reverse/final drive unit.
Weight: 30 tons 4 cwt.
Driving Wheels: 3′ 7″.
Maximum tractive effort: 15,300 lb.

| 91 | 92 |

DIESEL MULTIPLE UNITS

The numbers of diesel cars have been checked to September 6th, 1958

Unless otherwise stated, all multiple-unit trains are gangwayed within each set, with guard's and luggage compartment at the inner end of motor brake coaches, and seating is in open saloons with centre and/or end doors. The letter L in the headings indicates an

Open vehicle fitted with toilet facilities ; K indicates a side corridor vehicle with toilet. Two standard lengths of underframe are in use, namely 56 ft. 11 in. and 63 ft. 5 in. but the actual body lengths vary by a few inches for the same type of underframe. The dimensions shown are the length over body and the overall width.

Several of the types listed are sub-divided by reason of detail or mechanical differences. For example, a certain number of cars in a class may have a different seating arrangement or a different make of engine but are otherwise similar to the main batch. Such differences are noted in the heading to the class and given a reference mark by which the relevant dimensions or details and the cars concerned can be identified. The type of set in which each class is formed is shown at the head of the details for that class.

Motor Brake Second

(TWIN UNITS)

Built by: **Derby Works, B.R.**
Engines: Two B.U.T. (Leyland) 6-cyl. horizontal type of 150 b.h.p.
  *Two Rolls Royce 8-cyl. horizontal type of 238 b.h.p.
  †Two B.U.T. (Leyland) 6-cyl. horizontal type of 230 b.h.p.
Transmission: **Mechanical.** Cardan shaft and freewheel to four-speed epicyclic gearbox and further cardan shaft to final drive.
  *Hydraulic. Torque converter.
  †Mechanical. Cardan shaft and free wheel to Self Changing Gears Ltd. automatic four-speed gearbox and further cardan shaft to final drive.
Body: 64′ 6″ × 9′ 3″.
Weight: {35 tons 10 cwt.
  {37 tons 10 cwt.†
Seats 2nd: 62.

E50000*	E50015	E50030
E50001	E50016	E50031
E50002	E50017	E50032
E50003	E50018	E50033
E50004	E50019	E50034
E50005	E50020	E50035
E50006	E50021	E50036
E50007	E50022	E50037
E50008	E50023	E50038
E50009	E50024	E50039
E50010	E50025	E50040
E50011	E50026	E50041
E50012	E50027	E50042
E50013	E50028	E50043
E50014	E50029	E50044

E50045	E50047	E50049†
E50046	E50048	

Cars 50001–48 are to be equipped with 230 h.p. B.U.T. engines shortly.

Motor Brake Second

(W.R. THREE-CAR SUBURBAN)

Built by: **Derby Works, B.R.**
Engines: Two B.U.T. (Leyland) 6-cyl. horizontal type of 150 b.h.p.
Transmission: **Mechanical.** Cardan shaft and freewheel to four-speed epicyclic gearbox and further cardan shaft to final drive.
Body: 64′ 0″ × 9′ 3″. Non-gangwayed, side doors to each seating bay.
Weight: 35 tons 10 cwt.
Seats 2nd: 65.

W50050	W50065	W50080
W50051	W50066	W50081
W50052	W50067	W50082
W50053	W50068	W50083
W50054	W50069	W50084
W50055	W50070	W50085
W50056	W50071	W50086
W50057	W50072	W50087
W50058	W50073	W50088
W50059	W50074	W50089
W50060	W50075	W50090
W50061	W50076	W50091
W50062	W50077	
W50063	W50078	
W50064	W50079	

Motor Second

(W.R. THREE-CAR SUBURBAN)

Built by: **Derby Works, B.R.**
Engines: Two B.U.T. (Leyland) 6-cyl. horizontal type of 150 b.h.p.
Transmission: **Mechanical.** Cardan shaft and freewheel to four-speed epicyclic gearbox and further cardan shaft to final drive.
Body: 64′ 0″ × 9′ 3″. Non-gangwayed, side doors to each seating bay.
Weight: 35 tons 10 cwt.
Seats 2nd: 95.

W50092	W50106	W50120
W50093	W50107	W50121
W50094	W50108	W50122
W50095	W50109	W50123
W50096	W50110	W50124
W50097	W50111	W50125
W50098	W50112	W50126
W50099	W50113	W50127
W50100	W50114	W50128
W50101	W50115	W50129
W50102	W50116	W50130
W50103	W50117	W50131
W50104	W50118	W50132
W50105	W50119	W50133

Motor Brake Second

(TWIN UNITS)

Built by: **Metropolitan Cammell.**
Engines: Two Rolls-Royce 6-cyl. horizontal type of 180 b.h.p.
  *Two Rolls Royce 6-cyl. type supercharged to 230 b.h.p.
Transmission: **Mechanical.** Cardan shaft and freewheel to four-speed epicyclic gearbox and further cardan shafts to final drive.
Body: 57′ 0″ × 9′ 3″.
Weight: 33 tons.
Seats 2nd: 52.

M50134	M50136*	M50137
M50135		

Motor Composite (L)

(N.E. FOUR-CAR UNITS)

Built by: **Metropolitan Cammell.**
Engines: Two B.U.T. (A.E.C.) 6-cyl. horizontal type of 150 b.h.p.

Transmission: **Mechanical.** Cardan shaft and freewheel to four-speed epicyclic gearbox and further cardan shaft to final drive.
Body: 57′ 0″ × 9′ 3″.
Weight: 32 tons.
Seats 1st: 12.
  2nd: 45.

E50138	E50143	E50148
E50139	E50144	E50149
E50140	E50145	E50150
E50141	E50146	E50151
E50142	E50147	

Motor Brake Second

(TWIN UNITS)

Built by: **Metropolitan Cammell.**
Engines: Two B.U.T. (A.E.C.) 6-cyl. horizontal type of 150 b.h.p.
Transmission: **Mechanical.** Cardan shaft and freewheel to four-speed epicyclic gearbox and further cardan shaft to final drive.
Body: 57′ 0″ × 9′ 3″.
Weight: 32 tons.
Seats 2nd:

E50152	E50154	E50156
E50153	E50155	E50157

Motor Composite (L)

(TWIN UNITS)

Built by: **Metropolitan Cammell.**
Engines: Two B.U.T. (A.E.C.) 6-cyl. horizontal type of 150 b.h.p.
Transmission: **Mechanical.** Cardan shaft and freewheel to four-speed epicyclic gearbox and further cardan shaft to final drive.
Body: 57′ 0″ × 9′ 3″.
Weight: 32 tons.
Seats 1st: 12.
  2nd: 53.

E50158	E50160	E50162
E50159	E50161	E50163

Motor Brake Second

(TWIN UNITS)

For Details see E50152-7

E50164	E50166	E50167
E50165		

Motor Composite (L)
(TWIN UNITS)
For Details see E50158-63

E50168	E50170	E50171
E50169		

Motor Composite (L)
(N.E. FOUR-CAR UNITS)

Built by: **Metropolitan Cammell.**
Engines: B.U.T. (A.E.C.) 6-cyl. horizontal type of 150 b.h.p.
Transmission: **Mechanical.** Cardan shaft and freewheel to four-speed epicyclic gearbox and further cardan shaft to final drive.
Body: 57′ 0″ × 9′ 3″.
Weight: 32 tons.
Seats 1st: 12.
     2nd: 53.

E50172	E50182	E50191
E50174	E50183	E50192
E50175	E50184	E50193
E50176	E50185	E50194
E50177	E50186	E50195
E50178	E50187	E50196
E50179	E50188	E50197
E50180	E50189	
E50181	E50190	

Motor Brake Second
(TWIN UNITS)

Built by: **Metropolitan Cammell.**
Engines: Two B.U.T. (A.E.C.) 6-cyl. horizontal type of 150 b.h.p.
Transmission: **Mechanical.** Cardan shaft and freewheel to four-speed epicyclic gearbox and further cardan shaft to final drive.
Body: 57′ 0″ × 9′ 3″.
Weight: 32 tons.
Seats 2nd: 52

E50198	E50207	E50216
E50199	E50208	E50217
E50200	E50209	E50218
E50201	E50210	E50219
E50202	E50211	E50220
E50203	E50212	E50221
E50204	E50213	E50222
E50205	E50214	E50223
E50206	E50215	E50224

E50225	E50228	E50231
E50226	E50229	E50232
E50227	E50230	E50233

Motor Composite (L)
(N.E. FOUR-CAR UNITS)
For Details see E50138-45

E50234	E50238	E50242
E50235	E50239	E50243
E50236	E50240	E50244
E50237	E50241	E50245

Motor Brake Second
(TWIN UNITS)

Built by: **Metropolitan Cammell.**
Engines: Two B.U.T. (A.E.C.) 6-cyl. horizontal type of 150 b.h.p.
Transmission: **Mechanical.** Cardan shaft and freewheel to four-speed epicyclic gearbox and further cardan shaft to final drive.
Body: 57′ 0″ × 9′ 3″.
Weight: 31 tons 10 cwt.
Seats 2nd:

E50246	E50247	E50248

Motor Brake Second
(TWIN UNITS)

Built by: **Metropolitan Cammell.**
Engines: Two B.U.T. (A.E.C.) 6-cyl. horizontal type of 150 b.h.p.
Transmission: **Mechanical.** Cardan shaft and freewheel to four-speed epicyclic gearbox and further cardan shaft to final drive.
Body: 57′ 0″ × 9′ 3″.
Weight: 31 tons 10 cwt.
Seats 2nd:

E50250	E50254	E50258
E50251	E50255	E50259
E50252	E50256	
E50253	E50257	

Motor Composite (L)
(TWIN UNITS)

Built by: **Metropolitan Cammell.**
Engines: Two B.U.T. (A.E.C.) 6-cyl. horizontal type of 150 b.h.p.
Transmission: **Mechanical.** Cardan shaft and freewheel to four-speed epicyclic gearbox and further cardan shaft to final drive.

Body: 57' 0" × 9' 3".
Weight: 31 tons 10 cwt.
Seats 1st:
 2nd:

E50260	E50264	E50268
E50261	E50265	E50269
E50262	E50266	
E50263	E50267	

Motor Composite (L)
(N.E. THREE-CAR UNITS)

Built by: **Metropolitan Cammell.**
Engines: Two Rolls Royce 6-cyl. horizontal type of 180 b.h.p.
Transmission: **Mechanical.** Cardan shaft and freewheel to four-speed epicyclic gearbox and further cardan shaft to final drive.
Body: 57' 0" × 9' 3".
Weight:
Seats 1st: 12
 2nd: 53.

E50270	E50274	E50278
E50271	E50275	E50279
E50272	E50276	
E50273	E50277	

Motor Brake Second
(N.E. THREE-CAR UNITS)

Built by: **Metropolitan Cammell.**
Engine: Rolls Royce 6-cyl. horizontal type of 180 b.h.p.
Transmission: **Mechanical.** Cardan shaft and freewheel to four-speed epicyclic gearbox and further cardan shaft to final drive.
Body: 57' 0" × 9' 3".
Weight: 33 tons.
Seats 2nd: 52.

E50280	E50285	E50290
E50281	E50286	E50291
E50282	E50287	E50292
E50283	E50288	
E50284	E50289	

Motor Brake Second
(TWIN UNITS)

Built by: **Metropolitan Cammell.**
Engines: Two B.U.T. (A.E.C.) 6-cyl. horizontal type of 150 b.h.p.
Transmission: **Mechanical.** Cardan shaft and freewheel to four-speed epicyclic gearbox and further cardan shaft to final drive.
Body: 57' 0" × 9' 3".
Weight:
Seats 2nd:

E50293	E50295	E50296
E50294		

Motor Brake Second
(L.M. THREE-CAR UNITS)

Built by: **Metropolitan Cammell.**
Engines:
Transmission: **Mechanical.** Cardan shaft and freewheel to four-speed epicyclic gearbox and further cardan shaft to final drive.
Body: 57' 0" × 9' 3".
Weight:
Seats 2nd: 52.

M50303	M50309	M50315
M50304	M50310	M50316
M50305	M50311	M50317
M50306	M50312	M50318
M50307	M50313	M50319
M50308	M50314	M50320

Motor Composite (L)
(L.M. THREE-CAR UNITS)

Built by: **Metropolitan Cammell.**
Engines:
Transmission: **Mechanical.** Cardan shaft and freewheel to four-speed epicyclic gearbox and further cardan shaft to final drive.
Body: 57' 0" × 9' 3".
Weight:
Seats 1st 12.
 2nd: 53.

M50321	M50327	M50333
M50322	M50328	M50334
M50323	M50329	M50335
M50324	M50330	M50336
M50325	M50331	M50337
M50326	M50332	M50338

E50359	E50371*	E50383*
E50360	E50372*	E50384*
E50361	E50373*	E50385*
E50362	E50374*	E50386*
E50363	E50375*	E50387*
E50364	E50376*	E50388*
E50365	E50377*	E50389*
E50366	E50378*	M50390*
E50367	E50379*	M50391*
E50368	E50380*	M50392*
E50369	E50381*	M50393*
E50370	E50382*	M50394*

Motor Brake Second
(TWIN UNITS)
Built by: **Gloucester R.C. & W. Co.**
Engines: Two B.U.T. (A.E.C.) 6-cyl. horizontal type of 150 b.h.p.
Transmission: **Mechanical.** Cardan shaft and freewheel to four-speed epicyclic gearbox and further cardan shaft to final drive.
Body: 57′ 6″ × 9′ 3″.
Weight: 30 tons 5 cwt.
Seats 2nd: 52.

SC50339	SC50346	M50353
SC50340	SC50347	M50354
SC50341	SC50348	M50355
SC50342	SC50349	M50356
SC50343	M50350	M50357
SC50344	M50351	M50358*
SC50345	M50352	

* Fitted with C.A.V. Ltd. automatic gear change equipment.

Motor Brake Second
(TWIN UNITS)
Built by: **Park Royal Vehicles.**
Engines: Two B.U.T. (A.E.C.) 6-cyl. horizontal type of 150 b.h.p.
Transmission: **Mechanical.** Cardan shaft and freewheel to four-speed epicyclic gearbox and further cardan shaft to final drive.
Body: 57′ 6″ × 9′ 3″.
Weight: 33 tons 8 cwt.
Seats 2nd: 52.

M50395	M50401	M50407
M50396	M50402	M50408
M50397	M50403	M50409
M50398	M50404	M50410
M50399	M50405	
M50400	M50406	

Motor Brake Second
(TWIN UNITS)
Built by: **Cravens.**
Engines: Two B.U.T. (Leyland) (A.E.C.*) 6-cyl. horizontal type of 150 b.h.p.
Transmission: **Mechanical.** Cardan shaft and freewheel to four-speed epicyclic gearbox and further cardan shaft to final drive.
Body: 57′ 6″ × 9′ 3″.
Weight: 30 tons.
Seats 2nd: 52.

Motor Brake Second
(TWIN UNITS)
Built by: **D. Wickham & Co. Ltd.**
Engines: Two B.U.T. (Leyland) 6-cyl. horizontal type of 150 b.h.p.
Transmission: **Mechanical.** Cardan shaft and freewheel to four-speed epicyclic gearbox and further cardan shaft to final drive.

Body: 57' 0" × 9' 3".
Weight: 27 tons 10 cwt.
Seats 2nd: 59.

E50415	E50417	E50419
E50416	E50418	

Motor Brake Second

(L.M. THREE-CAR UNITS)

Built by: **Birmingham C. & W. Co.**
Engines: Two B.U.T. (Leyland) 6-cyl. horizontal type of 150 b.h.p.
Transmission: **Mechanical.** Cardan shaft and freewheel to four-speed epicyclic gearbox and further cardan shaft to final drive.
Body: 57' 6" × 9' 3".
Weight: 31 tons.
Seats 2nd: 52.

M50420	M50422	M50423
M50421		

Motor Composite (L)

(L.M. THREE-CAR UNITS)

Built by: **Birmingham C. & W. Co.**
Engines: Two B.U.T. (Leyland) 6-cyl. horizontal type of 150 b.h.p.
Transmission: **Mechanical.** Cardan shaft and freewheel to four-speed epicyclic gearbox and further cardan shaft to final drive.
Body: 57' 6" × 9' 3".
Weight: 31 tons.
Seats 1st: 12.
2nd: 54.

M50424	M50426	M50427
M50425		

Motor Brake Second

(L.M. THREE-CAR UNITS)
For Details see M50420-3

M50428	M50446	M50464
M50429	M50447	M50465
M50430	M50448	M50466
M50431	M50449	M50467
M50432	M50450	M50468
M50433	M50451	M50469
M50434	M50452	M50470
M50435	M50453	M50471
M50436	M50454	M50472
M50437	M50455	M50473
M50438	M50456	M50474
M50439	M50457	M50475
M50440	M50458	M50476
M50441	M50459	M50477
M50442	M50460	M50478
M50443	M50461	M50479
M50444	M50462	
M50445	M50463	

Motor Composite (L)

(L.M. THREE-CAR UNITS)
For Details see M50424-7.

M50480	M50498	M50516
M50481	M50499	M50517
M50482	M50500	M50518
M50483	M50501	M50519
M50484	M50502	M50520
M50485	M50503	M50521
M50486	M50504	M50522
M50487	M50505	M50523
M50488	M50506	M50524
M50489	M50507	M50525
M50490	M50508	M50526
M50491	M50509	M50527
M50492	M50510	M50528
M50493	M50511	M50529
M50494	M50512	M50530
M50495	M50513	M50531
M50496	M50514	
M50497	M50515	

Motor Brake Second
(TWIN UNITS)

Built by: **Birmingham C. & W. Co.**
Engines: Two B.U.T. (Leyland) 6-cyl.
  horizontal type of 150 b.h.p.
Transmission: **Mechanical.** Cardan
  shaft and freewheel to four-speed
  epicyclic gearbox and further cardan
  shaft to final drive.
Body: 57′ 6″ × 9′ 3″.
Weight: 31 tons.
Seats 2nd: 52.

M50532	M50536	M50540
M50533	M50537	M50541
M50534	M50538	
M50535	M50539	

Motor Composite (L)
(N.E. FOUR-CAR UNITS)

Built by: **Birmingham C. & W. Co.**
Engines: Two B.U.T. (Leyland) 6-cyl.
  horizontal type of 150 b.h.p.
Transmission: **Mechanical.** Cardan
  shaft and freewheel to four-speed
  epicyclic gearbox and further cardan
  shaft to final drive.
Body: 57′ 6″ × 9′ 3″.
Weight: 31 tons.
Seats 1st: 12.
  2nd: 51.

E50542	E50549	E50567
E50543	E50550	E50568
E50544	E50551	E50569
E50545	E50563	E50570
E50546	E50564	E50571
E50547	E50565	E50572
E50548	E50566	

Motor Brake Second
(TWIN UNITS)

Built by: **Birmingham C. & W Co.**
Engines: Two B.U.T. (Leyland) 6-cyl.
  horizontal type of 150 b.h.p.

Transmission: **Mechanical.** Cardan
  shaft and freewheel to four-speed
  epicyclic gearbox and further cardan
  shaft to final drive.
Body: 57′ 6″ × 9′ 3″.
Weight: 31 tons.
Seats 2nd: 52.

E50594	E50596	E50598
E50595	E50597	

Motor Brake Second
(TWIN UNITS)

Built by: **Derby Works, B.R.**
Engines: Two B.U.T. (A.E.C.) 6-cyl.
  horizontal type of 150 b.h.p.
Transmission: **Mechanical.** Cardan
  shaft and freewheel to four-speed
  epicyclic gearbox and further cardan
  shaft to final drive.
Body: 57′ 6″ × 9′ 2″.
Weight: 27 tons.
Seats 2nd.

E50599	E50606	E50613
E50600	E50607	E50614
E50601	E50608	E50615
E50602	E50609	E50616
E50603	E50610	E50617
E50604	E50611	E50618
E50605	E50612	E50619

Motor Second (L)
(W.R. THREE-CAR CROSS-COUNTRY)

Built by: **Swindon Works B.R.**
Engines: Two B.U.T. 6-cyl. horizontal
  type of 150 b.h.p.
Transmission: **Mechanical.** Cardan
  shaft and freewheel to four-speed
  epicyclic gearbox and further cardan
  shaft to final drive.
Body: 64′ 6″ × 9′ 3″.
Weight: 36 tons 10 cwt.
Seats 2nd: 68.

W50647	W50650	W50653
W50648	W50651	W50654
W50649	W50652	W50655

W50656	W50670	W50684
W50657	W50671	W50685
W50658	W50672	W50686
W50659	W50673	W50687
W50660	W50674	W50688
W50661	W50675	W50689
W50662	W50676	W50690
W50663	W50677	W50691
W50664	W50678	W50692
W50665	W50679	W50693
W50666	W50680	W50694
W50667	W50681	W50695
W50668	W50682	
W50669	W50683	

Motor Composite (L)
(N.E. THREE-CAR UNITS)

Built by: **Metropolitan Cammell.**
Engines: Two Rolls Royce 6-cyl. horizontal type of 180 b.h.p.
Transmission: **Mechanical.** Cardan shaft and freewheel to four-speed epicyclic gearbox and further cardan shaft to final drive.
Body: 57' 0" × 9' 3".
Weight:
Seats 1st: 12.
  2nd: 53.

E50745	E50746	E50747

Motor Brake Composite
(W.R. THREE-CAR CROSS-COUNTRY)

Built by: **Swindon Works B.R.**
Engines: Two B.U.T. 6-cyl. horizontal type of 150 b.h.p.
Transmission: **Mechanical.** Cardan shaft and freewheel to four-speed epicyclic gearbox and further cardan shaft to final drive.
Body: 64' 6" × 9' 3".
Weight: 36 tons 7 cwt.
Seats 1st: 18.
  2nd: 16.

W50696	W50713	W50730
W50697	W50714	W50731
W50698	W50715	W50732
W50699	W50716	W50733
W50700	W50717	W50734
W50701	W50718	W50735
W50702	W50719	W50736
W50703	W50720	W50737
W50704	W50721	W50738
W50705	W50722	W50739
W50706	W50723	W50740
W50707	W50724	W50741
W50708	W50725	W50742
W50709	W50726	W50743
W50710	W50727	W50744
W50711	W50728	
W50712	W50729	

Motor Composite (L)
(N.E. FOUR-CAR UNITS)

Built by: **Metropolitan Cammell.**
Engines: Two B.U.T. (A.E.C.) 6-cyl. horizontal type of 150 b.h.p.
Transmission: **Mechanical.** Cardan shaft and freewheel to four-speed epicyclic gearbox and further cardan shaft to final drive.
Body: 57' 0" × 9' 3".
Weight:
Seats 1st:
  2nd:

E50748	E50750	E50751
E50749		

Motor Brake Second
(L.M. THREE-CAR UNITS)

Built by: **Cravens.**
Engines: Two B.U.T. (Leyland) 6-cyl. horizontal type of 150 b.h.p.
Transmission: **Mechanical.** Cardan shaft and freewheel to four-speed epicyclic gearbox and further cardan shaft to final drive.
Body: 57' 6" × 9' 3".
Weight: 30 tons.
Seats 2nd: 52.

M50752	M50767	M50782
M50753	M50768	M50783
M50754	M50769	M50784
M50755	M50770	
M50756	M50771	
M50757	M50772	
M50758	M50773	
M50759	M50774	
M50760	M50775	
M50761	M50776	
M50762	M50777	
M50763	M50778	
M50764	M50779	
M50765	M50780	
M50766	M50781	

Motor Composite (L)

(L.M. THREE-CAR UNITS)

Built by: **Cravens.**
Engines: Two B.U.T. (Leyland) 6-cyl. horizontal type of 150 b.h.p.
Transmission: **Mechanical.** Cardan shaft and freewheel to four-speed epicyclic gearbox and further cardan shaft to final drive.
Body: 57′ 6″ × 9′ 3″.
Weight: 30 tons.
Seats 1st: 12.
2nd: 51.

M50785	M50799	M50813
M50786	M50800	M50814
M50787	M50801	M50815
M50788	M50802	M50816
M50789	M50803	M50817
M50790	M50804	
M50791	M50805	
M50792	M50806	
M50793	M50807	
M50794	M50808	
M50795	M50809	
M50796	M50810	
M50797	M50811	
M50798	M50812	

Motor Brake Second

(W.R. THREE-CAR SUBURBAN)

For Details see W50050-91

W50818	W50836	W50854
W50819	W50837	W50855
W50820	W50838	W50856
W50821	W50839	W50857
W50822	W50840	W50858
W50823	W50841	W50859
W50824	W50842	W50860
W50825	W50843	W50861
W50826	W50844	W50862
W50827	W50845	W50863
W50828	W50846	W50864
W50829	W50847	W50865
W50830	W50848	W50866
W50831	W50849	W50867
W50832	W50850	W50868
W50833	W50851	W50869
W50834	W50852	W50870
W50835	W50853	

Motor Second

(W.R. THREE-CAR SUBURBAN)

For Details see W50092-50133

W50871	W50887	W50903
W50872	W50888	W50904
W50873	W50889	W50905
W50874	W50890	W50906
W50875	W50891	W50907
W50876	W50892	W50908
W50877	W50893	W50909
W50878	W50894	W50910
W50879	W50895	W50911
W50880	W50896	W50912
W50881	W50897	W50913
W50882	W50898	W50914
W50883	W50899	W50915
W50884	W50900	W50916
W50885	W50901	W50917
W50886	W50902	W50918

W50919	W50921	W50923
W50920	W50922	

Motor Brake Second

(TWIN UNITS)

For Details see SC50339-M50358

SC51108	SC51115	SC51122
SC51109	SC51116	SC51123
SC51110	SC51117	SC51124
SC51111	SC51118	SC51125
SC51112	SC51119	SC51126
SC51113	SC51120	SC51127
SC51114	SC51121	

Motor Brake Second

(W.R. THREE-CAR SUBURBAN)

For Details see W50050-91

W51128	W51133	W51138
W51129	W51134	W51139
W51130	W51135	W51140
W51131	W51136	
W51132	W51137	

Motor Second

(W.R. THREE-CAR SUBURBAN)

For Details see W50092-50133

W51141	W51146	W51151
W51142	W51147	W51152
W51143	W51148	W51153
W51144	W51149	
W51145	W51150	

Motor Brake Second

(TWIN UNITS)

Built by: **Metropolitan Cammell.**
Engines: Two B.U.T. (A.E.C.) 6-cyl. horizontal type of 150 b.h.p.
Transmission: **Mechanical.** Cardan shaft and freewheel to four-speed epicyclic gearbox and further cardan shaft to final drive.
Body: 57' 0" × 9' 3".
Weight : 32 tons.
Seats 2nd: **52**

M51174	M51201	SC51228
M51175	M51202	SC51229
M51176	M51203	SC51230
M51177	E51204	SC51231
M51178	E51205	SC51232
M51179	E51206	SC51233
M51180	E51207	SC51234
M51181	E51208	SC51235
M51182	E51209	SC51236
M51183	E51210	SC51237
M51184	E51211	SC51238
M51185	E51212	SC51239
M51186	E51213	SC51240
M51187	E51214	SC51241
M51188	E51215	SC51242
M51189	E51216	SC51243
M51190	E51217	SC51244
M51191	E51218	SC51245
M51192	E51219	SC51246
M51193	E51220	SC51247
M51194	E51221	SC51248
M51195	E51222	SC51249
M51196	E51223	SC51250
M51197	SC51224	SC51251
M51198	SC51225	SC51252
M51199	SC51226	SC51253
M51200	SC51227	

Motor Brake Second

(TWIN UNITS)

Built by: **Cravens.**
Engines: Two B.U.T. (A.E.C.) 6-cyl. horizontal type of 150 b.h.p.
Transmission: **Mechanical.** Cardan shaft and freewheel to four-speed epicyclic gearbox and further cardan shaft to final drive.
Body: 57' 6" × 9' 3".
Weight: 30 tons.
Seats 2nd: 52.

E51254	E51260	E51266
E51255	E51261	E51267
E51256	E51262	E51268
E51257	E51263	E51269
E51258	E51264	E51270
E51259	E51265	E51271

Motor Brake Second

(SINGLE UNITS)

Built by: **Gloucester R.C. & W. Co.**
Engines: Two B.U.T. (A.E.C.) 6-cyl. horizontal type of 150 b.h.p.
Transmission: **Mechanical.** Cardan shaft and freewheel to four-speed epicyclic gearbox and further cardan shaft to final drive.
Body: 64' 6" × 9' 3".
    Non-gangwayed, side doors to each seating bay.
Weight: 35 tons.
Seats 2nd: 65.

W55000	W55007	W55014
W55001	W55008	W55015
W55002	W55009	W55016
W55003	W55010	W55017
W55004	W55011	W55018
W55005	W55012	W55019
W55006	W55013	

Motor Parcels Van

Built by: **Cravens.**
Engines: Two B.U.T. (A.E.C.) 6-cyl. horizontal type of 150 b.h.p.
Transmission: **Mechanical.** Cardan shaft and freewheel to four-speed epicyclic gearbox and further cardan shaft to final drive.
Body: 57' 6" × 9' 3".
Weight: 30 tons.

M55997	M55998	M55999

Driving Trailer Composite (L)

(TWIN UNITS)

Built by: **Derby Works B.R.**
Body: 64' 6" × 9' 3".
Weight: 29 tons 10 cwt.
Seats 1st: 12.
    2nd: 62.

E56000	E56005	E56010
E56001	E56006	E56011
E56002	E56007	E56012
E56003	E56008	E56013
E56004	E56009	E56014

E56015	E56027	E56039
E56016	E56028	E56040
E56017	E56029	E56041
E56018	E56030	E56042
E56019	E56031	E56043
E56020	E56032	E56044
E56021	E56033	E56045
E56022	E56034	E56046
E56023	E56035	E56047
E56024	E56036	E56048
E56025	E56037	E56049
E56026	E56038	

Driving Trailer Composite (L)

(TWIN UNITS)

Built by: **Metropolitan Cammell.**
Body: 57' 0" × 9' 3".
Weight: 24 tons 4 cwt.
Seats 1st: 12.
    2nd: 53.

E56050	E56069	E56088
E56051	E56070	E56089
E56052	E56071	M56090
E56053	E56072	M56091
E56054	E56073	M56092
E56055	E56074	M56093
E56056	E56075	
E56057	E56076	
E56058	E56077	
E56059	E56078	
E56060	E56079	
E56061	E56080	
E56062	E56081	
E56063	E56082	
E56064	E56083	
E56065	E56084	
E56066	E56085	
E56067	E56086	
E56068	E56087	

Driving Trailer
Composite (L)
(TWIN UNITS)

Built by: **Gloucester R. C. & W. Co.**
Body: 57′ 6″ × 9′ 3″.
Weight: 24 tons 15 cwt.
Seats 1st: 12.
   2nd: 54.

SC56094	SC56101	M56108
SC56095	SC56102	M56109
SC56096	SC56103	M56110
SC56097	SC56104	M56111
SC56098	M56105	M56112
SC56099	M56106	M56113
SC56100	M56107	

Driving Trailer
Composite (L)
(TWIN UNITS)

Built by: **Cravens.**
Body: 57′ 6″ × 9′ 3″.
Weight: 23 tons.
Seats 1st: 12.
   2nd: 51.

E56114	E56130	M56146
E56115	E56131	M56147
E56116	E56132	M56148
E56117	E56133	M56149
E56118	E56134	
E56119	E56135	
E56120	E56136	
E56121	E56137	
E56122	E56138	
E56123	E56139	
E56124	E56140	
E56125	E56141	
E56126	E56142	
E56127	E56143	
E56128	E56144	
E56129	M56145	

Driving Trailer
Composite (L)
(TWIN UNITS)

Built by: **Park Royal Vehicles.**
Body: 57′ 6″ × 9′ 3″.
Weight: 26 tons 7 cwt.
Seats 1st: 16.
   2nd: 48.

M56150	M56156	M56162
M56151	M56157	M56163
M56152	M56158	M56164
M56153	M56159	M56165
M56154	M56160	
M56155	M56161	

Driving Trailer
Composite (L)
(TWIN UNITS)

Built by: **D. Wickham & Co. Ltd.**
Body: 57′ 0″ × 9′ 3″.
Weight: 20 tons 10 cwt.
Seats 1st: 16.
   2nd: 50.

E56170	E56172	E56174
E56171	E56173	

Driving Trailer
Composite (L)
(TWIN UNITS)

Built by: **Birmingham R.C. & W. Co.**
Body: 57′ 6″ × 9′ 3″.
Weight:
Seats 1st: 12.
   2nd: 54.

M56175	M56179	M56183
M56176	M56180	M56184
M56177	M56181	
M56178	M56182	

Driving Trailer
Composite (L)
(TWIN UNITS)

Built by: **Birmingham R.C. & W. Co.**
Body: 57′ 6″ × 9′ 3″.
Weight:
Seats 1st: 12.
    2nd: 51.

E56185	E56187	E56189
E56186	E56188	

Driving Trailer
Composite (L)
(TWIN UNITS)

Built by: **Derby Works, B.R.**
Body: 57′ 6″ × 9′ 2″.
Weight: 21 tons.
Seats 1st:
    2nd:

E56190	E56197	E56204
E56191	E56198	E56205
E56192	E56199	E56206
E56193	E56200	E56207
E56194	E56201	E56208
E56195	E56202	E56209
E56196	E56203	E56210

Driving Trailer
Composite (L)
(TWIN UNITS)
For Details see E56050-93

E56218	E56219	E56220

Driving Trailer Second
(For use with Single Unit cars Nos. W55000, etc.)

Built by: **Gloucester R.C. & W. Co.**
Body: 64′ 0″ × 9′ 3″.
  Non-gangwayed, side doors to each
  seating bay.
Weight:
Seats 2nd: 95.

W56291	W56294	W56297
W56292	W56295	W56298
W56293	W56296	W56299

Driving Trailer
Composite (L)
(TWIN UNITS)
For Details see SC56094-M56113

SC56300	SC56307	SC56314
SC56301	SC56308	SC56315
SC56302	SC56309	SC56316
SC56303	SC56310	SC56317
SC56304	SC56311	SC56318
SC56305	SC56312	SC56319
SC56306	SC56313	

Driving Trailer
Composite (L)
(TWIN UNITS)

Built by: **Metropolitan Cammell.**
Body: 57′ 0″ × 9′ 3″.
Weight: 24 tons 4 cwt.
Seats 1st: 12.
    2nd: 53.

M56332	M56359	SC56386
M56333	M56360	SC56387
M56334	M56361	SC56388
M56335	E56362	SC56389
M56336	E56363	SC56390
M56337	E56364	SC56391
M56338	E56365	SC56392
M56339	E56366	SC56393
M56340	E56367	SC56394
M56341	E56368	SC56395
M56342	E56369	SC56396
M56343	E56370	SC56397
M56344	E56371	SC56398
M56345	E56372	SC56399
M56346	E56373	SC56400
M56347	E56374	SC56401
M56348	E56375	SC56402
M56349	E56376	SC56403
M56350	E56377	SC56404
M56351	E56378	SC56405
M56352	E56379	SC56406
M56353	E56380	SC56407
M56354	E56381	SC56408
M56355	SC56382	SC56409
M56356	SC56383	SC56410
M56357	SC56384	SC56411
M56358	SC56385	

Driving Trailer
Composite (L)

Built by: **Cravens.**
Body: 57′ 6″ × 9′ 3″.
Weight: 23 tons.
Seats 1st: 12.
 2nd: 51.

E56412	E56418	E56424
E56413	E56419	E56425
E56414	E56420	E56426
E56415	E56421	E56427
E56416	E56422	E56428
E56417	E56423	E56429

Trailer Composite
(W.R. THREE-CAR SUBURBAN)

Built by: **Derby Works B.R.**
Body: 63′ 8¾″ × 9′ 3″. Non-gangwayed,
 side doors to each seating bay.
Weight: 28 tons 10 cwt.
Seats 1st: 28.
 2nd: 74.

W59000	W59011	W59022
W59001	W59012	W59023
W59002	W59013	W59024
W59003	W59014	W59025
W59004	W59015	W59026
W59005	W59016	W59027
W59006	W59017	W59028
W59007	W59018	W59029
W59008	W59019	W59030
W59009	W59020	W59031
W59010	W59021	

Trailer Second
(W.R. THREE-CAR SUBURBAN)

Built by: **Derby Works B.R.**
Body: 63′ 8¾″ × 9′ 3″. Non-gangwayed,
 side doors to each seating bay.
Weight: 28 tons 10 cwt.
Seats 2nd: 106.

W59032	W59036	W59040
W59033	W59037	W59041
W59034	W59038	
W59035	W59039	

Trailer Second (L)
(N.E. FOUR-CAR UNITS)

Built by: **Metropolitan Cammell.**
Body: 57′ 0″ × 9′ 3″.
Weight: 25 tons.
Seats 2nd: 61.

E59042	E59045	E59048
E59043	E59046	
E59044	E59047	

Trailer Brake Second (L)
(N.E. FOUR-CAR UNITS)

Built by: **Metropolitan Cammell.**
Body: 57′ 0″ × 9′ 3″.
Weight: 25 tons.
Seats 2nd: 45.

E59049	E59052	E59055
E59050	E59053	
E59051	E59054	

Trailer Second (L)
(N.E. FOUR-CAR UNITS)

Built by: **Metropolitan Cammell.**
Body: 57′ 0″ × 9′ 3″.
Weight: 25 tons.
Seats 2nd: 71.

E59060	E59065	E59070
E59061	E59066	E59071
E59062	E59067	E59072
E59063	E59068	
E59064	E59069	

Trailer Brake Second
(N.E. FOUR-CAR UNITS)

Built by: **Metropolitan Cammell.**
Body: 57′ 0″ × 9′ 3″.
Weight: 25 tons.
Seats 2nd: 53.

E59073	E59078	E59083
E59074	E59079	E59084
E59075	E59080	E59085
E59076	E59081	
E59077	E59082	

Trailer Second (L)
(N.E. FOUR-CAR UNITS)
For Details see E59042-8

E59086	E59088	E59090
E59087	E59089	E59091

Trailer Brake Second (L)
(N.E. FOUR-CAR UNITS)
For Details see E59049-55

E59092	E59094	E59096
E59093	E59095	E59097

Trailer Second (L)
(N.E. THREE-CAR UNITS)

Built by: **Metropolitan Cammell.**
Body: 57′ 0″ × 9′ 3″.
Weight: 24 tons 10 cwt.
Seats 2nd: 75.

E59100	E59104	E59108
E59101	E59105	E59109
E59102	E59106	
E59103	E59107	

Trailer Brake Second (L)
(N.E. FOUR-CAR UNITS)

Built by: **Metropolitan Cammell.**
Body: 57′ 0″ × 9′ 3″.
Weight:
Seats 2nd:

E59112	E59113

Trailer Second (L)
(L.M. THREE-CAR UNITS)

Built by: **Metropolitan Cammell.**
Body: 57′ 0″ × 9′ 3″.
Weight:
Seats 2nd: 71.

M59114	M59120	M59126
M59115	M59121	M59127
M59116	M59122	M59128
M59117	M59123	M59129
M59118	M59124	M59130
M59119	M59125	M59131

Trailer Composite (L)
(L.M. THREE-CAR UNITS)

Built by: **Birmingham R. C. & W. Co.**
Body: 57′ 0″ × 9′ 3″.
Weight: 24 tons.
Seats 1st: 12.
     2nd: 54.

M59132	M59143	M59154
M59133	M59144	M59155
M59134	M59145	M59156
M59135	M59146	M59157
M59136	M59147	M59158
M59137	M59148	M59159
M59138	M59149	M59160
M59139	M59150	M59161
M59140	M59151	M59162
M59141	M59152	M59163
M59142	M59153	M59164

M59165	M59175	M59185
M59166	M59176	M59186
M59167	M59177	M59187
M59168	M59178	
M59169	M59179	
M59170	M59180	
M59171	M59181	
M59172	M59182	
M59173	M59183	
M59174	M59184	

Trailer Buffet Second (L)
(W.R. THREE-CAR CROSS-COUNTRY)

Built by: **Swindon Works B.R.**
Body: 64′ 6″ × 9′ 3″.
Open second with small buffet and counter at one end.
Weight: 30 tons 12 cwt.
Seats 2nd: 64.

W59255	W59271	W59287
W59256	W59272	W59288
W59257	W59273	W59289
W59258	W59274	W59290
W59259	W59275	W59291
W59260	W59276	W59292
W59261	W59277	W59293
W59262	W59278	W59294
W59263	W59279	W59295
W59264	W59280	W59296
W59265	W59281	W59297
W59266	W59282	W59298
W59267	W59283	W59299
W59268	W59284	W59300
W59269	W59285	W59301
W59270	W59286	

Trailer Second (L)
(N.E. FOUR-CAR UNITS)

Built by: **Birmingham R.C. & W. Co.**
Body: 57′ 0″ × 9′ 3″.
Weight:
Seats 2nd:

E59188	E59192	E59196
E59189	E59193	E59197
E59190	E59194	
E59191	E59195	

Trailer Second (L)
(N.E. THREE-CAR UNITS)

Built by: **Metropolitan Cammell.**
Body: 57′ 0″ × 9′ 3″.
Weight: 24 tons 10 cwt.
Seats 2nd: 75.

E59302	E59303	E59304

Trailer Brake Second (L)
(N.E. FOUR-CAR UNITS)

Built by: **Birmingham R.C. & W. Co.**
Body: 57′ 0″ × 9′ 3″.
Weight:
Seats 2nd:

E59209	E59213	E59217
E59210	E59214	E59218
E59211	E59215	
E59212	E59216	

Trailer Second (L)
(N.E. FOUR-CAR UNITS)

Built by: **Metropolitan Cammell.**
Body: 57′ 0″ × 9′ 3″.
Weight:
Seats 2nd:

E59305	E59306

Trailer Second (L)
(L.M. THREE-CAR UNITS)

Built by: **Cravens.**
Body: 57' 6" × 9' 3".
Weight: 23 tons.
Seats 2nd: 69.

M59307	M59314	M59321
M59308	M59315	M59322
M59309	M59316	M59323
M59310	M59317	M59324
M59311	M59318	M59325
M59312	M59319	
M59313	M59320	

Trailer Composite
(W.R. THREE-CAR SUBURBAN)
For Details see W59000-31

W59326	W59343	W59360
W59327	W59344	W59361
W59328	W59345	W59362
W59329	W59346	W59363
W59330	W59347	W59364
W59331	W59348	W59365
W59332	W59349	W59366
W59333	W59350	W59367
W59334	W59351	W59368
W59335	W59352	W59369
W59336	W59353	W59370
W59337	W59354	W59371
W59338	W59355	W59372
W59339	W59356	W59373
W59340	W59357	W59374
W59341	W59358	W59375
W59342	W59359	W59376

Trailer Composite
(W.R. THREE-CAR SUBURBAN)
For Details see W59000-31

W59438	W59443	W59448
W59439	W59444	W59449
W59440	W59445	W59450
W59441	W59446	
W59442	W59447	

Motor Brake Second
(S.R. HASTINGS UNITS)

Unit numbers 1001–7*
1011–9†
1031–7‡

Built by: **Eastleigh Works B.R.**
Engine: English Electric 4-cyl. type 4SRKT Mark II of 500 b.h.p. at 850 r.p.m.
Transmission: **Electric.** Two nose-suspended axle-hung traction motors.
Body: 58' 0" × 8' 2½" *
64' 6" × 8' 2½" †‡
Guard's, luggage compartment, engine room and full width driving compartment at outer end of car.
Weight: 54 tons 2 cwt.*
55 tons 0 cwt.†‡
Seats 2nd: 22*
30†‡

S60000*	S60016†	S60032‡
S60001*	S60017†	S60033‡
S60002*	S60018†	S60034‡
S60003*	S60019†	S60035‡
S60004*	S60020†	S60036‡
S60005*	S60021†	S60037‡
S60006*	S60022†	S60038‡
S60007*	S60023†	S60039‡
S60008*	S60024†	S60040‡
S60009*	S60025†	S60041‡
S60010*	S60026†	S60042‡
S60011*	S60027†	S60043‡
S60012*	S60028†	S60044‡
S60013*	S60029†	S60045‡
S60014†	S60030†	
S60015†	S60031†	

Motor Brake Second
(S.R. TWIN UNITS)

Unit numbers 1101–22

Built by: **Eastleigh Works, B.R.**
Engine: English Electric 4-cyl. type 4SRKT Mark II of 500 b.h.p. at 850 r.p.m.
Transmission: **Electric.** Two nose-suspended axle-hung traction motors.
Body: 64' 0" × 9' 3".

Guard's, luggage compartment, engine room and full width driving compartment at outer end of car. Non-gangwayed, side door to each seating bay.
Weight: 56 tons 0 cwt.
Seats 2nd: 52.

S60100	S60108	S60116
S60101	S60109	S60117
S60102	S60110	S60118
S60103	S60111	S60119
S60104	S60112	S60120
S60105	S60113	S60121
S60106	S60114	
S60107	S60115	

Trailer Second (L)
(S.R. HASTINGS UNITS)

Unit numbers 1001–7*
1011–9†
1031–7‡

Built by: **Eastleigh Works, B.R.**
Body: 58′ 0″ × 8′ 2½″.*
64′ 6″ × 8′ 2½″†‡.
Weight: 29 tons.*
30 tons.†‡
Seats 2nd: 52*
60†‡

S60500*	S60516*	S60532†
S60501*	S60517*	S60533†
S60502*	S60518*	S60534†
S60503*	S60519*	S60535†
S60504*	S60520*	S60536†
S60505*	S60521†	S60537†
S60506*	S60522†	S60538†
S60507*	S60523†	S60539†
S60508*	S60524†	S60540†
S60509*	S60525†	S60541†
S60510*	S60526†	S60542†
S60511*	S60527†	S60543†
S60512*	S60528†	S60544†
S60513*	S60529†	S60545†
S60514*	S60530†	S60546†
S60515*	S60531†	S60547†

S60548‡	S60553‡	S60558‡
S60549‡	S60554‡	S60559‡
S60550‡	S60555‡	S60560‡
S60551‡	S60556‡	S60561‡
S60552‡	S60557‡	

Trailer First (K)
(S.R. HASTINGS UNITS)

Unit numbers 1001–7*
1011–9†
1031–7‡

Built by: **Eastleigh Works, B.R.**
Body: 58′ 0″ × 8′ 2½″*
64′ 6″ × 8′ 2½″†‡
Side corridor with seven* (eight†‡) first class compartments with side door to each compartment.
Weight: 30 tons*
31 tons †‡
Seats 1st: 42*
48†‡

S60700*	S60708†	S60716‡
S60701*	S60709†	S60717‡
S60702*	S60710†	S60718‡
S60703*	S60711†	S60719‡
S60704*	S60712†	S60720‡
S60705*	S60713†	S60721‡
S60706*	S60714†	S60722‡
S60707†	S60715†	

Trailer Buffet
(S.R. HASTINGS UNITS)

Unit numbers 1031–7

Built by: **Eastleigh Works B.R.**
Body: 64′ 6″ × 8′ 2½″.
Buffet with kitchen and bar; self-contained seating saloon.
Weight: 35 tons.
Seats: 21.

S60750	S60753	S60756
S60751	S60754	
S60752	S60755	

Driving Trailer
Composite (L)
(S.R. TWIN UNITS)

Unit numbers 1101–22

Built by: **Eastleigh Works, B.R.**
Body: 64′ 0″ × 9′ 3″.
  Non-gangwayed, side door to each seating bay or compartment. 5-bay 2nd saloon and 2 1st compartments with intermediate lavatories, 2nd class compartment next to driving compartment.
Weight: 32 tons 0 cwt.
Seats 1st: 13.
  2nd: 62.

S60800	S60808	S60816
S60801	S60809	S60817
S60802	S60810	S60818
S60803	S60811	S60819
S60804	S60812	S60820
S60805	S60813	S60821
S60806	S60814	
S60807	S60815	

Motor Brake Second
(TWIN UNITS)

Built by: **Derby Works B.R.**
Engines: Two B.U.T. (Leyland) 6-cyl. horizontal type of 125 b.h.p.
Transmission: **Hydro-Mechanical.** Lysholm Smith (Leyland) torque converter to final drive.
Body: 57′ 0″ × 9′ 2″.
Weight: 26 tons.
Seats 2nd: 61.

E79000	E79003	E79006
E79001	E79004	E79007
E79002	E79005	

Motor Brake Second
(TWIN UNITS)

Built by: **Derby Works B.R.**
Engines: Two B.U.T. (A.E.C.) 6-cyl. horizontal type of 150 b.h.p.
Transmission: **Mechanical.** Cardan shaft and freewheel to four-speed epicyclic gearbox and further cardan shaft to final drive.
Body: 57′ 6″ × 9′ 2″.
Weight: 27 tons.
Seats 2nd: 61.
  56*.

M79008	E79021*	E79034*
M79009	E79022*	E79035*
M79010	E79023*	E79036*
M79011	E79024*	E79037*
M79012	E79025*	E79038*
M79013	E79026*	E79039*
M79014	E79027*	E79040*
M79015	E79028*	E79041*
M79016	E79029*	E79042*
M79017	E79030*	E79043*
M79018	E79031*	E79044*
M79019	E79032*	E79045*
M79020	E79033*	E79046*

Motor Brake Second
(TWIN UNITS)

Built by: **Metropolitan Cammell.**
Engines: Two B.U.T. (A.E.C.) 6-cyl. horizontal type of 150 b.h.p.
Transmission: **Mechanical.** Cardan shaft and freewheel to four-speed epicyclic gearbox and further cardan shaft to final drive.
Body: 57′ 0″ × 9′ 3″.
Weight: 31 tons 10 cwts.
Seats 2nd: 57.
  53*.

E79047	E79053	E79059
E79048	E79054	E79060
E79049	E79055	E79061
E79050	E79056	E79062
E79051	E79057	E79063
E79052	E79058	E79064

E79065	E79072	M79079*
E79066	E79073	M79080*
E79067	E79074	M79081*
E79068	E79075	M79082*
E79069	M79076*	
E79070	M79077*	
E79071	M79078*	

Motor Brake Second (L)
(INTER-CITY UNITS)

Built by: **Swindon Works B.R.**
Engines: Two B.U.T. (A.E.C.) 6-cyl. horizontal type of 150 b.h.p.
Transmission: **Mechanical.** Cardan shaft and freewheel to four-speed epicyclic gearbox and further cardan shaft to final drive.
Body: 64′ 6″ × 9′ 3″.
Guard's and luggage compartment at outer end. Two types of car: " leading "* with full width driving compartment, gangwayed at inner end only; " intermediate "† with side driving compartment, gangwayed at both ends.
Weight: 38 tons.
Seats 2nd: 52.

W79083†	W79093*	SC79103*
W79084†	W79094*	SC79104*
W79085†	SC79095†	SC79105*
W79086†	SC79096*	SC79106*
W79087†	SC79097*	SC79107*
W79088†	SC79098*	SC79108*
W79089†	SC79099*	SC79109*
W79090†	SC79100*	SC79110*
W79091*	SC79101*	SC79111*
W79092*	SC79102*	

Motor Brake Second
(TWIN UNITS)

Built by: **Derby Works B.R.**
Engines: Two B.U.T. 6-cyl. horizontal type of 150 b.h.p.

Transmission: **Mechanical.** Cardan shaft and freewheel to four-speed epicyclic gearbox and further cardan shaft to final drive.
Body: 57′ 6″ × 9′ 2″.
Weight: 27 tons.
Seats 2nd: 52.

M79118	M79129	E79140
M79119	M79130	M79141
M79120	M79131	M79142
M79121	M79132	M79143
M79122	M79133	M79144
M79123	M79134	M79145
M79124	M79135*	M79146
M79125	M79136	M79147
M79126	E79137	M79148
M79127	E79138	M79149
M79128	E79139	

* *Fitted with Self Changing Gears Ltd. automatic four-speed gearbox.*

Motor Second
(N.E. FOUR-CAR UNITS)

Built by: **Derby Works B.R.**
Engines: Two B.U.T. (A.E.C.) 6-cyl. horizontal type of 150 b.h.p.
Transmission: **Mechanical.** Cardan shaft and freewheel to four-speed epicyclic gearbox and further cardan shaft to final drive.
Body: 57′ 6″ × 9′ 2″.
Weight: 27 tons.
Seats 2nd: 64.

E79150	E79152	E79154
E79151	E79153	

Motor Second (L)
(INTER-CITY UNITS)

Built by: **Swindon Works B.R.**
Engines: Two B.U.T. (A.E.C.) 6-cyl. horizontal type of 150 b.h.p.
Transmission: **Mechanical.** Cardan shaft and freewheel to four-speed Wilson

gearbox and further cardan shaft to final drive.

Body: 64′ 6″ × 9′ 3″.

Gangwayed both ends. Side driving compartment at one end.

Weight: 39 tons 3 cwt.

Seats 2nd: 64.

SC79155	SC79160	SC79165
SC79156	SC79161	SC79166
SC79157	SC79162	SC79167
SC79158	SC79163	SC79168
SC79159	SC79164	

Motor Brake Second

(TWIN UNITS)
For Details see M79118-49

M79169	M79174	M79179
M79170	M79175	M79180
M79171	M79176	M79181
M79172	M79177	
M79173	M79178	

Motor Brake Second

(TWIN UNITS)
For Details see M79008-20

M79184	M79186	M79188
M79185	M79187	

Motor Composite (L)

(TWIN UNITS)

Built by: **Derby Works B.R.**

Engines: Two B.U.T. (A.E.C.) 6-cyl. horizontal type of 150 b.h.p.

Transmission: **Mechanical.** Cardan shaft and freewheel to four-speed epicyclic gearbox and further cardan shaft to final drive.

Body: 57′ 6″ × 9′ 2″.

Weight: 27 tons.

Seats 1st: 16.

2nd: 53.

M79189	M79191	M79193
M79190	M79192	

Driving Trailer Composite (L)

(TWIN UNITS)

Built by: **Derby Works B.R.**

Body: 57′ 6″ × 9′ 2″.

Weight: 20 tons.

Seats 1st: 16.

2nd: 53.

These cars have been converted from driving trailer seconds.

E79250	E79255	E79260
E79251	E79256	E79261
E79252	E79257	E79262
E79253	E79258	
E79254	E79259	

Driving Trailer Second (L)

(TWIN UNITS)

Built by: **Metropolitan Cammell.**

Body: 57′ 0″ × 9′ 3″.

Weight: 25 tons.

Seats 2nd: 71.

E79263	E79273	E79283
E79264	E79274	E79284
E79265	E79275	E79285
E79266	E79276	E79286
E79267	E79277	E79287
E79268	E79278	E79288
E79269	E79279	E79289
E79270	E79280	E79290
E79271	E79281	E79291
E79272	E79282	

Trailer Brake Second (L)
(N.E. FOUR-CAR UNITS)

Built by: **Derby Works B.R.**
Body: 57′ 6″ × 9′ 2″.
Weight: 20 tons 10 cwt.
Seats 2nd: 45.

E79325	E79327	E79329
E79326	E79328	

Trailer Second (L)
(N.E. FOUR-CAR UNITS)

Built by: **Derby Works B.R.**
Body: 57′ 6″ × 9′ 2″.
Weight: 20 tons 10 cwt.
Seats 2nd: 61.

E79400	E79402	E79404
E79401	E79403	

Trailer Buffet First (K)
(INTER-CITY UNITS)

Built by: **Swindon Works B.R.**
Body: 64′ 6″ × 9′ 3″.
  Side corridor with three first class
  compartments. Buffet with kitchen,
  bar and saloon.
Weight: 34 tons.
Seats 1st: 18.
  Buffet: 12.

W79440	SC79443	SC79446
W79441	SC79444	SC79447
SC79442	SC79445	

Trailer First (K)
(INTER-CITY UNITS)

Built by: **Swindon Works B.R.**
Body: 64′ 6″ × 9′ 3″.
  Side corridor with seven first class
  compartments and end doors.

Weight: 33 tons 9 cwt.
Seats 1st: 42.

W79470	SC79475	SC79480
W79471	SC79476	SC79481
W79472	SC79477	SC79482
W79473	SC79478	
SC79474	SC79479	

Motor Composite (L)
(TWIN UNITS)

Built by: **Derby Works B.R.**
Engines: Two B.U.T. (Leyland) 6-cyl.
  horizontal type of 125 b.h.p.
Transmission: **Hydro-Mechanical.**
  Lysholm Smith (Leyland) torque
  converter to final drive.
Body: 57′ 6″ × 9′ 2″.
Weight:
Seats 1st: 16.
  2nd: 53.

E79500	E79503	E79506
E79501	E79504	E79507
E79502	E79505	

Motor Composite
(N.E. FOUR-CAR UNITS)

Built by: **Derby Works B.R.**
Engines: Two B.U.T. (A.E.C.) 6-cyl.
  horizontal type of 150 b.h.p.
Transmission: **Mechanical.** Cardan
  shaft and freewheel to four-speed
  epicyclic gearbox and further cardan
  shaft to final drive.
Body: 57′ 6″ × 9′ 2″.
Weight: 26 tons 10 cwt.
Seats 1st: 20.
  2nd: 36.

E79508	E79510	E79512
E79509	E79511	

Driving Trailer Composite (L)
(TWIN UNITS)

Built by: **Derby Works B.R.**
Body: 57′ 6″ × 9′ 2″.
Weight: 21 tons.
Seats 1st: 9.
16*.
2nd: 53.

M79600	M79609	E79618*
M79601	M79610	E79619*
M79602	M79611	E79620*
M79603	M79612	E79621*
M79604	E79613*	E79622*
M79605	E79614*	E79623*
M79606	E79615*	E79624*
M79607	E79616*	E79625*
M79608	E79617*	

Driving Trailer Composite (L)
(TWIN UNITS)

Built by: **Metropolitan Cammell.**
Body: 57′ 0″ × 9′ 3″.
Weight:
Seats 1st: 12.
2nd: 53.

M79626	M79629	M79632
M79627	M79630	
M79628	M79631	

Driving Trailer Composite (L)
(TWIN UNITS)
For Details see M79600-E79625

M79639	M79643	M79647
M79640	M79644	M79648
M79641	M79645	M79649
M79642	M79646	M79650

M79651	M79663	M79675
M79652	M79664	M79676
M79653	M79665	M79677
M79654	M79666	M79678
M79655	M79667	M79679
M79656	M79668	M79680
M79657	M79669	M79681
E79658*	M79670	M79682
E79659*	M79671	M79683
E79660*	M79672	M79684
E79661*	M79673	
M79662	M79674	

> For reasons of clarity the 4-wheel units below are not in strict numerical order.

Motor Second
(FOUR-WHEEL UNITS)

Built by: **British United Traction Co.**
Engine: B.U.T. (A.E.C.) 6-cyl. horizontal type of 125 b.h.p.
Transmission: **Mechanical.** Cardan shaft and freewheel to four-speed epicyclic gearbox and further cardan shaft to final drive.
Body: 37′ 6″ × 9′ 0″. Non-gangwayed. Driving compartment at each end.
Weight: 15 tons 0 cwt.
Seats 2nd: 34.

M79740   M79745   M79748

Motor Brake Second
(FOUR-WHEEL UNITS)

Built by: **British United Traction Co.**
Engine: B.U.T. (A.E.C.) 6-cyl. horizontal type of 125 b.h.p.
Transmission: **Mechanical.** Cardan shaft and freewheel to four-speed

epicyclic gearbox and further cardan shaft to final drive.
Body: 37' 6" × 9' 0". Non-gangwayed. Driving compartment at each end.
Weight: 15 tons 0 cwt.
Seats 2nd: 28.

M79742	M79744	M79750
M79743		

Trailer Second

(FOUR-WHEEL UNITS)

Built by: **British United Traction Co.**
Body: 37' 6" × 9' 0". Non-gangwayed.
Weight: 10 tons 10 cwt.
Seats 2nd: 48.

M79741	M79747	M79749
M79746		

Motor Brake Second

(SINGLE UNITS)

Built by: **Derby Works B.R.**
Engine: Two B.U.T. (A.E.C.) 6-cyl. horizontal type of 150 b.h.p.
Transmission: **Mechanical.** Cardan shaft and freewheel to four-speed epicyclic gearbox and further cardan shaft to final drive.
Body: 57' 6" × 9' 2".
Driving compartment at each end.
Non-gangwayed.
Weight: 27 tons.
Seats 2nd: 52.

M79900	M79901

Four-Wheel Railbus

Built by: **Bristol/E.C.W.**
Engine: Gardner 6.H.L.W 6-cyl. type of 112 b.h.p. at 1,700 r.p.m.
Transmission: **Mechanical.** Cardan shaft and freewheel to Self-Changing Gears five-speed epicyclic gearbox and further cardan shaft to final drive.
Body: 42' 4" × 9' 3". Non-gangwayed.
Weight: 13 tons 10 cwt.
Seats 2nd: 56.

SC79958	SC79959

Four-Wheel Railbus

Built by: **Waggon und Maschinenbau.**
Engine: Buessing 150 b.h.p. at 1,900 r.p.m.
Transmission: **Mechanical.** Cardan shaft to ZF electro-magnetic six-speed gearbox.
Body: 41' 10". × 8' 8 $\frac{5}{16}$". Non-gangwayed.
Weight: 15 tons.
Seats 2nd: 56.

E79960	E79962	E79964
E79961	E79963	

Four-Wheel Railbus

Built by: **D. Wickham & Co.**
Engine: Meadows 6-cyl. type 6HDT500 of 105 b.h.p. at 1,800 r.p.m.
Transmission: **Mechanical.** Freeborn-Wickham disc and ring coupling driving Self-Changing Gears four-speed epicyclic gearbox and cardan shaft to final drive.
Body: 38' 0" × 9' 0". Non-gangwayed.
Weight: 11 tons 5 cwt.
Seats 2nd: 44.

SC79965	SC79967	SC79969
SC79966	SC79968	

Four-Wheel Railbus

Built by: **Park Royal Vehicles.**
Engine: B.U.T. (A.E.C.) 6-cyl. horizontal type of 150 b.h.p.
Transmission: **Mechanical.** Cardan shaft and freewheel to Self-Changing Gears four-speed epicyclic gearbox and further cardan shaft to final drive.
Body: 42' 0" × 9' 3". Non-gangwayed.
Weight: 15 tons.
Seats 2nd: 50.

SC79970	M79972	SC79974
M79971	M79973	

Four-Wheel Railbus

Built by: **A.C. Cars Ltd.**
Engine: B.U.T. (A.E.C.) 6-cyl. horizontal type of 150 b.h.p.
Transmission: **Mechanical.** Cardan shaft and freewheel to four-speed epicyclic gearbox and further cardan shaft to final drive.
Body: 36' 0" × 8' 11".
Weight: 11 tons.
Seats 2nd: 46.

W79975	W79977	SC79979
W79976	W79978	

Battery Railcar
Motor Brake Second
(TWIN UNIT)

Built by: **Derby Works B.R.**
Electrical Equipment: Two 100 kW Siemens Schuckert nose-suspended traction motors powered by 216 lead-acid cell batteries of 1070 amp/hour capacity.
Body: 57' 6" × 9' 2".
Weight:
Seats 2nd: 52

SC79998

Battery Railcar
Driving Trailer Composite
(TWIN UNIT)

Built by: **Derby Works B.R.**
Body: 57' 6" × 9' 2".
Weight:
Seats 1st: 12   *2nd:* 53

SC79999

Experimental Unit

This unit is not in public service but is undergoing trials. The two coaches were converted from former L.M.S. steam-hauled Open Brake Thirds and the motor bogies were recovered from withdrawn Euston-Watford electric units.
Engine: Ruston-Paxman type 6ZHHL of 450 b.h.p. in each coach.
Transmission: **Electric.**
Body: 57' 0" × 9' 3".
Weight: 51 tons 10 cwt.
Seats: —

9821   9828

G.W.R. Railcars

Car No.	Date	Engines	Total b.h.p.	Seats 2nd.
5/7	1935	2	242	70
8	1936	2	242	70
13–15	1936	2	242	70
17*	1936	2	242	—
19–32†	1940	2	210	48
33, 38‡	1942	4	420	92
34*	1941	2	210	—

* Parcels cars.
‡ Twin-coach unit with buffet facilities. Adjoining statistics apply per 2-car unit.
† These cars may work in pairs with an additional ordinary coach between.

W5W	W17W	W24W	W30W
W7W	W19W	W25W	W31W
W8W	W20W	W26W	W32W
W13W	W21W	W27W	W33W
W14W	W22W	W28W	W34W
W15W	W23W	W29W	W38W

Class 5P/5F 1Co-Co1 No. 10202   [*P. H. Groom*

Type 4 A1A-A1A D600 *Active*   [*P. J. Sharpe*

Type 4 B-B No. D800 *Sir Brian Robertson*   [*J. A. Coiley*

Barclay 153 b.h.p. 0-4-0 diesel mechanical shunter (E.R. class DY1) No. 11503
[*R. K. Evans*

Ruston & Hornsby 165 b.h.p. 0-4-0 diesel mechanical shunter (E.R. class DY5) No. 11507
[*Ruston & Hornsby*

North British 330 b.h.p. 0-4-0 diesel hydraulic shunter No. D2900
[*J. A. Young*

Drewry 204 b.h.p. 0-6-0 diesel mechanical shunter No. 11102   [R. E. Vincent

0-6-0 diesel electric shunter (E.R. class DEJ3) No. 12066   [R. J. Buckley

400 b.h.p. diesel electric shunter (E.R. class DEJ4) No. D3609   R. K. Evans

The English Electric " Deltic " Co-Co locomotive [M. Mensing

Type 4 English Electric 2,000 b.h.p. ICo-Col No. D202 [B. K. B. Green

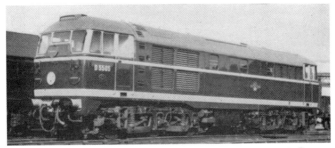

Type 2 Brush Traction 1,250 b.h.p. AIA-AIA No. D5505 [R. K. Evans

Type 2 Derby/B.T.H. 1,160 b.h.p. Bo-Bo No. D5000　　　　　　　[R. J. Buckley

Type 2 Birmingham R.C. & W. Co. 1,160 b.h.p. Bo-Bo No. D5300　　[G. W. Morrison

Type 2 Metropolitan Vickers 1,200 b.h.p. Co-Bo No. D5700　　　　[A. N. Yeates

Type I English Electric 1,000 b.h.p. Bo-Bo No. D8006   *[R. K. Evans*

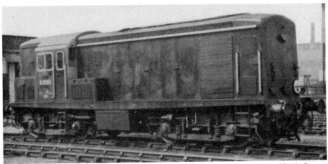

Type I B.T.H. 800 b.h.p. Bo-Bo No. D8205   *[R. K. Evans*

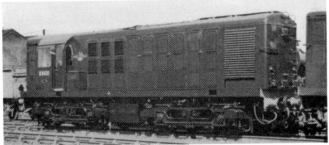

Type I North British 800 b.h.p. Bo-Bo No. D8401   *R. K. Evans*

Top: Class DEJI 0-6-0 diesel electric shunter, built at Doncaster, No. 15001 [*P. J. Sharpe; Centre:* 0-6-0 diesel electric shunter, built at Ashford, No. 15218 [*R. K. Evans; Bottom:* S.R. diesel electric shunter No. 15202 [*R. K. Evans*

Metropolitan-Cammell motor composite M50333   [*P. J. Sharpe*

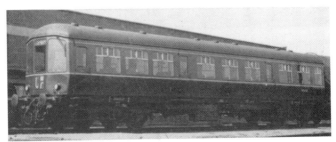

Park Royal driving trailer composite M56150   [*P. J. Sharpe*

Cravens motor brake second M50755   [*P. J. Sharpe*

Two-car experimental unit 9821 and 9828

A two-car Gloucester R.C. & W. Co. unit passes Millers Dale Junction *en route* for Buxton
[*Alan H. Bryant*]

Twelve-car diesel electric train for the Charing Cross–Hastings service

[G. M. Kichenside

First-class trailer of the 8′ 0¾″ wide Hastings stock

[G. M. Kichenside

Two-car diesel electric unit 1112 for S.R. Hampshire services

[D. Fereday Glenn

Scottish Region six-car Inter-city unit built at Swindon   [*J. L. Stevenson*

Swindon-built three-car Cross-Country unit   [*M. Mensing*

Two Derby-built three-car suburban units in service in South Wales   [*S. Rickard*

Park Royal railbus No. M79972   [P. J. Sharpe

Waggon -und Maschinenbau railbus No. E79661   [British Railways

A.C. Cars railbus No. SC79979   [British Railways

Bristol/Eastern Coachworks railbus No. SC79958

[P. J. Sharpe

B.U.T. four-wheel motor brake second No. M79742

[G. M. Kichenside

Gloucester R.C. & W. Co. driving trailer second No. W56295

[P. J. Sharpe

S.R. ELECTRIC LOCOMOTIVES

Co-Co   7P/5F   Class CC

*Introduced 1941: Raworth & Bulleid design for S.R.

†Introduced 1948: Later design with detail differences.

Weight: 99 tons 14 cwt.*
        104 tons 14 cwt.†

Driving Wheels: 3′ 7″

T.E.: 40,000 lb.*
    45,000 lb.†

Voltage: 660 D.C.

Current Collection: Overhead and third rail, with flywheel-driven generator for gaps in third rail.

20001*	20002*	20003†

Total 3

Also Bo-Bo No. **DS74** and Bo No. **DS75** which are service locomotives.

EASTERN & NORTH EASTERN LOCOMOTIVES

Bo-Bo   Class EMI

*Introduced 1941: Metropolitan-Vickers and Gresley design for L.N.E.R.
Remainder. Introduced 1950.
Production design with detail alterations.
Weight: 87 tons 18 cwt.
Driving Wheels: 4′ 2″.
T.E.: 25,000 lb.   Voltage: 1,500 D.C.
Current Collection: Overhead.

26000*	26015	26030	26045
26001	26016	26031	26046
26002	26017	26032	26047
26003	26018	26033	26048
26004	26019	26034	26049
26005	26020	26035	26050
26006	26021	26036	26051
26007	26022	26037	26052
26008	26023	26038	26053
26009	26024	26039	26054
26010	26025	26040	26055
26011	26026	26041	26056
26012	26027	26042	26057
26013	26028	26043	**Total**
26014	26029	26044	**58**

*26000 named *Tommy*.

Bo-Bo   Class ESI

Built 1902: Brush & Thomson-Houston shunting design for N.E.R.
Weight: 46 tons.

Voltage: 600 D.C.   T.E.: 25,000 lb.
Current collection: Overhead and third rail.

26500	26501	**Total 2**

Bo-Bo   Class EBI

Introduced 1946: L.N.E.R. rebuild of N.E.R. Raven freight design (introduced 1914) for banking work on Manchester-Wath line.

Weight: 74 tons 8 cwt.

Driving Wheels: 4′ 0″.

T.E.: 37,600 lb.   Voltage: 1,500 D.C.
Current collection: Overhead.

26510	**Total I**

Co-Co   Class EM2

Introduced 1954: Metropolitan-Vickers and L.N.E.R. design, development of EMI with six axles and higher speed range.
Weight: 102 tons.
Driving Wheels: 4′ 2″.
T.E.: 45,000 lb.   Voltage: 1,500 D.C.
Current collection: Overhead.

27000	27002	27004	27006
27001	27003	27005	**Total 7**

EASTERN & NORTH EASTERN ELECTRIC UNIT NUMBERS

LIVERPOOL ST.–SOUTHEND 4-CAR ELECTRIC TRAIN UNITS

01s	05s	09s	13s	17s	21s	25s	29s
02s	06s	10s	14s	18s	22s	26s	30s
03s	07s	11s	15s	19s	23s	27s	31s
04s	08s	12s	16s	20s	24s	28s	32s

LIVERPOOL ST.–SHENFIELD 3-CAR ELECTRIC TRAIN UNITS

01	11	21	31	41	51	61	71	81	91
02	12	22	32	42	52	62	72	82	92
03	13	23	33	43	53	63	73	83	
04	14	24	34	44	54	64	74	84	
05	15	25	35	45	55	65	75	85	
06	16	26	36	46	56	66	76	86	
07	17	27	37	47	57	67	77	87	
08	18	28	38	48	58	68	78	88	
09	19	29	39	49	59	69	79	89	
10	20	30	40	50	60	70	80	90	

GRIMSBY–IMMINGHAM ELECTRIC TRAMS

1	11	15	18	21	24	27	30	33
4	12	16	19	22	25	28	31	
5	14	17	20	23	26	29	32	

SOUTH TYNESIDE ELECTRIC MOTOR COACHES

E65311	E65314	E65317	E65320	E65323
E65312	E65315	E65318	E65321	E65324
E65313	E65316	E65319	E65322	E65325

Motor Parcels Van E68000

NORTH TYNESIDE ELECTRIC TWIN-UNIT MOTOR COACHES

E29101E	E29113E	E29124E	E29135E	E29146E	E29157E
E29102E	E29114E	E29125E	E29136E	E29147E	E29158E
E29103E	E29115E	E29126E	E29137E	E29148E	E29159E
E29104E	E29116E	E29127E	E29138E	E29149E	E29160E
E29105E	E29117E	E29128E	E29139E	E29150E	E29161E
E29106E	E29118E	E29129E	E29140E	E29151E	E29162E
E29107E	E29119E	E29130E	E29141E	E29152E	E29163E
E29108E	E29120E	E29131E	E29142E	E29153E	E29164E
E29109E	E29121E	E29132E	E29143E	E29154E	
E29110E	E29122E	E29133E	E29144E	E29155E	
E29111E	E29123E	E29134E	E29145E	E29156E	

	Motor Coaches			Motor Parcels Vans	
E29165E		E29166E	E29467E		E29468E

L.M. ELECTRIC MOTOR COACH NUMBERS

LONDON DISTRICT

OPEN STOCK

OPEN STOCK			M28267M	M28281M	M28292M
M28000M	M28246M	M28258M	M28269M	M28282M	M28294M
M28224M	M28248M	M28259M	M28270M	M28283M	M28295M
M28225M	M28249M	M28260M	M28272M	M28284M	M28296M
M28226M	M28252M	M28261M	M28273M	M28285M	M28297M
M28228M	M28253M	M28262M	M28274M	M28286M	M28298M
M28229M	M28254M	M28263M	M28275M	M28287M	M28299M
M28230M	M28255M	M28264M	M28277M	M28288M	
M28237M	M28256M	M28265M	M28279M	M28289M	
M28242M	M28257M	M28266M	M28280M	M28290M	

COMPARTMENT STOCK

COMPARTMENT STOCK			M28013M	M28018M	M28022M
M28001M	M28005M	M28009M	M28014M	M28019M	M28023M
M28002M	M28006M	M28010M	M28015M	M28020M	M28024M
M28003M	M28007M	M28011M	M28016M	M28021M	M28025M
M28004M	M28008M	M28012M	M28017M		

B.R. STOCK

B.R. STOCK			M61160	M61170	M61180
M61133	M61142	M61151	M61161	M61171	M61181
M61134	M61143	M61152	M61162	M61172	M61182
M61135	M61144	M61153	M61163	M61173	M61183
M61136	M61145	M61154	M61164	M61174	M61184
M61137	M61146	M61155	M61165	M61175	M61185
M61138	M61147	M61156	M61166	M61176	M61186
M61139	M61148	M61157	M61167	M61177	M61187
M61140	M61149	M61158	M61168	M61178	M61188
M61141	M61150	M61159	M61169	M61179	M61189

LIVERPOOL–SOUTHPORT

COMPARTMENT STOCK

COMPARTMENT STOCK			OPEN STOCK		
M28301M	M28305M	M28308M	M28311M	M28314M	M28317M
M28302M	M28306M	M28309M	M28312M	M28315M	M28318M
M28303M	M28307M	M28310M	M28313M	M28316M	M28319M
M28304M					

M28321M	M28331M	M28341M	M28352M	M28358M	M28364M
M28322M	M28332M	M28342M	M28353M	M28359M	M28365M
M28323M	M28333M	M28343M	M28354M	M28360M	M28366M
M28324M	M28334M	M28344M	M28355M	M28361M	M28367M
M28325M	M28335M	M28345M	M28356M	M28362M	M28368M
M28326M	M28336M	M28347M	M28357M	M28363M	M28369M
M28327M	M28337M	M28348M			
M28328M	M28338M	M28349M			
M28329M	M28339M	M28350M			
M28330M	M28340M	M28351M			

BAGGAGE CARS

M28496M M | 28497M

WIRRAL & MERSEY

M28371M	M28379M	M28387M	M28394M	M28678M	M28685M
M28372M	M28380M	M28388M	M28672M	M28679M	M28686M
M28373M	M28381M	M28389M	M28673M	M28680M	M28687M
M28374M	M28382M	M28390M	M28674M	M28681M	M28688M
M28375M	M28383M	M28391M	M28675M	M28682M	M28689M
M28376M	M28384M	M28392M	M28676M	M28683M	M28690M
M28377M	M28385M	M28393M	M28677M	M28684M	
M28378M	M28386M				

MANCHESTER–BURY

M28500M	M28506M	M28512M	M28518M	M28525M	M28531M
M28501M	M28507M	M28513M	M28519M	M28526M	M28532M
M28502M	M28508M	M28514M	M28521M	M28527M	M28533M
M28503M	M28509M	M28515M	M28522M	M28528M	M28434M
M28504M	M28510M	M28516M	M28523M	M28529M	M28535M
M28505M	M28511M	M28517M	M28524M	M28530M	M28537M

LANCASTER– MORECAMBE–HEYSHAM

M28219M	M28221M
M28220M	M28222M

MANCHESTER, S. JUNCT. & ALTRINCHAM

M28571M	M28579M	M28587M
M28572M	M28580M	M28588M
M28573M	M28581M	M28589M
M28574M	M28582M	M28590M
M28575M	M28583M	M28591M
M28576M	M28584M	M28592M
M28577M	M28585M	M28593M
M28578M	M28586M	M28594M

MANCHESTER–GLOSSOP–HADFIELD

M59401E	M59403E	M59405E	M59407E
M59402E	M59404E	M59406E	M59408E

SOUTHERN REGION ELECTRIC MOTOR UNIT NUMBERS

(Number to be seen on front and rear of each set)

TWO-CAR NON-CORRIDOR MOTOR UNITS

Motor Brake Second, Driving Trailer Composite.

(2-NOL.)

1813	1822	1831	1842
1814	1823	1832	1844
1815	1824	1834	1845
1816	1825	1836	1846
1817	1826	1837	1847
1818	1827	1839	1848
1820	1829	1840	1849
1821	1830	1841	1850

TWO-CAR MOTOR LAVATORY UNITS

Motor Lavatory Brake Second, Driving Trailer Lavatory Composite.

(2-BIL.)

2001†	2021	2040	2059
2002†	2022	2041	2060
2003†	2023	2042	2061
2004†	2024	2043	2062
2005†	2025	2044	2063
2006†	2026	2045	2064
2007†	2027	2046	2065
2008†	2028	2047	2066
2009†	2029	2048	2067
2010†	2030	2049	2068
2011	2031	2050	2069*
2012	2032	2051	2070
2013	2033	2052	2071
2015	2034	2053	2072
2016	2035	2054	2073
2017	2036	2055	2074
2018	2037	2056*	2075
2019	2038	2057	2076
2020	2039	2058	2077

2078	2096	2115	2135
2079	2097	2116	2136
2080	2098	2117	2137
2081	2099	2118	2138
2082	2100*	2120	2139
2083	2101	2121	2140
2084	2103	2122	2141
2085	2104	2123	2142
2086	2105	2124	2143
2087	2106	2125	2144
2088*	2107	2126	2145
2089	2108	2127	2146
2090	2109	2128	2147
2091	2110	2129	2148
2092	2111	2130	2149
2093	2112	2132	2150
2094	2113	2133*	2151
2095	2114	2134	2152

† 88 2nd seats instead of 84 and all-electric control gear.

* BIL Motor Coach and HAL trailer.

TWO-CAR MOTOR LAVATORY UNITS

Motor Brake Second, Driving Trailer Lavatory Composite.

(2-HAL.)

2601	2612	2623	2634
2602	2613	2624	2635
2603	2614	2625	2636
2604	2615	2626	2637
2605	2616	2627	2638
2606	2617	2628	2639
2607	2618	2629	2640
2608	2619	2630	2641
2609	2620	2631	2642
2610	2621	2632	2643
2611	2622	2633	2644

2645	2660	2674	2689
2647	2661	2675	2690
2648	2662	2676	2691
2649	2663	2677	2692
2650	2664	2678	2693
2651	2665	2679	2694
2652	2666	2681	2695
2653	2667	2682	2696
2654	2668	2683	2697
2655	2669	2684	2698
2656	2670	2685	2699
2657	2671	2686	2700
2658	2672	2687	
2659	2673	2688	

FOUR-CAR MOTOR LAVATORY UNITS

Motor Brake Second, Composite, Lavatory Composite, Motor Brake Second.

(4-LAV.)

2921	2930	2939	2948
2922	2931	2940	2949
2923	2932	2941	2950
2924	2933	2942	2951
2925	2934	2943	2952
2926*	2935	2944	2953
2927	2936	2945	2954†
2928	2937	2946	2955†
2929	2938	2947	

* One motor coach with electro-pneumatic control gear.

† With electro-pneumatic control gear.

SIX-CAR MOTOR CORRIDOR UNITS (with Pullman Car)

Gangwayed within set

Motor Brake Second, Second, Composite, Composite Pullman, Composite, Motor Brake Second.

(6-PUL.)

3001	3007	3013	3019
3002	3008	3015	3020
3003	3009	3016	3041*
3004	3010	3017	3042*
3005	3011	3018	3043*
3006	3012		

* Ex- " 6-CIT " Units. Trailers (except Pullman) formerly Firsts.

SIX-CAR MOTOR CORRIDOR UNITS (with Pantry Car)

Gangwayed within set

Motor Brake Second, Second, First, Pantry First, Second, Motor Brake Second.

(6-PAN.)

3021	3026	3030	3034
3022	3027	3031	3035
3023	3028	3032	3036
3024	3029	3033	3037
3025			

FIVE-CAR PULLMAN MOTOR UNITS

(For " Brighton Belle " Service)

All-Pullman

Gangwayed within set.

Motor Second, Second, First, First, Motor Second.

(5-BEL.)

3051	3052	3053

FOUR-CAR KITCHEN CORRIDOR MOTOR UNITS

Gangwayed throughout.

Motor Brake Second, First (and First Dining), Kitchen Second Dining, Motor Brake Second.

(4-RES.)

3054	3059	3065	3069
3055	3061	3066	3070
3056	3062	3067	3071
3057	3064	3068	3072

FOUR-CAR BUFFET CORRIDOR MOTOR UNITS

Gangwayed throughout.

Motor Brake Second, Composite, Buffet, Motor Brake Second.

(4-BUF.)

3073	3077	3080	3083
3074	3078	3081	3084
3075	3079	3082	3085
3076			

FOUR-CAR CORRIDOR MOTOR UNITS

Gangwayed throughout.

Motor Brake Second, Second, Composite, Motor Brake Second.

(4-COR.)

3101	3116	3131	3145
3102	3117	3132	3146
3103	3118	3133	3147
3104	3119	3134	3148
3105	3120	3135	3149
3106	3121	3136	3150
3107	3122	3137	3151
3108	3123	3138	3152
3109	3124	3139	3153
3110	3125	3140	3154
3111	3126	3141	3155
3112	3127	3142	3156
3113	3128	3143	3157
3114	3129	3144	3158
3115	3130		

FOUR-CAR DOUBLE DECK SUBURBAN UNITS

Motor Brake Second, 2 Trailer Seconds, Motor Brake Second.

(4-DD.)

4001	4002

FOUR-CAR NON-CORRIDOR SUBURBAN UNITS

See table for formation.

(4-SUB.)

4101	4289	4332	4375
4102	4290	4333	4376
4103	4291	4334	4377
4104	4292	4335	4378
4105	4293	4336	4379
4106	4294	4337	4380
4107	4295	4338	4381
4108	4296	4339	4382
4109	4297	4340	4383
4110	4298	4341	4384
4111	4299	4342	4385
4112	4301	4343	4386
4113	4302	4344	4387
4114	4303	4345	4501
4115	4304	4346	4502
4116	4305	4347	4503
4117	4306	4348	4504
4118	4307	4349	4505
4119	4308	4351	4506
4120	4309	4352	4507
4121	4310	4353	4508
4122	4311	4354	4509
4123	4312	4355	4510
4124	4313	4356	4511
4125	4314	4357	4512
4126	4315	4358	4513
4127	4316	4359	4514
4128	4317	4360	4515
4129	4318	4361	4516
4130	4319	4362	4517
4277	4320	4363	4518
4278	4321	4364	4601
4279	4322	4365	4602
4280	4323	4366	4603
4281	4324	4367	4604
4282	4325	4368	4605
4283	4326	4369	4606
4284	4327	4370	4607
4285	4328	4371	4621
4286	4329	4372	4622
4287	4330	4373	4623
4288	4331	4374	4624

4625	4658	4691	4723
4626	4659	4692	4724
4627	4660	4693	4725
4628	4661	4694	4726
4629	4662	4695	4727
4630	4663	4696	4728
4631	4664	4697	4729
4632	4665	4698	4730
4633	4666	4699	4731
4634	4667	4700	4732
4635	4668	4701	4733
4636	4669	4702	4734
4637	4670	4703	4735
4638	4671	4704	4736
4639	4672	4705	4737
4640	4673	4706	4738
4641	4674	4707	4739
4642	4675	4708	4740
4643	4676	4709	4741
4644	4677	4710	4742
4645	4678	4711	4743
4646	4679	4712	4744
4647	4680	4713	4745
4648	4681	4714	4746
4649	4682	4715	4747
4650	4683	4716	4748
4651	4684	4717	4749
4652	4685	4718	4750
4653	4686	4719	4751
4654	4687	4720	4752
4655	4688	4721	4753
4656	4689	4722	4754
4657	4690		

5030	5123	5169	5216
5031	5124	5170	5217
5032	5125	5171	5218
5033	5126	5172	5219
5034	5127	5173	5220
5035	5128	5174	5221
5036	5129	5175	5222
5037	5130	5176	5223
5038	5131	5177	5224
5039	5132	5178	5225
5040	5133	5179	5226
5041	5134	5180	5227
5042	5135	5181	5228
5043	5136	5182	5229
5044	5137	5183	5230
5045	5138	5184	5231
5046	5139	5185	5232
5047	5140	5186	5233
5048	5141	5187	5234
5049	5142	5188	5235
5050	5143	5189	5236
5051	5144	5190	5237
5052	5145	5191	5238
5053	5146	5192	5239
5101	5147	5193	5240
5102	5148	5194	5241
5103	5149	5195	5242
5104	5150	5196	5243
5105	5151	5197	5244
5106	5152	5198	5245
5107	5153	5199	5246
5108	5154	5200	5247
5109	5155	5201	5248
5110	5156	5202	5249
5111	5157	5203	5250
5112	5158	5205	5251
5113	5159	5206	5252
5114	5160	5207	5253
5115	5161	5208	5254
5116	5162	5209	5255
5117	5163	5210	5256
5118	5164	5211	5257
5119	5165	5212	5258
5120	5166	5213	5259
5121	5167	5214	5260
5122	5168	5215	5261

FOUR-CAR NON-CORRIDOR SUBURBAN UNITS

See table for formation.

(4-EPB)

5001	5008	5015	5022
5002	5009	5016	5024
5003	5010	5017	5025
5004	5011	5018	5026
5005	5012	5019	5027
5006	5013	5020	5028
5007	5014	5021	5029

5262	5266	5269	5272
5263	5267	5270	5273
5264	5268	5271	5274
5265			

N.B.—These units are still being delivered.

TWO-CAR MOTOR LAVATORY UNITS

Motor Brake Saloon Second, Driving Trailer Lavatory Composite.

(2-HAP.)

5601	5610	5619	5628
5602	5611	5620	5629
5603	5612	5621	5630
5604	5613	5622	5631
5605	5614	5623	5632
5606	5615	5624	5633
5607	5616	5625	5634
5608	5617	5626	5635
5609	5618	5627	5636

N.B.—These units are still being delivered.

TWO-CAR NON-CORRIDOR SUBURBAN UNITS

(B.R. Standard design)

Motor Brake Saloon Second, Driving Trailer Second (part Saloon).

(2-EPB)

5701	5715	5729	5743
5702	5716	5730	5744
5703	5717	5731	5745
5704	5718	5732	5746
5705	5719	5733	5747
5706	5720	5734	5748
5707	5721	5735	5749
5708	5722	5736	5750
5709	5723	5737	5751
5710	5724	5738	5752
5711	5725	5739	5753
5712	5726	5740	5754
5713	5727	5741	5755
5714	5728	5742	5756

5757	5773	5788	5803
5758	5774	5789	5804
5759	5775	5790	5805
5760	5776	5791	5806
5761	5777	5792	5807
5762	5778	5793	5808
5763	5779	5794	5809
5764	5780	5795	5810
5765	5781	5796	5811
5767	5782	5797	5812
5768	5783	5798	5813
5769	5784	5799	5814
5770	5785	5800	5815
5771	5786	5801	5816
5772	5787	5802	

N.B.—These units are still being delivered.

TWO-CAR MOTOR LAVATORY UNITS

(B.R.Standard design)

Motor Brake Saloon Second, Driving Trailer Lavatory Composite (part Saloon).

(2-HAP.)

6001	6013	6025	6037
6002	6014	6026	6038
6003	6015	6027	6039
6004	6016	6028	6040
6005	6017	6029	6041
6006	6018	6030	6042
6007	6019	6031	6043
6008	6020	6032	6044
6009	6021	6033	6045
6010	6022	6034	
6011	6023	6035	
6012	6024	6036	

N.B.—These units are still being delivered.

FOUR-CAR CORRIDOR BUFFET UNITS

(B.R. Standard design)

Gangwayed throughout.

Motor Brake Second, Composite, Buffet, Motor Brake Second.

(4-BEP.)

7001	7016	7031	7045
7002	7017	7032	7046
7003	7018	7033	7047
7004	7019	7034	7048
7005	7020	7035	7049
7006	7021	7036	7050
7007	7022	7037	7051
7008	7023	7038	7052
7009	7024	7039	7053
7010	7025	7040	7054
7011	7026	7041	7055
7012	7027	7042	7056
7013	7028	7043	7057
7014	7029	7044	7058
7015	7030		

N.B.—These units are still being delivered.

FOUR-CAR CORRIDOR UNITS

(B.R. Standard design)

Gangwayed throughout.

Motor Brake Second, Composite, Second, Motor Brake Second.

(4-CEP.)

7101	7116	7131	7145
7102	7117	7132	7146
7103	7118	7133	7147
7104	7119	7134	7148
7105	7120	7135	7149
7106	7121	7136	7150
7107	7122	7137	7151
7108	7123	7138	7152
7109	7124	7139	7153
7110	7125	7140	7154
7111	7126	7141	7155
7112	7127	7142	7156
7113	7128	7143	7157
7114	7129	7144	7158
7115	7130		

N.B.—These units are still being delivered.

WATERLOO AND CITY LINE MOTOR COACH NOS.

51	54	57	60
52	55	58	61
53	56	59	62

FOUR–CAR SUBURBAN (4–SUB & 4–EPB) UNITS

Make-up, Seating Capacity, etc.

Unit Nos.	Type	Motor Coaches	Trailer Coaches	Seating Capacity
4101–4110	All-Steel Built 1941/5	9 compt.	1 10 compt. 1 11 compt.	468
4111–4120	All-Steel Built 1946	8 compt.	1 9 compt. 1 10 compt.	420
4121–4130	All-Steel Built 1946	Semi-Saloon	1 Semi-Saloon 1 9 compt.	382

4277–4299	All-Steel Built 1948-9	Saloon	I I	Saloon 10 compt.	386
4300-25	Augmented W-Section Built 1925	7 compt.	I I	9 compt. All-Steel* 10 compt.	350 338*
4326-38 4340-49 51-4	Augmented E-Section Built 1925/6	8 compt.	I I	9 compt. All-Steel 10 compt.	370
4339	Augmented E-Section Built 1925/6	I-7 compt. I-8 compt.	I I	9 compt. All-Steel 10 compt.	360
4355-4363	All-Steel Built 1947/8	8 compt.	2	10 compt.	432
4364-4376	All-Steel Built 1947/8	8 compt.	I I	9 compt. 10 compt.	420
4377	All-Steel Built 1947	8 compt.	I I	9 compt. Saloon	402
4378-4387	All-Steel Built 1948	Saloon	I I	Saloon 10 compt.	386
4501-18	Reformed L.B.S.C.R. converted S.R. (4501/11 have one or two converted ex-L.S.–W.R. coaches)	I-7 compt. I-8 compt.† († 7-compt. on unit 4501)	2	10 compt.	350 340†
4601-4607	All-Steel bodies on original or new underframes Rebuilt 1949/50	Semi-Saloon	2	10 compt.	404
4621-4666		Saloon	I I	Saloon 10 compt.*	386*
4667-4754	New all-steel bodies (1950–7) on original underframes	Saloon	I I	Saloon 10 compt.	386
5001-53, 5101-5274		Saloon	I I	Saloon 10 compt.*	386*

*Except units **4313, 4688/96, 4723/8/33/9, 5005, 5220,** which have 9 compt. trailers thus reducing the number of seats by 12.

GLASGOW UNDERGROUND

Motor Coach Nos.

I	6	14	17	21	25	29	57
2	II	15	18	23	27	30	58
3	12	16	20	24	28	55	59
						56	60

SWANSEA & MUMBLES

Tramcar Nos.

| 1 | | 3 | | 5 | | 7 | | 9 | | 11 | | 13 |
| 2 | | 4 | | 6 | | 8 | | 10 | | 12 | | |

BRIGHTON CORPORATION—VOLK'S ELECTRIC RAILWAY

Car No.	Seating Capacity	Sides	H.P. of Motor
1	40	Open	Approximately 7
2	40	Open	,,
3	40	Sliding Doors	,,
4	40	,, ,,	,,
5	40	,, ,,	,,
6	40	,, ,,	,,
7	40	,, ,,	,,
8	36	Open	,, 10/12
9	36	Open	,, ,,

Cars Nos. 8 and 9 were originally trailers purchased from Southend, and the trucks were reconstructed and motorised by Brighton Corporation Transport.

MANX ELECTRIC RAILWAY

No.	Seating Capacity	Type	No.	Seating Capacity	Type
1	36	Saloon*	20	48	Saloon
2	36	Saloon*	21	48	Saloon
5	36	Saloon	22	48	Saloon
6	36	Saloon	25	56	Open
7	36	Saloon	26	56	Open
9	36	Saloon	27	56	Open
14	56	Open	28	56	Open
15	56	Open	29	56	Open
16	56	Open	30	56	Open
17	56	Open	31	56	Open
18	56	Open	32	56	Open
19	48	Saloon	33	56	Open

* With open front end.

A nine-car train of E.R. 1949 Shenfield stock approaches Brentwood   [*C. R. L. Coles*

B.R. standard electric stock built in 1956 for the Liverpool St.–Southend service
[*R. E. Vincent*

Class EB1 Bo-Bo No. 26510   [*C. C. B. Herbert*

251

Class EM1 Bo-Bo's Nos. 26039 and 26042   [P. J. Lynch

Class EM2 Co-Co No. 27000 leaves Thurgoland tunnel with a local train for Sheff

A six-coach train of former L.N.W.R. saloon stock, with Oerlikon equipment, leaves Kenton for Euston [G. M. *Kichenside*

L.M.S.-built compartment type motor coach M28023M [G. M. *Kichenside*

Six-coach train of B.R. standard stock for L.M.R. London area services [G. M. *Kichenside*

A twelve-coach train, with a 6-PUL unit leading, leaves the Quarry tunnel, near Merstham, bound for Littlehampton   [S. Creer

The up " Brighton Belle " passes South Croydon   [R. Russell

The first B.R. standard express unit appeared in 1956.   4-CEP set 7102 passes Redhill
                    [G. Daniels

2-BIL semi-fast units on a down Alton and Portsmouth train   [*British Railways*

Two 2-HAL units work an up Brighton slow train.   [*British Railways*

Shortly to be withdrawn are the 2-NOL units. This is the driving trailer of unit 1841
[*G. M. Kichenside*

First published 1958
This edition 2003

ISBN 0 7110 2974 1

Published by Ian Allan Publishing

an imprint of Ian Allan Publishing Ltd, Hersham, Surrey, KT12 4RG.

Printed by Ian Allan Printing Ltd, Hersham, Surrey, KT12 4RG.

Code: 0301/B2

Front cover: Stanier Class 5MT No 45439 seen with a special at Bushy troughs.
T. B, Owen

Back cover, top: The last steam locomotive to be constructed at Crewe Works, BR
Standard Class 9F No 92250. *D. P. Williams*

Back cover, bottom: No D8401 one of the Pilot Scheme designs manufactured by NBL.
P. H. Groom